*"Men ever had, and ever will
 have, leave
To coin new words well suited
 to the age.
Words are like leaves, some
 wither ev'ry year,
And ev'ry year a younger race
 succeeds."*

Horace, Ars Poetica
Trans., Earl of Roscommon
Wentworth Dillon

The language of science is complex and everchanging. In order to comprehend and appreciate the fascinating world of the scientist and our age of electronics, nuclear energy, and space, one must stay abreast of this language. The YOUNG PEOPLE'S SCIENCE DICTIONARY is the most complete science dictionary available for young people. Its user gains a head start in today's world of mushrooming knowledge. Designed as a companion volume to the YOUNG PEOPLE'S SCIENCE ENCYCLOPEDIA, the new YOUNG PEOPLE'S SCIENCE DICTIONARY is an outstanding contribution to science education that will be welcomed by young and old alike in home, school, or library.

22 Na Zy

Young People's Science Dictionary

by the Editors of the

YOUNG PEOPLE'S SCIENCE ENCYCLOPEDIA

in cooperation with

The Science Center

National College of Education
Evanston, Illinois

 **𝒫** CHILDRENS PRESS ™

CHICAGO

Photographs

Page 2: Skylab space station (NASA)

Page 3: *Top to Bottom:*
Wheatfield (U.S.D.A. Photo)
Technician capping Abbokinase (Abbott Laboratories)
Spider (Macmillan Science Company)
View of Earth (NASA)
Space Shuttle (NASA)
Bahama coral reef (Macmillan Science Company)

Cover: Design by Sandra Gelak
Fringed Gentian (James P. Rowan)
Wisconsin Farmland (James P. Rowan)
Arctic Fox (James P. Rowan)

Library of Congress Catalog Card Number: 67-17925

TABLE OF CONTENTS

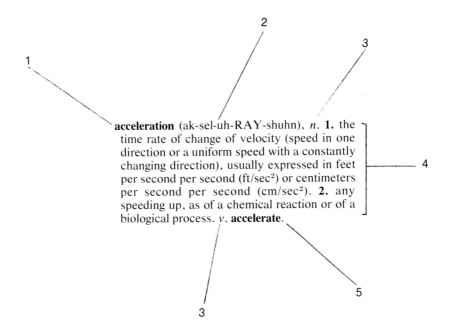

acceleration (ak-sel-uh-RAY-shuhn), *n.* **1.** the time rate of change of velocity (speed in one direction or a uniform speed with a constantly changing direction), usually expressed in feet per second per second (ft/sec^2) or centimeters per second per second (cm/sec^2). **2.** any speeding up, as of a chemical reaction or of a biological process. *v.* **accelerate.**

1. **ENTRY WORD** appears in bold face type.

2. **PRONUNCIATION** appears enclosed in parentheses. The syllable that is to be stressed in the pronunciation is printed in large type.

3. **PART OF SPEECH** is printed in italic type. Part of speech shows how the word is used.

4. **DEFINITIONS** tell the meaning of the entry word. If a word has more than one meaning each definition is set off by a number 1, 2, etc.

5. **RUN-ON WORDS** appear at the end of the definition in bold face type. The word is undefined because its meaning is similar to the entry word. Part of speech is indicated in italics.

6. **CROSS-REFERENCES** also appear in bold face at the end of the definition. They refer the reader to other entries for further information.

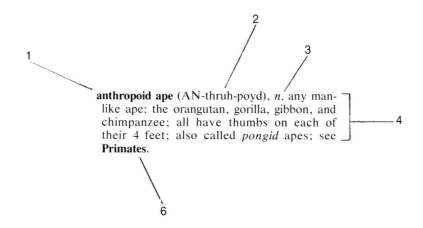

anthropoid ape (AN-thruh-poyd), *n.* any man-like ape: the orangutan, gorilla, gibbon, and chimpanzee; all have thumbs on each of their 4 feet; also called *pongid* apes; see **Primates.**

PRONUNCIATION KEY

(stress is put on syllable in LARGE LETTERS)

VOWELS

a—*a* as in *lap* or *Al*
ah—*a* as in *calm*, *o* as in *constant*
ai—*a* as in *care*
ay—*a* as in *late*
ee—*e* as in *deep*
ey—*i* as in *iris*, when standing alone in syllable
i—*i* as in *pin*
ih—*i* as in *pin*, when standing alone in syllable
oh—*o* as in *stone*
oy—*oi* as in *coil*, *oy* as in *boy*
uh—*u* as in *but*, *e* as in *matter*
y—*i* as in *line*, when part of a syllable
yoo—*u* as in *fuse*

CONSONANTS

f—*ph* as in *phase*
g—*g* as in *gap*
j—*g* as in *gem*
k—*c* as in *cat*
kw—*qu* as in *quake*
s—*c* as in *cell*, *s* as in *slip*
sh—*sh* as in *shell*
z—*s* as in *please*, *x* as in *xenon*
zh—*si* as in *fusion*, *ti* as in *equation*
Remainder of consonants are said as written

N

n, symbol for a variable quantity, especially: **1.** used in a general chemical formula, such as $C_nH_{2n}+2$, the general formula for the methane series. **2.** in genetics, the number of chromosomes in a gamete (ovum or sperm); see **meiosis.**

N, symbol for **nitrogen.**

Na, symbol for **sodium** (formerly called *natrium*).

nacre, alternate term for **mother-of-pearl.**

nadir (NAY-duhr), *n.* that spot on the celestial sphere found by drawing a line through the observer and down through the earth; 180° from the zenith; see also **azimuth** picture.

naiad (NY-uhd), *n.* the immature aquatic form of any insect that undergoes incomplete metamorphosis, as the dragonfly; see also **metamorphosis.**

Naiadales (ny-uh-DAY-leez), *n.* an order of monocot aquatic or marsh herbs, usually with small flowers with green perianth and often without petals; seeds have little or no endosperm; most have tiny scales at base of leaf. The 7 fam-

(Left) Arrowhead, a water plantain, *Sagittaria latifolia;* (center) elodea, *Anacharis occidentalis:* (right) eel grass, *Zostera marina*

ilies include the pondweed or eel-grass family (*Zosteraceae*), the water-plantain family (*Alismataceae*), and the frogbit or elodea family (*Hydrochartiaceae*). All are used as aquarium plants; order is also called *Helobiales.*

nail, *n.* a horny tissue at the ends of digits of many mammals.

Najadales, alternate spelling of **Naiadales.**

Nansen bottle (NAN-suhn), a bottle open at both ends, for sampling water in ocean depths; when the bottle is lowered on a line to the desired depth, a sliding weight on the line trips a mechanism which closes both ends of the bottle, trapping water; named for Fridtjof Nansen (1861-1930), Norwegian explorer and oceanographer.

napalm (NAY-pahm), *n.* a combustible substance made of jellied gasoline, used in chemical warfare; burns on contact, with intense heat.

naphtha (NAF-thuh, NAP-thuh), *n.* any of a group of flammable, oily organic compounds derived from petroleum, with boiling range between gasoline and kerosene; used as fuel and solvent.

naphthalene (NAF-thuh-leen, NAP-), *n.* a white, flaky, crystalline organic compound with a strong aromatic odor; insoluble in water; used as a moth repellent, and an important intermediate for making fungicides, dyes, and explosives; formula, $C_{10}H_8$.

narcotic (nahr-KAH-tik), *n.* any drug that dulls pain and induces sleep, especially opium and its derivatives; can be habit-forming; extreme amounts cause coma (*narcosis*) or death. *adj.* **narcotic.**

naris (NAIR-uhs), alternate term for **nostril.**

nasal (NAY-zuhl), *adj.* relating to the nose.

nasturtium family (nas-TUHR-shuhm), see **Geraniales.**

native, *adj.* **1.** belonging to the biota of an ecosystem that occurs naturally in an area without the interference of man, as kangaroos are native to Australia. **2.** found in nature in pure form, such as *native* copper.

natrium, former name for **sodium.**

natural gas, a mixture of gaseous chemicals, paraffin hydrocarbons, and other gases coming from the earth and often found with petroleum; used as fuel and as a chemical intermediate; composition varies but is chiefly the lighter hydrocarbons —methane, propane—mixed with hydrogen, nitrogen, the carbon oxides, and (in some finds) helium; see also **LNG.**

natural history, 1. the study of natural objects such as plants, animals, and minerals. **2.** a descriptive story giving the natural development of some object or process in nature, as the *natural history* of glacial bogs or of coastal birds.

natural immunity, a condition of natural resistance to a particular disease due to the body's inherited physical constitution; see also **acquired immunity.**

natural laws, a body of scientific laws that hold true throughout the universe as far as can be determined by observation and experimentation.

natural resource, all the land, water, energy, mineral wealth, and naturally occurring plants and animals in any region.

natural science, any of the scientific studies of nature, especially astronomy, physics, chemistry, biology, and geology; thus, any modern science except the social sciences.

natural selection, the biological concept that as each new generation of organisms arises and possesses new combinations of traits (due to sexual recombinations of genes or to mutations), then those patterns of traits that better enable the new organisms to adjust to the environment they meet will be selected for survival.

nature (NAY-chuhr), *n.* the universe; the total of all the events, organisms, and matter that occur in the universe; especially, all such phenomena as they occur without being affected by man. *adj.* **natural.**

nauplius (NAW-plee-uhs), *n.,* *pl.* **-plii.** the larval form of many hard-shelled crustaceans, having an oval unsegmented body and 3 pairs of appendages, as well as one large, central eye; first stage after egg.

nausea (NAW-zee-uh, -shuh), *n.* the sensation of digestive or related discomfort without usual sense of pain, "feeling sick to the stomach." In extreme cases it may lead to automatic vomiting.

nautical mile, a unit of linear measurement for ships and aircraft, equal to 1 minute on the circle of the earth, or about 6,076 feet. The *international nautical mile* is 6,076.103 feet; contrast with **statute mile.**

nautilus (NAW-tuh-luhs), see **Cephalopoda.**

navel (NAY-vuhl), *n.* a button-like scar and (often) a depression on the abdomen of mammals where the umbilical cord was attached during embryonic life before birth.

navigation (nav-uh-GAY-shuhn), *n.* the art or science of locating position and plotting courses of ships and aircraft. *v.* **navigate.**

Nb, symbol for **niobium.**

Nd, symbol for **neodymium.**

Ne, symbol for **neon.**

Neanderthal man (nee-AN-duhr-tawl), a prehistoric race of man, *Homo neanderthalensis;* reconstructions indicate a short, broad-shouldered type with low and retreating forehead, heavy brow ridges, and knees bent forward when walking; lived between 200,000 and 100,000 years ago.

neap tide (NEEP), a tide when the difference between high and low tide is the least; occurs just after the first and third quarters of the lunar month.

nearsighted, *adj.* having a condition in which faraway objects are not seen clearly; due to the focusing of distant objects before their images reach the retina, resulting in a blurred image; medically, *nearsightedness* is called *myopia.*

nebula (NEB-yoo-luh), *n., pl.* **-las, -lae. 1.** in astronomy, a faint, cloudy patch in the sky consisting of stars too distant to be seen separately, or

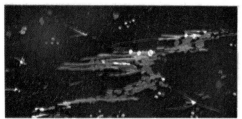

Veil Nebula, near Cygnus, may be the remains of a supernova; gas particles collide, emitting colored light

a mass of gaseous matter. **2.** in medicine, a small, cloudy patch on the cornea of the eye.

nebular hypothesis, a theory of the origin of the solar system which states that it was a mass of hot, gaseous matter (a nebula) that gradually cooled, shrank, and formed the sun and planets; also called *Laplace theory.*

necrosis (nuh-KROH-sis), *n.* changes in plant and animal tissues due to the death of cells resulting from physical injury, reduced blood supply, or harmful actions of bacteria.

nectar (NEK-tuhr), *n.* a sweet liquid from certain glands (*nectaries*) in or near the flowers of many plants; attracts bees and hummingbirds.

needle, *n.* **1.** a slender, pointed, straight or bent piece of heavy steel wire set in a handle and used in dissecting animals. **2.** the simple, narrow leaf of most conifers.

negative charge, the electrical or valence charge of an atom, radical, or other substance that has an excess of electrons, as Cl^-, $NO_3{}^-$.

nekton (NEK-tuhn), *n.* collectively, all organisms in the ocean that are capable of active locomotion; contrast with **plankton.** *adj.* **nektonic.**

Nemathelminthes (nem-uh-thel-MIN-theez), see **Nematoda.**

nematocyst (nuh-MAT-uh-sist), *n.* a flask-shaped, stinging device with barbs and a long slender filament ejected by certain cells in hydra, jellyfishes, and other coelenterates; see **Coelenterata.**

Nematoda (nem-uh-TOH-duh), *n.* the phylum of invertebrates known as *roundworms,* characterized by an elongated, unsegmented, cylindrical body, a digestive tract open at both ends, an ex-

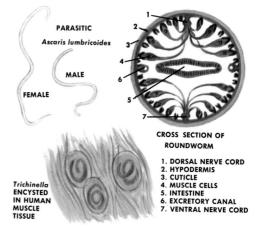

PARASITIC

Ascaris lumbricoides

MALE

FEMALE

Trichinella ENCYSTED IN HUMAN MUSCLE TISSUE

CROSS SECTION OF ROUNDWORM

1. DORSAL NERVE CORD
2. HYPODERMIS
3. CUTICLE
4. MUSCLE CELLS
5. INTESTINE
6. EXCRETORY CANAL
7. VENTRAL NERVE CORD

cretory system of two lateral tubes; *nematodes* include eelworm, pinworm, trichina, ascaris, and hookworm; phylum is sometimes called *Nemathelminthes.*

Neocene (NEE-uh-seen), *n.* in some geologic time calculations, an epoch of the Tertiary Period, including the Miocene and Pliocene epochs; see **geologic time table.**

neodymium (nee-oh-DIM-ee-uhm), *n.* a metallic chemical element in the rare-earth family; its salts are used to color glass and glazes; symbol Nd; at. no., 60; at. wt., 144.24; isolated by Welsbach in 1885.

Neolithic (nee-oh-LITH-ik), *adj.* dating from human cultures of the late Stone Age, about 5,000 years ago, when man had domesticated animals, practiced weaving and pottery-making, and tilled the soil.

neon (NEE-ahn), *n.* a chemical element in the rare gas family; colorless, odorless, and very unreactive; used chiefly to fill neon sign tubes; symbol Ne; at. no., 10; at. wt., 20.183; first identified by Ramsay and Travers in 1898.

neoprene (NEE-uh-preen), *n.* polychloroprene, a man-made rubber; more resistant to gas, heat, and oil than natural rubber.

nephology (ne-FAHL-uh-jee), *n.* the study of clouds; a division of meteorology.

nephoscope (NEF-uh-skohp), *n.* an instrument for measuring the height of clouds, their direction of movement, and their speed.

nephridium (nuh-FRID-ee-uhm), *n., pl.* **-idia.** the excretory organ of certain segmented worms and mollusks roughly corresponding to the kidneys in vertebrates.

nephrite (NEF-ryt), *n.* a translucent mineral similar to jadeite but of less brilliant green color; also occurs in grays and whites; hardness 6-6½; a source of jade.

nephritis (nuh-FRY-tis), *n.* inflammation of the kidneys, characterized by albumin and sometimes blood in the urine; most common type is called *Bright's disease.*

nephron (NEF-rahn), *n.* any of the numerous secreting structures in the kidney of vertebrates; in man, consists of the *renal corpuscle* including

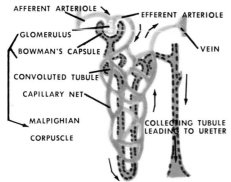

Bowman's capsule (that takes waste from the glomerulus), the proximal tubule, Henle's loop, and the distal tubule.

Neptune (NEP-tyoon), *n.* one of the largest planets of the solar system, with a diameter about 3.5 times that of the earth; a mean distance of about 2 billion, 800 million miles from the sun; takes about 165 years to revolve around the sun.

neptunium (nep-TYOO-nee-uhm), *n.* a man-made, radioactive chemical element in the actinide series; symbol Np; *at. no.,* 93; mass number of most stable isotope, 237; first prepared by McMillan and Abelson in 1940.

nerve, *n.* a cord or bundle of fibers which carries impulses of sensation and motion between the brain and other parts of the nervous system, and to the other parts of the body.

nerve cell, alternate term for **neuron.**

nerve impulse, a wave of excitation progressing along nerve fibers and acting as a stimulus to muscle, gland, organ, or other nerve cells; occurs by electrochemical changes.

nervous system (NUHR-vuhs), the body system of nerves, nerve cells, and nerve centers which acts to receive stimuli and to send nerve impulses; regulates and coordinates the parts of the body; see also **brain.**

nest, *n.* a structure built or a place used by an animal for shelter and concealment, and mostly as a home for its young during development.

nettle family, see **Urticales.**

neural (NOO-ruhl), *adj.* referring to a nerve or the nervous system.

neuralgia (noo-RAL-juh), *n.* a sharp, intermittent pain along the path of a nerve, usually accompanied by heightened sensitivity of the skin in the same area.

neural tube, a structure in the embryo of vertebrates from which the entire nervous system develops; forms from ectoderm.

neurilemma (noo-ruh-LEM-uh), *n.* the thin, cellular covering of a nerve fiber.

neuritis (noo-RY-tis), *n.* acute or chronic inflammation of one or many nerves accompanied by continuous pain; complicates many infectious diseases; also caused by pressure on a nerve due to a tumor or calcium deposits in arthritis.

neurodermatitis (noo-roh-duhr-muh-TY-tis), *n.* a chronic allergy of the skin characterized by itching scaly patches; affected by emotional state.

neuroglia (noo-RAHG-lee-uh), *n.* branching cells of various forms composing the supporting tissues which bind together the nervous elements of the nervous system.

neurohormone (noo-roh-HAWR-mohn), *n.* any of several hormones that stimulate nerve action, as *adrenalin.*

neurohumor (noo-roh-HYOO-muhr), *n.* a substance originating in a neuron that can stimulate another neuron or a muscle; unlike a neurohormone, it acts at the place it is given off; acetylcholine is an example.

neurology (noo-RAHL-uh-jee), *n.* the study of nerves and the nervous system, especially of the diseases affecting them.

neuron, *n.* the smallest living unit of nervous tissue; specialized in carrying a nerve impulse;

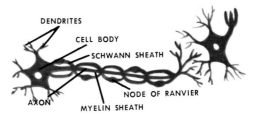

having specially developed properties of irritability and conductivity; also called *nerve cell.*

neutral (NOO-truhl), *adj.* **1.** in electricity, having neither positive nor negative charge; zero charge. **2.** in chemistry, having neither acid nor basic reaction, as salts are *neutral.* **3.** in biology, lacking sex organs (*neuter*).

Main parts of the human nervous system

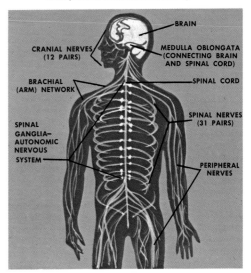

neutralization (noo-truh-luh ZAY-shuhn), *n.* **1.** in chemistry, the reduction of the acidity or alkalinity of a substance, usually a solution, by adding another substance which reacts with it. **2.** in physics, the removal of an electric charge on an object by adding an equal amount of opposite charge. *v.* **neutralize.**

neutrino (noo-TREE-noh), *n.* a nuclear particle, smaller than a neutron, that has no electrical charge and a mass close to zero.

neutron (NOO-trahn), *n.* one of 2 major particles that make up the nucleus of an atom; mass slightly greater than a proton, but with a charge of zero.

neutron star, a small dense star made mostly of neutrons. It rotates at high speeds.

neutron activation analysis, method of determining the elements present in material; a beam of neutrons makes the sample radioactive; the resultant radiation is analyzed; each element has its own peculiar radiation.

new candle, alternate term for **candela.**

newt (NOOT), *n.* any amphibious salamander with slender body, long tail, and short legs; usually found in Europe, Asia, and North America; adults, called *efts,* about 4 inches long; eat insects, snails, and worms; see **Amphibia.**

newton, *n.* the unit of force in the mks system: force which gives acceleration of 1 meter per second per second to a mass of 1 kilogram.

Newton's Law of Motion, any of 3 laws: **1.** a body at rest remains at rest and a body in motion remains in motion in the same path unless acted upon by an external force. **2.** the acceleration (change of motion) which a force gives to a mass is directly porportional to the force and inversely proportional to the mass. **3.** for every force there is an equal force, or reaction, in the opposite direction; stated by Sir Isaac Newton, English scientist.

New World, *adj.* native to North and South America, as certain *New World* porcupines; used to distinguish similar types from other continents.

Ni, symbol for **nickel.**

niacin (NY-uh-suhn), *n.* one of the B-complex vitamins essential to man for the prevention of pellegra; an organic acid occurring as colorless, odorless, needle-like crystals; derived from nicotine, and found in lean meat, fish, whole grains, milk, and yeast; formula, C_5H_4NCOOH; also called *nicotinic acid.*

niche (NITCH), *n.* in ecology, a habitat providing needed conditions for the life of any one species in an ecological system; if environment changes, the species must also change or locate a similar niche; see also **ecosystem.**

nickel (NIK-uhl), *n.* a silvery gray, metallic chemical element; ductile, malleable, and strong; used in electroplating to give a tough, corrosion-resistant, polished surface; a catalyst and alloying element; symbol Ni; *at. no.,* 28; *at. wt.,* 58.71; isolated by Cronstedt in 1751.

nicotine (NIK-uh-teen), *n.* a poisonous, thick, oily alkaloid found in tobacco; may be a carcinogen; used in medicines and insecticides; formula, $C_5H_4NC_4H_7NCH_3$.

nicotinic acid (nik-uh-TIN-ik), an alternate term for **niacin.**

nictitating membrane (NIK-ti-tay-ting), a transparent third eyelid present in many vertebrates which helps to keep the eye clean; in mammals, reduced to a small pink area at the inner edge of each eye.

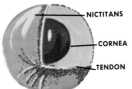

Nictitating membrane of a turkey (*Meleagris gallopavo*) covering part of the eyeball — NICTITANS, CORNEA, TENDON

nightshade family, see **Polemoniales.**

nimbostratus (NIM-boh-STRAH-tuhs), *n.* a dark, low-lying cloud that covers the sky and brings rain or snow; also called *nimbus.*

nimbus, see **nimbostratus.**

niobium (ny-OH-bee-uhm), *n.* a shiny, whitish, metallic chemical element; used in stainless steel and high-temperature alloys; symbol Nb; *at. no.,* 41; *at. wt.,* 92.906; isolated by Hatchett in 1801; also called *columbium* by metallurgists.

Nissl body (NIS-uhl), a dark-staining, fairly large body in the cytoplasm of nerve cells; contains ribonucleic acid and protein; function not known.

nit, *n.* the egg of a louse or other insect in order Anoplura; ectoparasitic on man and other mammals; usually cemented to strands of hair or fibers of clothing when laid.

niter, see **potassium nitrate.**

nitrate (NY-trayt), *n.* the radical, NO_3^-, or any compound containing this radical, as KNO_3.

nitration (ny-TRAY-shuhn), *n.* the process of treating with nitric acid, HNO_3, or other nitrate, or making a nitrate from other substances.

nitric (NY-trik), *adj.* referring to compounds in which nitrogen has a higher valence than in the corresponding nitrous compounds, such as nitric acid, HNO_3, where valence is +5; contrast with **nitrous.**

nitric acid, a colorless to yellow, fuming, corrosive inorganic acid; used to make fertilizers and important as a chemical intermediate; formula, HNO_3.

nitrification (ny-truh-fuh-KAY-shuhn), *n.* the process of combining with nitrogen or nitrogen compounds, as treating soil with nitrates; see **denitrifying bacterium.** *v.* **nitrify.**

nitrogen (NY-truh-juhn), *n.* a gaseous chemical element, almost 80% of the atmosphere; necessary for the life of plants and animals; colorless, odorless, nonflammable; used to make ammonia and other chemical compounds, and to fill incandescent lamps; symbol N; *at. no.,* 7; *at. wt.,* 14.0067; identified by Rutherford in 1772.

nitrogen fixation, the process in which nitrogen in the air is changed into useful nitrogen compounds by soil bacteria that live in the roots of legumes (as peas, beans), and by lightning that combines nitrogen with oxygen.

nitroglycerin (ny-truh-GLIH-suhr-uhn), *n.* a yellowish, thick, flammable, explosive liquid derived from glycerol and nitric acid; used for explosives and medicines; formula, $C_3H_5(NO_3)_3$.

nitrous (NY-truhs), *adj.* referring to compounds in which nitrogen has a lower valence than similar nitric compounds, as nitrous acid, HNO_2, with a valence of +3; contrast with **nitric.**

No, symbol for **nobelium.**

nobelium (noh-BEL-ee-uhm), *n.* a man-made, radioactive chemical element in the actinide series; symbol No; *at. no.,* 102; mass number of most stable isotope, 254; prepared at Nobel Institute of Physics in Sweden in 1957.

noble gas, alternate term for **rare gas.**

nocturnal (nahk-TUHR-nuhl), *adj.* characteristically active at night; *nocturnal* animals are more or less inactive during the day and feed at night; contrast with **diurnal.**

node (NOHD), *n.* **1.** a knot or swelling in any tissue. **2.** in botany, a point on a plant stem from which leaves or buds sprout. **3.** in astronomy, either of the points at which a celestial body cuts any given plane. **4.** any of the evenly spaced points of no vibration in the movement of a sound wave through a medium. **5.** alternate term for **lymph gland.**

nomenclature (NOH-muhn-klay-chuhr), *n.* **1.** in chemistry, the orderly system used to name compounds, especially organic compounds, as ethane, where the *eth-* means 2 carbons and the *-ane* means a straight chain hydrocarbon—C_2H_6 or CH_3CH_3. **2.** in biology, **classification.**

This chart shows height reached by an object at any given time after being thrown upward with known initial velocity. Dotted line shows an example: if a ball is tossed upward with initial velocity of 117 ft./sec., it will be 100 ft. high in one second; after 6¼ sec., it will again be 100 ft. high but falling. A ruler intersects the curve at 6¼.	150 100 50 0 Height (feet) Time (sec.) Velocity (ft./sec.) 80 100 120 140 160

nomograph (NOH-muh-graf), *n.* a graph for solving equations by laying a straightedge from one line to another and reading the answer from the point at which a third line is intersected; also called *alignment chart.*

nonconductor (nahn-kuhn-DUHK-tuhr), *n.* a material that does not transport any form of energy (particularly heat or electric energy) to any notable degree; often called an *insulator.*

North Pole, 1. the most northern point on the earth's surface, coinciding with the end of the earth's axis; its zenith is about 1° from the North Star. **2.** the north magnetic pole, several hundred miles from the geologic North Pole.

North Star, the bright star seen in the Northern Hemisphere that is almost directly above the earth's northern axis; also called *Polaris.*

nose, *n.* in some vertebrates, the part of the face containing the nostrils; see also **nostril.**

nose cone, the front tip of a missile or satellite, specially designed for protection from the heat of atmospheric friction.

nostril (NAHS-tril), *n.* an external opening of a passage in the respiratory system of air-breathing vertebrates; may contain olfactory nerves for smelling; usually occur as a pair of openings in the nose; in some whales there is only one, called a *blow-hole;* also called *naris.*

notochord (NOH-tuh-kawrd), *n.* a rodlike, stiffening structure occurring in all chordate embryos and in adults of some primitive chordates; the axis around which the spinal column develops in vertebrates.

nova (NOH-vuh), *n., pl.* **novae.** a star that grows suddenly brighter and then gradually grows dimmer, returning to its original luminosity.

novocaine (NOH-vuh-kayn), *n.* a colorless or white crystalline alkaloid, *procaine hydrochloride;* related to cocaine; used as a local anesthetic and in medicine; formula, $C_{13}H_{20}O_2N_2 \cdot HCl$.

noxious (NAHK-shuhs), *adj.* harmful or injurious to the health of an organism.

Np, symbol for **neptunium.**

nuclear (NOO-klee-uhr), *adj.* **1.** related to the nucleus of a cell. **2.** related to the nucleus of an atom.

nuclear energy, the energy involved in the binding together of an atomic nucleus, which may be liberated usefully by fission of the nucleus, or by fusion reactions of nuclei.

nuclear fission, the splitting of an atomic nucleus, usually achieved by bombardment with high-energy neutrons and involving the formation of new atoms and freeing of large amounts of energy.

nuclear particle, any of the fundamental particles making up the nuclei of atoms; especially the

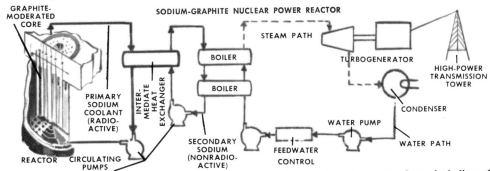

GRAPHITE-MODERATED CORE — SODIUM-GRAPHITE NUCLEAR POWER REACTOR — STEAM PATH — BOILER — TURBOGENERATOR — HIGH-POWER TRANSMISSION TOWER — BOILER — PRIMARY SODIUM COOLANT (RADIO-ACTIVE) — INTERMEDIATE HEAT EXCHANGER — CONDENSER — WATER PUMP — SECONDARY SODIUM (NONRADIO-ACTIVE) — WATER PATH — REACTOR — CIRCULATING PUMPS — FEEDWATER CONTROL

nonmetal, *n.* a substance that is a poor conductor of heat and electricity and is not malleable, ductible, or lustrous, such as sulfur, rubber.

Northern Hemisphere, that part of Earth lying north of the equator.

northern lights, an alternate term for *aurora borealia;* see **aurora.**

neutron and *proton;* sometimes including the *meson, hyperon, neutrino,* or other particles not necessarily strictly nuclear; see also **antiparticle, mass-twin.**

nuclear physics, the branch of physical science that is concerned with study of atomic nuclei and related atomic phenomena.

nuclear reactor, a device so constructed as to make possible chain-reaction nuclear fissions; originally called an *atomic pile;* consists of fuel, moderator, and shielding devices; used in production of nuclear energy which may be converted to electrical power, preparation of isotopes, and other applications.

nuclei (NOO-klee-ey), plural of **nucleus.**

nucleic acid (noo-KLAY-ik), any of the compounds found in all living cells, usually combined with proteins to form nucleoproteins. They are complex, high-molecular weight compounds of carbon, hydrogen, oxygen, nitrogen, and phosphorus, as in DNA and RNA.

nucleolus (noo-KLEE-uh-luhs), *n.* a small, round, conspicuous body found in the nucleus of many cells; composition differs from the rest of the nucleus; function is uncertain but it probably temporarily stores RNA.

nucleon (NOO-klee-ahn), *n.* any nuclear particle, especially a proton or neutron.

nucleonics (noo-klee-AHN-iks), *n.* that branch of nuclear physics that deals with the synthesis or analysis of systems containing or interacting with free nuclear or atomic particles or radiation.

nucleon number, the sum of the protons and neutrons in the nucleus of an atom.

nucleoprotein (NOO-klee-oh-PROH-tee-in), *n.* any protein found combined with nucleic acids, occurring especially in the cell nuclei of living organisms.

nucleus (NOO-klee-uhs), *n., pl.* **nuclei. 1.** in physics and chemistry, the central part of an atom that has a positive charge and makes up most of its mass. It is composed of protons and neutrons (except for hydrogen whose nucleus contains only a proton). **2.** in biology, the central mass of protoplasm in animal and plant cells which governs cellular activity; see **cell. 3.** in astronomy, the small, bright part in a comet head. *adj.* **nuclear.**

nuclide (NOO-klyd), *n.* an atom (especially its nucleus) of specific atomic number and mass number, or a collection of such atoms; written as $_6C^{14}$ (carbon has atomic number 6 and one of its isotopes contains 14 nucleons).

numerical control, the use of a computer to control the manufacture of small quantities of items, particularly those items needing a great many precise but different operations.

nut, *n.* a dry, indehiscent fruit with a hard pericarp or wall, as acorn and filbert; see **fruit.**

nutmeg family, see **Ranales.**

nutrient (NOO-tree-uhnt), *n.* a substance used by an organism for carrying on its cellular functions; a food.

nutrition (noo-TRISH-uhn), *n.* the process of taking food material into a living organism and converting it into substances (*nutrients*) used for growth, repair, and energy.

nylon (NY-lahn), *n.* any strong synthetic fiber, plastic, or other material composed of polymerized amides; used for clothing, adhesives, insulators, and many household and industrial items.

nymph (NIMF), *n.* the immature form of an insect that undergoes an incomplete metamorphosis; resembles the adult except lacks wings and reproductive organs; grasshopper is an example.

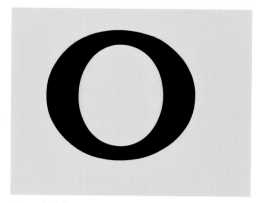

O, symbol for **oxygen.**

OAO, abbreviation for **orbital astronautical satellite.**

oasis (oh-AY-sis), *n.* a region in a desert area that has vegetation and water.

obesity (oh-BEE-si-tee), *n.* a body condition in which fat is stored in the tissues, due to too many calories consumed and too little energy expended; a person is *obese* if his weight is more than 10% over the recommended weight for his size and age.

objective (ahb-JEK-tiv), **1.** *n.* the lens in a microscope or telescope which is closest to the observed object. **2.** *adj.* referring to any event that can be observed by any person.

oblate spheroid (AHB-layt SFEE-royd), a ball-shaped body or object that is slightly flattened at 2 opposite spots (poles); a term describing the earth's shape.

observatory (ahb-ZUHR-vuh-toh-ree), *n.* any place specially equipped for observation of celestial objects, usually with large telescopes.

obsidian (ahb-SID-ee-uhn), *n.* a glassy, dark-colored volcanic rock composed chiefly of silica; see **rock** picture.

obstetrics (ahb-STET-riks), *n.* the branch of medicine concerned with the care and treatment of women before, during, and after childbirth and related disorders and complications.

occipital (ahk-SIP-uh-tuhl), *adj.* relating to the back of the skull.

occluded front (uh-KLOOD-uhd), a weather front formed when a cold front meets a warm front and elevates the warm air.

occultation (ah-kuhl-TAY-shuhn), *n.* the cutting off of light from a celestial body by the passage of another between it and Earth; especially, the cutting off (eclipsing) of light by the moon as it passes between a star and Earth.

ocean (OH-shuhn), *n.* **1.** the massive body of salt water covering over two-thirds of the earth's surface and containing animal and plant life of its own. **2.** any of 5 principal geological divisions of the above: the Atlantic, Pacific, Indian, Arctic, or Antarctic oceans.

oceanography (oh-shuh-NAHG-ruh-fee), *n.* the scientific study of the oceans including their geography, geology, chemistry, and biology, and the various relationships among these.

ocellus (oh-SEL-uhs), *n., pl.* **-li. 1.** a simple eye of certain invertebrates, mainly arthropods, consisting of light-sensitive cells, pigments and nerve fibers. **2.** an eye-like colored spot found on wings of butterflies and moths and on bird feathers, as the peacock's.

octane (AHK-tayn), *n.* one of several isomers of octane; specifically, *n-octane,* a colorless, flammable, liquid paraffin hydrocarbon; used as a solvent, combustion stimulant, and for organic synthesis; formula, C_8H_{18}.

octane number, a number indicating the antiknock quality of an automotive fuel; shows degree of similarity to a standard fuel.

octopus (AHK-tuh-puhs), see **Cephalopoda.**

ocular (AHK-yuh-luhr), **1.** *adj.* relating to the eye or of the nature of an eye. **2.** *n.* the eyepiece of an optical instrument.

odometer (oh-DAHM-uh-tuhr), *n.* an instrument used to measure distance traveled; one type measures distance a vehicle moves; another type measures distance traveled along a line or curve on a graph or architectural plan.

Odonata (oh-duh-NAH-tuh), *n.* an order of insects with toothlike biting mouth parts, 2 pairs of membranous wings, incomplete metamorphosis, and aquatic larvae; examples are dragonflies and damsel flies.

odontology (oh-dahn-TAHL-uh-jee), *n.* the study of the teeth and surrounding tissues, including the prevention and cure of diseases affecting them; dentistry.

oersted (UHR-sted), *n.* the unit of magnetic intensity in the cgs system: intensity where a force of one dyne acts on a unit magnetic pole; also, the intensity 1 cm from a unit magnetic pole.

offspring, *n.* the new individuals produced by a set of parents; children or young.

OGO, abbreviation for **orbital geophysical observatory.**

ohm, *n.* a unit of electrical resistance: the resistance in a circuit when a potential difference of one volt produces a one-ampere current.

ohmmeter (OH-mee-tuhr), *n.* an instrument for direct measurement of electrical resistance by reading a scale showing effect of a resistor.

Ohm's law, the magnitude of an electric current in amperes, in an electric circuit, is directly proportional to the pressure, in volts, and inversely proportional to the resistance, in ohms; sometimes stated: amperes equal volts divided by ohms; named for Georg S. Ohm, German physicist.

oil, *n.* any liquid of high viscosity and a slippery, greasy feel, derived from animal, vegetable, or mineral sources. Oils generally fall into 3 types: *petroleum* or *mineral* oils (as lubricating oil); *fatty* oils from animal or plant fats (glycerol esters); and *essential* oils, also derived from plants and having a notable odor (peppermint oil).

Old World, *adj.* native of the Eastern Hemisphere, of the European continent especially, as certain *Old World* monkeys.

Oleales (oh-lee-AY-leez), see **Gentianales.**

olefin (OH-luh-fuhn), *n.* any of a class of unsaturated hydrocarbons containing double bonds, and having the general formula, C_nH_{2n}, as ethylene, C_2H_4.

oleomargarine (oh-lee-oh-MAHR-juh-rin), *n.* a mixture of animal and/or plant oils with skim milk churned to the consistency of butter; usually, vitamin A is added; used like butter.

olfactory (ahl-FAK-tuh-ree), *adj.* relating to the sense or the organs of smell.

Oligocene (OHL-ig-uh-seen), *n.* the second epoch of the Tertiary Period, characterized by development of mammals. It began about 35 million years ago; see **geologic time table.**

oligoclase (AH-lig-uh-klays), *n.* a type of plagioclase feldspar.

olive family, see **Gentianales.**

olivine (OH-luh-veen), *n.* a lustrous, green to brown mineral found in igneous and metamorphic rocks; composed of magnesium-iron silicates $(Fe,Mg)_2SiO_4$, with hardness 6½-7; used for refractories and cements; see **mineral** picture.

omasum (oh-MAY-suhm), *n.* the third stomach of cud-chewing mammals; located between the reticulum and abomasum; this is the stomach to which the cud returns after being chewed; see also **ruminant.**

ommateum (ahm-uh-TEE-uhm), the technical term for **compound eye.**

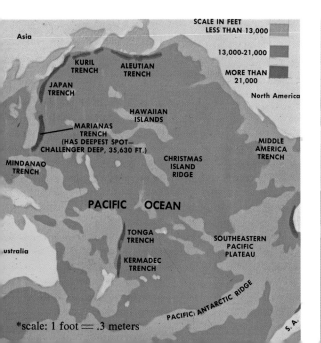

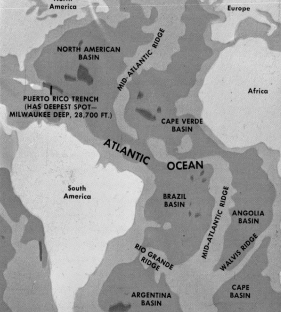

omnirange (AHM-ni-raynj), *n.* a radio navigation system in which a full range of bearings is transmitted by a radio station; a plane navigator may select any one of these bearings, and his instruments convert it to compass indications.

BEARINGS, OR RADIALS, FROM WHICH PILOT IS ABLE TO SET HIS COURSE

omnivorous (ahm-NIV-uh-ruhs), *adj.* referring to an animal which eats both plants and other animals. *n.* **omnivore.**

ontogeny (ahn-TAHJ-uh-nee), *n.* the development of an individual from the moment of fertilization of the egg through maturity, with some individual differences; contrast with **phylogeny.**

Onychophora (ahn-uh-KAHF-uh-ruh), *n.* a phylum of unsegmented, wormlike animals with slime glands on the head; found in dark places of moist, tropical areas; often considered a class of arthropods; see **peripatus.**

onyx (AHN-iks), *n.* a semiprecious stone, a form of chalcedony usually with layers of different colors.

oo-, (OH-oh), a word part meaning *egg;* also **oö-.**

oocyte (OH-uh-syt), *n.* a female germ cell in the maturation stage before it becomes a functional ovum and begins to divide.

oogenesis (OH-uh-jen-uh-sis), a type of *gametogenesis;* see **meiosis.**

oogonium (oh-uh-GOH-nee-uhm), *n. pl.* **-nia.** **1.** in animals, a female germ cell, during its multiplication stage preceding the maturation or *occyte* stages; occurs in the embryo. **2.** in certain algae and fungi, a cone-celled female reproductive structure usually consisting of a spherical sac containing one or more eggs.

opal (OH-puhl), *n.* SiO_2, any of various amorphous hydrated silicas used as gemstones; they may be dull or have a pearly luster, or be colorless; may reflect and refract light to show colors.

opalescent (oh-puh-LEHS-uhnt), *adj.* having or displaying colors like an opal; iridescent.

opaque (oh-PAYK), **1.** *adj.* pertaining to the quality of not letting light pass (not transparent) or not reflecting light (light-absorbing); contrast with **translucent. 2.** *n.* in photography, a substance used to block out parts of negatives.

open circulatory system, a system in which blood leaving the heart is confined to tubes which eventually lead into open tissue spaces *(lacunae);* the blood circulates through and back to a blood sinus around the heart; pores called *ostia* allow blood to re-enter the heart; found in crustaceans; contrast with **closed circulatory system.**

open-hearth process, a process for producing high-grade steel in which pig iron and scrap iron are melted and oxidized in a large, shallow furnace; fuel gas is burned above the metal mass and heat reflected down into the metal; impurities are removed by the addition of iron oxide as an oxidizing flux; slag leaves the hearth as a gas or is skimmed from the liquid surface; controlled alloy ingredients are then added.

operation (ahp-uh-RAY-shuhn), *n.* **1.** any complex procedure with many preparations before it can be executed. **2.** a surgical procedure, usually involving instruments, for correcting physical defects or otherwise improving a disorder.

operational (ahp-uh-RAY-shuh-nuhl), *adj.* in normal working condition; the *Nike-Hercules* missile is *operational.*

operculum (oh-PUHR-kyuh-luhm), *n.* a structure which acts as a lid or cover, as the gill covering of fishes, or the covering flap on capsules in many mosses.

ophthalmology (ahf-thal-MAHL-uh-jee), *n.* study of the eye and its diseases. An *ophthalmologist* is sometimes called an *oculist;* contrast with **optometry.**

ophthalmoscope (ahf-THAL-muh-skohp), *n.* an instrument used to study the inside of the eye, particularly the retina; consists of a mirror with a central hole through which light passes.

opiate (OH-pee-uht), *n.* any of various medicines containing opium or opium derivatives.

opium (OH-pee-uhm), *n.* a narcotic drug derived from the fluid found in the unripe seed capsules of the opium poppy; contains such alkaloids as morphine and codeine; used as a medicine to relieve pain and produce sleep.

opossum (uh-PAHS-uhm), see **Marsupialia.**

opposable (uh-POH-suh-buhl), *adj.* able to be put opposite something else; especially the *opposable* thumb of primates that can be placed opposite to the fingers.

opposite leaves, an arrangement in which 2 leaves appear opposite each other at each node.

opposition (ahp-uh-ZISH-uhn), *n.* in astronomy, the position of a planet when it is just opposite (180° from) the position of the sun as viewed from Earth.

opsonin (AHP-suh-nin), *n.* a blood serum component that makes invading bacteria more liable to destruction by phagocytes or white blood cells.

optical (AHP-ti-kuhl), *adj.* pertaining to sight and vision, or to the science of optics.

Zöllner's lines, a classic example of an optical illusion

optical illusion (ih-LOO-zhuhn), anything that deceives the eye by creating a false optical impression, such as Zöllner's parallel lines which appear to diverge or converge because of the placement of a series of diagonal cross lines.

optical maser, a maser operating in the visible spectrum, rather than in the microwave portion of the electromagnetic spectrum; see also **gaseous maser, maser.**

optic chiasma (ky-AS-muh), see **chiasma.**

optics (AHP-tiks), *n.* the study of light waves and of the phenomena related to them; includes design of optical equipment (lenses, mirrors).

optimum (AHP-tuh-muhm), *n.* the most advantageous conditions for something to occur: definite ranges of temperature and humidity, food abundance, etc., are part of a favorable or *optimum* environment. *adj.* **optimal.**

optometry (ahp-TAHM-uh-tree), *n.* the science of measuring the ability of the eyes to see and the prescription of corrective lenses or exercises; does not include drug prescriptions or surgery; see also **ophthalmology.**

Opuntiales (oh-puhn-chee-AY-leez), *n.* an order of American dicot fleshy herbs and woody plants,

(*Orchidaceae*) of ornamental epiphytes, usually with one petal different from the others. One orchid genus yields vanilla.

orchid family (AWR-kid), see **Orchidales.**

order, *n.* a group, in the classification of plants and animals, consisting of one or more families and forming a subdivision of a class; see also **classification.**

Ordovician (awr-doh-VISH-uhn), *n.* a period in the Paleozoic Era which began nearly 500 million years ago and lasted about 60 million years; algae were the only plants, and all animal life was marine; see **geologic time table.**

ore, *n.* a mineral or group of minerals from which useful substances, especially metals, can be obtained, as magnetite is an *iron* ore.

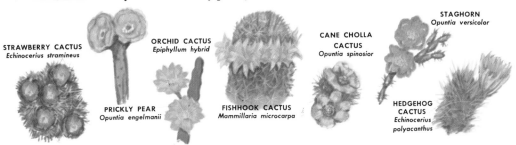

STRAWBERRY CACTUS
Echinocerius stramineus

ORCHID CACTUS
Epiphyllum hybrid

CANE CHOLLA CACTUS
Opuntia spinosior

STAGHORN
Opuntia versicolor

PRICKLY PEAR
Opuntia engelmanii

FISHHOOK CACTUS
Mammillaria microcarpa

HEDGEHOG CACTUS
Echinocerius polyacanthus

usually with small, spiny leaves and often with large, brilliantly colored, tubular flowers; stems are modified for holding water. The only family is the cactus family (*Cactaceae*) of 1700 species of which the largest is the *saquaro,* sometimes reaching 70 feet.

oral (AW-ruhl), OH-), *adj.* relating to the mouth.

orbit (AWR-bit), *n.* **1.** the path of any object as it revolves about some other object, whether it is the earth's path in revolving around the sun or an electron's path around the nucleus of an atom; may be circular, elliptical, or other section of a cone. The orbits of artificial satellites are usually elliptical. **2.** the bony socket in which the vertebrate eye is located.

orbital (AWR-bi-tuhl), **1.** *adj.* referring to an orbit. **2.** *n.* in quantum theory, the wave function of an electron corresponding to the older concept of its orbit.

orbital astronomical observatory, a satellite equipped for making astronomical observations and transmitting the observations back to Earth. *abbr.* **OAO.**

orbital capture, the interval in interplanetary space travel during which a satellite must remain on or near its target planet before it can take off for a return journey to Earth or other planet; this period is longest for planets nearest Earth.

orbital geophysical observatory, a satellite equipped for making geophysical observations (concerning distances, elevations, surface curvature, etc.) and transmitting the observations back to Earth. *abbr.* **OGO.**

Orchidales (awr-kid-AY-leez), *n.* an order of tropical and subtropical monocot plants having irregular flowers, one or 2 stamens fused to style, and numerous tiny seeds with little or no endosperm. There are 2 families: the small burmannia family (*Burmanniaceae*) of nongreen saprophytes, and the very large orchid family

organ (AWR-guhn), *n.* in biology, a group of cells or tissues so organized that it carries out specific functions; the leaf of a plant and the kidney of an animal are examples.

organelle (AWR-guh-nel), *n.* a specialized body in the protoplasm of a unicellular organism; functions like an organ system in a multicellular organism; a cell organ.

organic (awr-GAN-ik), *adj.* **1.** pertaining to, derived from, or composed of, living organisms. **2.** in chemistry, pertaining to compounds of carbon (except carbon gases and inorganic carbonates).

organic chemistry, the branch of chemistry that deals with the compounds of carbon (except carbon dioxide and monoxide, and the carbonates).

organism (AWR-guh-nizm), *n.* an individual living plant or animal.

organizer (AWR-gah-ny-zuhr), *n.* any region in an embryo, probably containing specific enzymes, that causes undifferentiated cells to differentiate in a specific direction; for example, if during an early stage of development, cells which normally

Representative orchids: (1) butterfly, *Epidendrum tampense;* (2) stream orchis, *Epipactis gigantea;* (3) grass orchid, *Calopogon pallidus;* (4) yellow lady's slipper, *Cipripedium calceolus;* (5) purple-fringe, *Habenaria psycodes;* (6) vanilla, *Vanilla planifolia*

produce skin are transplanted to the brain region, they become nerve cells rather than skin cells due to the influence of *organizers* in the brain.

orifice (AWR-uh-fis), *n.*   an opening or hole, such as the *cardiac orifice,* the opening of the esophagus into the stomach, or the mouthlike structure in some invertebrates; also called *os* or *aperture.*

origin (AWR-i-jin), *n.*   **1.** the first stage of existence of early ancestors of any organism.   **2.** in anatomy, the most fixed point of attachment for a muscle; or the attachment nearest the center of the body; see also **insertion.**

Orion (uh-RY-uhn), *n.*   **1.** the *Warrior,* a bright zodiacal constellation best seen in winter; 3 of the 25 brightest stars in the sky are in Orion: Rigel, Betelgeuse, and Bellatrix.   **2.** a proposed nuclear space ship much larger than any others, in the planning stage.

Ornithischia (awr-nuh-THIS-kee-uh), *n.*   an order of dinosaurs with birdlike hips; includes stegosaurus, trachodon, and triceratops; see **dinosaur.**

Representative osteichthyans, the true bony fishes

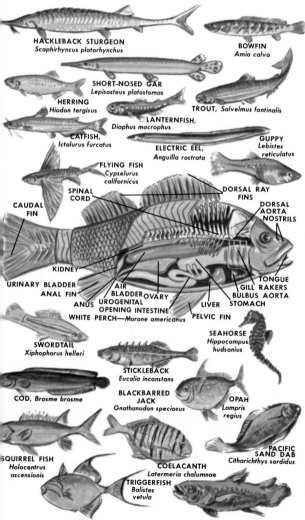

HACKLEBACK STURGEON
Scaphirhyncus platorhynchus

BOWFIN
Amia calva

SHORT-NOSED GAR
Lepisosteus platostomas

HERRING
Hiodon tergisus

TROUT, *Salvelmus fontinalis*

LANTERNFISH,
Diaphus macrophus

CATFISH,
Ictalurus furcatus

GUPPY
*Lebistes
reticulatus*

ELECTRIC EEL,
Anguilla rostrata

FLYING FISH
*Cypselurus
californicus*

SPINAL
CORD

DORSAL RAY
FINS

CAUDAL
FIN

DORSAL
AORTA
NOSTRILS

KIDNEY

TONGUE
GILL RAKERS
BULBUS AORTA
STOMACH

URINARY BLADDER
ANAL FIN

AIR
BLADDER OVARY

UROGENITAL
OPENING INTESTINE

LIVER

ANUS

WHITE PERCH—*Morone americanus*

PELVIC FIN

SWORDTAIL
Xiphophorus helleri

SEAHORSE
*Hippocampus
hudsonius*

STICKLEBACK
Eucalia inconstans

COD, *Brosme brosme*

BLACKBARRED
JACK
Gnathanodon speciosus

OPAH
*Lampris
regius*

SQUIRREL FISH
*Holocentrus
ascensionis*

PACIFIC
SAND DAB
Citharichthys sordidus

COELACANTH
Latermeria chalumnae

TRIGGERFISH
*Balistes
vetula*

ornithology (awr-nuh-THAHL-uh-jee), *n.*   the study of birds, their structure, habits, etc.

ornithopter (AWR-ni-thahp-tuhr), *n.*   an airplane designed to operate by imitating the flapping of a bird's wings; one of the early concepts in flight, but never workable except in small models.

orogeny (aw-RAH-juh-nee), *n.*   the process of mountain building, particularly when due to the earth's crust folding up; see **diastrophism.**

orology (oh-RAHL-uh-jee), *n.*   the study of mountains in all their details.

orpine family (OHR-pyn), see **Rosales.**

orthoclase (AWR-thuh-klays), *n.*   a type of feldspar with potassium as the basic metal, $KAlSi_3O_8$, with hardness 6; moonstone, a semi-precious stone, is an *orthoclase.*

orthodontia (awr-thuh-DAHN-shuh), *n.*   the branch of dentistry concerned with the straightening of irregular teeth.

orthogenesis (awr-thuh-JEN-uh-sis), *n.*   the evolution of organisms along definite lines predetermined or made possible by the possibilities within their individual heritage.

orthopedics (awr-thuh-PEED-iks), *n.*   the branch of medicine and surgery concerned with the diagnosis, correction, treatment, and cure of deformities and diseases of bones, joints, muscles, and other parts of the skeletal system in man.

Orthoptera (awr-THAHP-tuh-ruh), *n.*   an order of insects with the forewings thickened and hind wings folded fanlike under them, chewing mouth parts, and gradual metamorphosis; examples are grasshopper, cockroach and other roaches, cricket, walking stick, and praying mantis.

orthorhombic (awr-tho-RAHM-bik), *adj.*   referring to any crystal with 3 unequal, perpendicular axes; also called *rhombic* or *rhombohedral* system; see **crystal system.**

os, *n.*   **1.** (OHS), a mouth, opening, or entrance.   **2.** (AHS), a bone.

Os, symbol for **osmium.**

oscillate (AHS-uh-layt), *v.*   to move back and forth, as a pendulum or spring.   *n.* **oscillation.**

oscilloscope (ah-SIL-uh-skohp), *n.*   an electronic device for tracing on the fluorescent screen of a cathode-ray tube a luminous track which shows the wave form of electrical signals.

osmium (AHZ-mee-uhm), *n.*   a hard, white, metallic chemical element; used in alloys for pen points and electric light filaments and as a hydrogenation catalyst; symbol Os; *at. no.,* 76; *at. wt.,* 190.2; isolated by Tennant in 1804.

osmosis (ahs-MOH-sis), *n.*   diffusion through a semipermeable membrane of liquids having differing concentrations of solute; movement is normally of the solvent in such a direction as to equalize the pressure (*osmotic pressure*) of the concentrations.   *adj.* **osmotic.**

ossicle (AHS-uh-kuhl), *n.*   **1.** a small bone, such as any one of the group of 3 small bones in the middle ear of mammals known as the *auditory ossicles.*   **2.** any of the calcified plates or spines found in the body wall of echinoderms.

ossify (AHS-uh-fy), *v.*   to change gradually from cartilage into bone.   *n.* **ossification.**

Osteichthyes (ahs-tee-IK-thee-eez), *n.*   a class of vertebrates including fishes with bony skeletons, gill coverings, and fins supported by rays; examples are guppy, swordtail, flounder, sole, sea horse, and lobefins.

osteitis (ahs-tee-EY-tis), *n.* a frequently chronic inflammation of bone usually due to syphilis or tuberculosis.

osteoblast (AHS-tee-oh-blast), *n.* a cell which produces bone. After becoming surrounded by bone, the cell is called an *osteocyte.*

osteology (ahs-tee-AHL-uh-jee), *n.* the branch of vertebrate anatomy concerned with the study of the skeleton and its parts; the study of bones.

ostrich (AHS-trij, AWS-), see **Struthioniformes.**

otolith (OHT-uh-lith), *n.* a small calcified mass found in the internal ear of vertebrates and in the balancing organ of certain invertebrates.

otology (oh-TAHL-uh-jee), *n.* the branch of medicine concerned with the study of the ear and its diseases.

ounce, *n.* a unit of weight in several systems, as 1/16 pound in the avoirdupois system; see measurement tables on page 214.

outcrop, *n.* a place at which a mineral vein or underground rock formation comes to the surface of the earth, such as an *outcrop* of marble or coal. *v.* **outcrop.**

outerspace, that region of space between the stars or far-removed planets; especially, all space beyond the moon.

output, *n.* **1.** the energy delivered by a device; may be electrical, mechanical, chemical, etc. **2.** the physical location in a device where such energy is delivered; contrast with **input.**

ova, plural of **ovum.**

oval window, alternate term for **foramen ovale.**

ovary (OH-vuh-ree), *n.* **1.** in higher animals, the female reproductive gland containing immature germ cells called *ova* or *eggs* and the hormones regulating secondary sex characteristics; see **endocrine gland.** *adj.* **ovarian. 2.** in flowering plants, the enlarged lower portion of the pistil enclosing the ovule or immature seed; see also **flower** picture.

overshot, *adj.* describing a mechanism operated by water flowing above; used especially of any water wheel in which water contacts the blades at the top of the wheel.

overtone (OH-vuhr-tohn), *n.* any of the tones accompanying, and of higher frequency than, the fundamental tone produced by a musical instrument; see also **harmonic.**

oviduct (OH-vi-dukt), *n.* one of a pair of tubes leading from the ovaries to the outside of the body and through which the eggs of a female animal leave the body; also, in invertebrates, such tubes leading to another portion of the body which may be called a *uterus.*

oviparous (oh-VIP-uh-ruhs), *adj.* producing young by laying eggs outside the body, as birds, most reptiles, and fishes.

ovipositor (oh-vi-PAHZ-i-tuhr), *n.* an organ at the end of the abdomen of certain female insects used for depositing eggs.

ovoviviparous (oh-voh-vy-VIP-uh-ruhs), *adj.* producing living young from eggs developed and hatched within the body of the female as in certain reptiles, fishes, and a few insects.

ovulate (OH-vyuh-layt), *v.* to shed an egg or eggs from an ovary of a female animal; most ani-

mals ovulate at a particular time in a recurring cycle. *n.* **ovulation.**

ovule (OH-vyuhl), *n.* in flowering plants, a structure containing the female germ cell or egg within an embryo sac; after fertilization, it develops into a seed; located in the ovary; see also **flower** picture.

ovum (OH-vuhm), *n., pl.* **ova.** in animals, the female reproductive cell or egg which, after fertilization, develops into a new individual.

owl, see **Strigiformes.**

oxalic acid (ahk-SAL-ik), *n.* a poisonous, colorless crystalline organic acid found in certain plants (oxalis, rumex); used for processing textiles and leather; formula, $(COOH)_2$.

oxalis family (ahk-SAL-is), see **Geraniales.**

oxidation (ahks-uh-DAY-shuhn), *n.* **1.** the combination of a substance with oxygen, as burning of coal. **2.** any chemical reaction in which the positive valence is increased or the negative valence is decreased by loss of electrons, as the ferrous, Fe^{++}, ion is oxidized to ferric, Fe^{+++}.

oxide (AHKS-eyd), *n.* any compound containing oxygen, as ferric oxide, Fe_2O_3.

oxidize (AHKS-uh-dyz), *v.* **1.** to chemically add oxygen to a substance, as a metal is oxidized to form a metal oxide. **2.** to remove hydrogen from a compound. **3.** to increase the positive valence or decrease the negative valence of an element or radical by removing electrons.

oxidizing agent, 1. generally, any substance such as oxygen, the peroxides, the halogens, etc., which, essentially, adds oxygen to an element or compound. **2.** specifically, a substance in whose presence a compound assumes a higher degree of combination with oxygen by adding oxygen or an *electronegative* atom or radical (one that tends to attract electrons), or by removing hydrogen or an *electropositive* atom or radical (one that tends to give off electrons); contrast with **reducing agent.**

oxyacetylene (ahks-ee-uh-SET-uh-lihn), *adj.* referring to a mixture of oxygen and acetylene, especially when used in welding torches.

oxygen (AHKS-uh-juhn), *n.* a chemical element necessary for all plant and animal life; forms one-fifth of the air; a colorless, odorless, flammable gas; used to remove impurities in steel and for oxyacetylene welding; symbol O; *at. no.,* 8; *at. wt.,* 15.9994; identified independently by Scheele and Priestley in 1774. Oxygen, with atomic weight exactly 16.000, was the standard for atomic weights until 1961, when it was replaced by carbon-12, an isotope of carbon; see also **liquid oxygen.**

oxytocin (ahk-suh-TOH-sin), *n.* a hormone from the posterior pituitary that functions in lactation; a peptide made of 8 amino acids; formula, $C_{43}H_{66}N_{12}O_{12}S_2$; first hormone to be synthesized.

oyster, see **Pelecypoda.**

ozone (OH-zohn), *n.* a poisonous, explosive, bluish gas with a strong, penetrating odor; an allotropic form of oxygen, O_3; used as an oxidizing agent and for purifying and deodorizing air, drinking water, sewage, and industrial wastes.

ozonosphere (oh-ZOHN-uh-sfeer), *n.* a layer of the stratosphere that contains large amounts of ozone and absorbs ultraviolet radiation.

p, abbreviation for **per.**
P, symbol for **phosphorus.**
Pa, symbol for **protactinium.**

pacemaker, *n.* **1.** in biochemistry, any substance whose rate of reaction controls the speed of other reactions. **2.** in anatomy, the *pacemaker* of the heart is the sino-auricular node, in the right auricle; a bundle of tissue which begins the rhythm of heart movement.

pachyderm (PAK-uh-duhrm), *n.* common name applied to the group of thick-skinned, hoofed mammals such as the elephant and hippopotamus.

palate (PAL-uht), *n.* roof of the mouth; includes both the *hard palate* (bone at the front of mouth cavity) and the *soft palate* (soft part near the uvula); used in forming certain speech sounds and swallowing.

paleobotany (pay-lee-oh-BAHT-uh-nee), *n.* a branch of paleontology restricted to the study of plant fossils.

Paleocene (PAY-lee-oh-seen), *n.* an epoch in the Tertiary Period of geologic time, characterized by the appearance of early flowering plants and the first primates; lasted 10 million years to 55 million years ago; see **geologic time table.**

paleolithic (pay-lee-uh-LITH-ik), *adj.* referring to the Old Stone Age (between the *Eolithic* and the *Neolithic*), characterized by the development of pointed tools of bone and ivory and cave drawings.

paleontology (pay-lee-uhn-TAHL-uh-jee), *n.* the study of fossils as evidence of plants and animals that lived during earlier geological times. *adj.* **paleontological.**

Paleozoic (pay-lee-oh-ZOH-ik), *n.* the geologic era between the Proterozoic and Mesozoic, lasting from about 550 to 2400 million years ago; characterized by the first land plants and land-dwelling animals, amphibians, and reptiles; coal and oil deposits were starting to form; see **geologic time table.**

palisade (pal-uh-SAYD), *n.* **1.** a layer of tissue in plant leaves, under the epidermis; a type of parenchyma consisting of simple, cylindrical cells abundant in chloroplasts. **2.** any of the cells making up such a layer.

palladium (puh-LAY-dee-uhm), *n.* a precious, silvery-white, metallic chemical element; ductile and malleable; used as a catalyst, for low-current electrical contacts, and for strong, light, corrosion-resistant alloys; symbol Pd; *at. no.,* 46; *at. wt.,* 106.4; isolated by Wollaston in 1803.

palm, *n.* **1.** the part of the human hand between the wrist and the fingers, toward which the fingers close. **2.** the only family of plants in order **Palmales.**

Palmales (pahl-MAY-leez), *n.* an order of tropical or subtropical monocot woody plants with flower parts in groups of 3 and long, compound leaves of many leaflets. Order includes only one family, the economically important palm family (*Palmae*), which yields starch, coconut, dates, waxes, oils, and fibers.

COCONUT
Cocos nucifera

DATE PALM
Phoenix dactylifera

ROYAL PALM
Roystonea regia

WASHINGTON FAN
Washingtonia filifera

palmate (PAL-mayt), *adj.* **1.** shaped like a hand with extended fingers, as antlers or webbed feet of certain animals. **2.** referring to the compound leaves of certain plants, as the horse chestnut.

palmate venation, a type of netted veining in a leaf in which more than one main vein arises from the base of the leaf; see **leaf** picture.

palm family, see **Palmales.**

palmitin (PAL-muh-tuhn), *n.* a white, crystalline powder; a glycerol ester of palmitic acid; used in medicine, soap; formula, $C_3H_5(OC_{16}H_{31}O)_3$.

palpitation (pal-pi-TAY-shuhn), *n.* unusually fast beating of the heart, strong enough to be felt by the person. *v.* **palpitate.**

pancreas (PAN-kree-uhs), *n.* a gland which secretes a fluid containing several inactive digestive enzymes (amylopsin, steapsin, trypsin) and discharges it into the intestine; also contains specialized hormone-secreting cells, the islets of Langerhans; see **digestive system.** *adj.* **pancreatic.**

pancreatin (pan-KREE-uh-tin), *n.* a digestive enzyme mixture secreted by the pancreas; largely amylase, lipase, and trypsin; an extract from cattle and pigs is used in treating pancreas deficiency.

Pandanales (pan-duh-NAY-leez), *n.* an order of monocot plants with long, thin leaves, monoecious flowers with little or no perianth of bristles or scales formed into heads or spikes, a nutlike fruit, and a fleshy seed. The order includes 3 families: the cattail family (*Typhaceae*), the spiral-leaved screwpine or pandanus family (*Pandanaceae*), and the burreed family (*Sparganiaceae*).

140

pandanus family (pan-DAY-nuhs), see **Pandanales.**

pangolin (PANG-guh-lin), see **Pholidota.**

Papaverales (puh-pav-uh-RAY-leez), *n.* an order of dicot plants, mostly herbs, with alternate leaves and flower parts arranged in a circle, including 6 stamens, 2 longer than the other 4. Of 6 families, the largest is the mustard family (*Cruciferae*)—source of cabbage, cauliflower, broccoli, radish, turnip. Other families are the poppy family (*Papaveraceae*), source of opium and morphine; and the fumitory family (*Fumariaceae*), including bleeding heart and Dutchman's breeches; order also called *Rhoeadales.*

papaya family (puh-PY-uh), see **Parietales.**

papilla (puh-PIL-uh), *n., pl.* **-lae.** a small projection from the surface of a tissue, shaped something like a nipple; occurs on the tongue and skin in man and on various plant structures.

Pap test, a method of examining body tissue for early detection of cancer; the tissue is stained with special chemicals and examined under the microscope; cancer cells will take a stain that normal cells do not; named for G. N. Papanicolaou, Greek-American physician.

parabolic (pair-uh-BAHL-ik), *adj.* having or taking on the shape of a parabola; a reflector built as a *parabolic* curve focuses light, sound, or radio waves into a small beam.

parachute (PAIR-uh-shoot), *n.* a device of lightweight cloth for reducing speed of fall, or for other braking action, in the air; folds to small size when not needed, but opens into a large surface similar to an upside-down bowl when in use. *v.* **parachute.**

paraffin (PAIR-uh-fin), *n.* **1.** any chemically inert, saturated hydrocarbon of the methane-ethane-propane series. **2.** a mixture of such saturated hydrocarbons, used to make waxed materials (paper, candles), and for waterproofing and pharmaceuticals; usually a white, odorless, and tasteless solid.

parallax (PAIR-uh-laks), *n.* in astronomy, the apparent difference in the position of a heavenly body between the point of the observer and the point representing the center of the earth. *adj.* **parallactic.**

parallel (PAIR-uh-lel), *adj.* **1.** describing 2 or more objects, lines, etc., always an equal distance from each other, as *parallel* wires in a grid. **2.** in electricity, describing a circuit in which the elements are arranged so the same voltage is applied at each element; see **circuit.**

parallel venation, an arrangement in which veins in a leaf are parallel or linear to each other, as in grass and lily; see **leaf** picture.

paralysis (puh-RAL-i-sis), *n.* the loss of motor activity in the body's muscular system resulting from the interruption of nerve impulses in certain areas of the nervous system. *v.* **paralyze.** *adj.* **paralytic.**

paramagnetic (pair-uh-mag-NET-ik), *adj.* pertaining to substances, such as aluminum, that have a slight capability for being magnetized; magnetic susceptibility shows little increase with increase in magnetizing force. *n.* **paramagnetism.**

paramecium (pair-uh-MEE-see-uhm), *n., pl.* **-mecia.** any of a genus of ciliate protozoan ani-

(1) Broccoli, *Brassica oleracea var. Italica;* (2) radish, *Raphanus sativus;* (3) California poppy, *Eschscholtzia californica;* (4) kohlrabi, *B. oleracea var. caulorapa;* (5) black mustard, *B. nigra;* (6) oriental poppy, *Papaver orientale;* (7) Dutchman's breeches, *Dicentra cucullaria*

mals, including a species, *Paramecium caudatum,* commonly studied for its easily seen, typical protozoan characteristics; see also **Ciliata.**

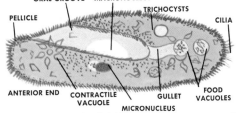

Common pond paramecium, *Paramecium caudatum*

ORAL GROOVE MACRONUCLEUS

TRICHOCYSTS

PELLICLE

CILIA

ANTERIOR END CONTRACTILE VACUOLE GULLET FOOD VACUOLES

MICRONUCLEUS

parapodium (pair-uh-POH-dee-uhm), *n., pl.* **-podia.** an unjointed, spiny projection used for locomotion in certain annelids such as sandworms.

parasite (PAIR-uh-syt), *n.* any plant or animal living on, or in, another plant or animal, the *host,* and obtaining food, shelter, and transportation from the host without performing any service in return. *adj.* **parasitic.**

parasitism (PAIR-uh-syt-izm), *n.* **1.** the condition of having parasites. **2.** the state of adapta-

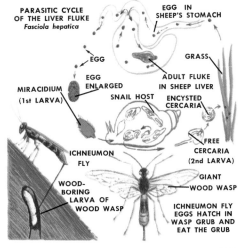

PARASITIC CYCLE OF THE LIVER FLUKE *Fasciola hepatica*

EGG IN SHEEP'S STOMACH

EGG

GRASS

EGG ENLARGED

ADULT FLUKE IN SHEEP LIVER

MIRACIDIUM (1st LARVA)

SNAIL HOST

ENCYSTED CERCARIA

ICHNEUMON FLY

FREE CERCARIA (2nd LARVA)

WOOD-BORING LARVA OF WOOD WASP

GIANT WOOD WASP

ICHNEUMON FLY EGGS HATCH IN WASP GRUB AND EAT THE GRUB

tion or behavior of an organism living within or upon another, at the other's expense; contrast with **symbiosis.**

parasitology (pair-uh-sy-TAHL-uh-jee), *n.* the study of parasites and the numerous relationships between them and their host organisms.

parasympathetic (pair-uh-sim-puh-THET-ik), *adj.* referring to certain nerves in the brain or to certain of the sacral spinal nerves; the *parasympathetic nervous system* is part of the autonomic nervous system; these nerves act in opposition to the sympathetic nervous system; see **autonomic nervous system, sympathetic nervous system.**

parathyroid gland (pair-uh-THY-royd), either of a pair of endocrine glands, secreting parathormone which controls the calcium content of the blood; see **endocrine gland.**

paratyphoid fever (pair-uh-TY-foid), an infectious disease resembling typhoid fever but milder; caused by different bacteria.

paregoric (pair-uh-GAWR-ik), *n.* a dilute solution of opium and camphor in alcohol; used as an analgesic to kill pain.

parenchyma (puh-REN-kuh-muh), *n.* **1.** a tissue of thin-walled storage cells found in many parts of a plant and retaining their ability to divide. **2.** in animals, the functional tissue of an organ, as contrasted with *connective* or *supporting* tissue. **3.** a loosely compacted, cellular tissue filling spaces between various organs and the body wall, found in flatworms and some roundworms.

paresis (puh-REE-sis), *n.* **1.** a chronic infection and inflammation of the brain and surrounding cerebral tissue occurring in advanced syphilis, resulting in progressive mental and physical deterioration and death. **2.** partial paralysis.

parhelion (pahr-HEEL-yuhn), *n.* any of several bright, round spots visible on a solar halo; also called *mock sun.*

parietal (puh-RY-uh-tuhl), *adj.* **1.** pertaining to the walls of a cavity in a living organism. **2.** pertaining to either of 2 bones of the vertebrate skull; see **skeletal system. 3.** pertaining to a plant ovule when borne on the ovary wall.

Parietales (puh-ry-uh-TAY-leez), *n.* a large dicot order of mainly tropical and subtropical plants with flowers that usually have 5 sepals

(1) Passion flower, *Passiflora alata-caerulea;* (2) tea, *Camellia sinensis;* (3) flowering camellia, *Camellia japonica;* (4) bird's-foot violet, *Viola pedata leariloba;* (5) hybrid garden pansy, *Viola tricolor;* (6) double hybrid tuberous begonia, *Begonia tuberhybrida;* (7) papaya, or papaw, *Carica papaya*

and petals and 5 or more stamens. Most have ovules attached to the ovary wall; this is called *parietal placentation,* from which the order gets its name. The 23 families include many ornamental and useful groups: the violet family (*Violaceae*), the passion-flower family (*Passi-*

floraceae), the tea family (*Theaceae*), the papaya family (*Caricaceae*), and the begonia family (*Begoniaceae*).

parietal eye, a "third eye" in the head of many lizards, with a cornea, lens, and retina; does not respond to light as an ordinary eye; appears to regulate the time a lizard spends in the sun.

Parkinson's disease, a chronic progressive disorder of the central nervous system caused by degenerative changes in cells and blood vessels in the basal brain ganglia; results in tremors, weakness, and muscular rigidity; cause is unknown.

parotid (puh-RAHT-id), *adj.* referring to either of a pair of large saliva-producing glands; badly swollen in mumps.

parrot, see **Psittaciformes.**

parrot fever, see **psittacosis.**

parsec (PAHR-sek), *n.* a measure of distance used in astronomy equal to 3¼ light years, or 19.2 trillion miles.

parsley family (PAHRS-lee), see **Umbellales.**

parthenocarpy (PAHR-thuh-noh-kahr-pee), *n.* the formation of fruit without the union of egg and sperm, as with seedless grapes and navel oranges; chemicals are usually used to start fruit development; occurs naturally in some plants.

parthenogenesis (pahr-thuh-noh-JEN-uh-sis), *n.* the development of an embryo from an unfertilized egg, such as regularly occurs in rotifers and certain algae.

particle physics, the study of the nuclear and other particles of atomic and subatomic matter.

parturition (pahr-tyuh-RISH-uhn), *n.* the process of bringing forth young; birth.

Pascal's Law (pas-KAL), a physical law stating that a confined fluid will transmit unreduced a change of pressure produced at any point, to all points in the fluid; more usefully applied to incompressible liquid fluids than gas fluids; named for Blaise Pascal, French scientist (1623–1662).

Passeriformes (pas-uh-ruh-FAWR-meez), *n.* the largest order of birds, with feet modified for perching; includes seed-eaters, insect-eaters, and omnivorous species. Examples are broadbill, flycatcher, robin, lyrebird, swallow, titmouse, and others. *adj.* **passerine.**

passion-flower family, see **Parietales.**

passive reflector satellite, a balloonlike sphere of aluminum-coated plastic that reflects radio waves from Earth back to the ground over long distances; a satellite of the *Echo* series.

pasteurize (PAS-tchuhr-eyz), *v.* to process a liquid (as milk) by heating it to destroy harmful bacteria; milk is usually heated to 142°-145°F for 30 minutes. *n.* **pasteurization.**

patch test, the application to the skin of a piece of gauze containing a substance to which a person may be sensitive. If redness appears, it is interpreted as a positive reaction; used to test for allergy, tuberculosis, and other conditions.

patella (puh-TEL-uh), *n.* **1.** the kneecap in man; see **skeletal system. 2.** part of the jointed leg of some arthropods. **3.** the low, conical, untwisted shell of the common limpet.

pathogen (PATH-uh-jen), *n.* any disease-producing organism such as certain bacteria, viruses, fungi, or animal parasites; specific diseases have specific pathogens. *adj.* **pathogenic.**

pathology (puh-THAHL-uh-jee), *n.* the study of the origin, nature, course, and treatment of diseases in animals and plants. *Pathologists* are specialized medical scientists and are especially interested in tissue changes. *adj.* **pathological.**

payload, *n.* the useful load of a missile, which may be a warhead, observation equipment, or similar material; originally, that part of a commercial aircraft's load from which revenue is obtained: passengers, freight, mail, etc.

Pb, symbol for **lead** (from Latin, *plumbum*).

Pd, symbol for **palladium.**

pea family, a large family (*Leguminosae*) of trees, shrubs, and herbs in dicot order *Rosales;* with compound leaves and podlike, dry, dehiscent fruits (*legumes*); includes common garden peas and beans, clover, alfalfa, licorice, peanut, and ornamental sweet pea; see also **Rosales.**

pearl (PURL), *n.* a gem produced by some mollusks (certain oysters) or an abnormal, hard structure created by many mollusks; consists of deposit of mother-of-pearl (*nacre*) and started by a grain of sand or other irritant.

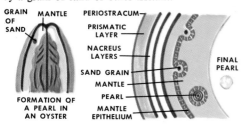

peat (PEET), *n.* partially decayed vegetable material found in marshy regions; the first stage of coal formation; often used as a heating fuel.

peccary (PEK-uh-ree), see **Artiodactyla.**

pectin (PEK-tin), *n.* any of a certain complex, high-molecular-weight polyuronides (related to carbohydrates) found in fruits and plants; occur as white powders or syrupy liquids; used for foods, cosmetics, jellies, colloids, and emulsifiers.

pectoral (PEK-tuh-ruhl), *adj.* relating to the chest or chest cavity, as a *pectoral* fin.

pediatrics (pee-dee-AT-riks), *n.* the branch of medicine concerned with the care of children and the prevention, diagnosis, and treatment of their disorders and diseases. *n.* **pediatrician.**

peduncle (PEE-duhn-kuhl), *n.* any of several stem or stalklike structures, as: **1.** a flower stalk. **2.** the stalk bearing the fruiting body of a fungus. **3.** the stalk by which certain invertebrates are attached to a supporting surface.

Pegasus (PEG-uh-suhs), *n.* the *Winged Horse,* a northern constellation most clearly seen in the winter; usually recognizable from the 4 bright stars that form the Great Square in Pegasus.

pegmatite (PEG-muh-tyt), *n.* a deposit of large crystals chiefly of quartz, feldspar, and muscovite, as a vein in or from a granite intrusion; many rare minerals, large plates of mica, and feldspar are mined from pegmatites.

Peking man (PEE-king), a prehistoric man of the early Pleistocene period, possibly half a million years ago; he was about 5 feet tall; scientific name is *Sinanthropus.*

pelage (PEL-ahj), *n.* the fur or hair covering of a mammal.

pelagic (puh-LAJ-ik), *adj.* pertaining to the open sea or to organisms living in water independent of the bottom and shores; usually refers only to marine organisms.

Pelecaniformes (pel-uh-kan-i-FAWR-meez), *n.* an order of web-footed birds that have all 4 toes included within the web; examples are pelicans, cormorants, and others.

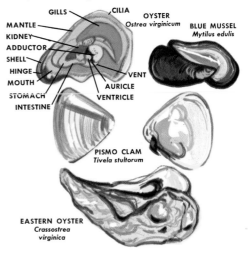

Pelecypoda (pel-uh-SIP-uh-duh), *n.* a class in phylum Mollusca of animals with body enclosed in a mantle with 2 lobes, shell with dorsal hinge, head and radula absent, and wedge-shaped, muscular foot. Mussels, clams, and oysters are *pelecypods;* class also called *Lamellibranchia.*

pelican (PEL-i-kuhn), see **Pelecaniformes.**

pellagra (puh-LAYG-ruh), *n.* a chronic dietary disease due to a deficiency of niacin, accompanied by skin eruptions, nervous disorders, and diarrhea.

pellicle (PEL-uh-kuhl), *n.* **1.** a thin covering layer on the surface of a cell. **2.** the covering sheath of a chromosome.

pelt, *n.* the skin of a mammal, with or without the hair or other covering.

pelvis (PEL-vis), *n.* the bowl-like cavity formed by several bones in the lower portion of the abdomen; supports the spinal column and contains the bladder, rectum, and reproductive organs; see **skeletal system.** *adj.* **pelvic.**

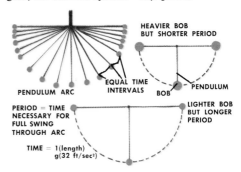

pendulum (PEN-juh-luhm), *n.* a body attached to one or more fixed points so that when undisturbed it has an equilibrium position and when displaced swings or oscillates around this position under the force of gravity; the period (time required for a full swing) depends on length of the string; see also **Foucault pendulum.**

peneplain (PEE-nuh-playn), *n.* **1.** any large land surface worn down to a nearly flat level. **2.** any such surface, though since leveled, lifted up to form a plateau and then eroded again.

penguin (PEN-gwin), see **Spheniseiformes.**

penicillin (pen-uh-SIL-in), *n.* the first antibiotic found useful in medicine, formed as a fermentation product of *Penicillium* mold when grown on a corn alcohol-carbohydrate medium.

penicillium (pen-i-SIL-ee-uhm), *n.* any of a genus of fungi commonly called blue-green molds, growing on moist, decaying organic matter; the natural producers of penicillin; see **Eumycophyta.**

peninsula (peh-NIN-suh-luh), *n.* a region of land projecting into a body of water; often long, narrow, and connected to the land by an isthmus.

penis (PEE-nis), *n.* the male reproductive organ of many animals which serves to inject sperm into the female during copulation.

Pennsylvanian (pen-sil-VAYN-yuhn), *n.* a geologic period late in the Paleozoic era, that began about 250 million years ago and lasted about 40 million years; coal beds began to form as great forests of trees decayed.

pentane (PEN-tayn), *n.* **1.** any of the 3 straight or branched-chain, 5-carbon isomers derived from methane. **2.** specifically, *n-pentane,* a colorless, flammable liquid with a pleasant odor; used as an anesthetic, solvent; formula, C_5H_{12}.

pentose (PEN-tohs), *n.* any of a group of 5-carbon sugars with the formula $C_5H_{10}O_5$; includes *arabinose,* from most plant gums, and *ribose,* found in nucleic acids.

penumbra (peh-NUHM-bruh), *n.* a partly lighted region between the umbra (full shadow) and the full light of a body, as in the eclipse of the moon; see **eclipse.**

pepper family, see **Piperales.**

pepsin, *n.* a stomach enzyme that converts proteins into peptones and other substances; when purified, occurs as an odorless, yellowish powder or colorless scales; used in medicine to aid in digestion.

peptic (PEP-tik), *adj.* relating to or concerned with digestion.

peptidase (PEP-ti-days), *n.* any enzyme, as pepsin, that hydrolyzes peptides made up of free amino (-NH_2) or carboxyl (-COOH) groups.

peptide, *n.* a group of 2 or more amino acids joined by the linking of amino groups of some acids to carboxyl groups of others.

peptone (PEP-tohn), *n.* any of a group of water-soluble proteins formed by various processes (as the action of pepsin in digestion); when isolated, occurs as a white to brownish powder; used for nutrient media in cultures.

per, a preposition meaning *for every* (unit amount of a . . .), as 40 pounds *per* square inch means 40 lbs. *for every* sq. in.; often indicated by a diagonal line, as lbs/in². *abbr.* **p.**

perception (puhr-SEP-shuhn), *n.* the conscious knowing, or awareness of, something resulting from knowledge gained by sensations, especially from the environment. *v.* **perceive.**

perching bird, any passerine bird; see **Passeriformes.**

perennial (puhr-EN-ee-uhl), *n.* any plant with a life span of more than 2 years; usually produces seeds annually after reaching maturity; trees and shrubs are perennials; contrast with **annual.** *adj.* **perennial.**

perfect flower, a flower having both male parts (stamens) and female parts (pistil or pistils), regardless of whether it has both sepals or petals; see **flower** picture.

perianth (PAIR-ee-anth), *n.* the sepals and petals of a flower, as a group.

pericardium (pair-uh-KAHR-dee-uhm), *n.* the sac-shaped serous membrane surrounding the heart of many animals, with structural variations in the different phyla. *adj.* **pericardial.**

pericarp (PAIR-uh-kahrp), *n.* the wall of a fruit that developed from the outer wall of an ovary in a flower; see **fruit** picture.

perigee (PAIR-i-jee), *n.* **1.** the point nearest to Earth in the orbit of an earth satellite, whether natural or artificial. **2.** the point at which any satellite comes closest to the object around which it orbits.

perihelion (pair-uh-HEE-lee-uhn), *n.* that point nearest to the sun reached by a planet, comet, or artificial satellite during its orbit; contrast with **aphelion.**

perilymph (PAIR-i-limf), *n.* a fluid in the labyrinth of the inner ear; transmits sound waves to the auditory nerve.

period (PEER-ee-uhd), *n.* an interval of time between 2 occurrences, especially: **1.** in astronomy, time elapsing between events, as between one new moon and the next. **2.** in geology, a division of an era characterized by specific changes in rocks and other phenomena; see **geologic time table. 3.** in physics, time necessary for a complete cycle to occur. *adj.* **periodic.**

periodic law, the theory that properties of chemical elements occur in groups, or *periods,* if the elements are arranged by increasing atomic number.

periodic table, the orderly arrangement of the chemical elements according to their atomic numbers. The table contains 9 basic groups, called *periods;* the elements in each of these have quite similar chemical and physical properties.

periosteum (pair-ee-AHS-tee-uhm), *n.* the layer of fibrous connective tissue that covers bones, except at the joints, and which produces new bone cells.

Velvet worm, *Peripatus,* the first animal of phylum Onychophora to be discovered; about 4 to 5 inches long

peripatus (puh-RIP-uh-tuhs), *n.* any of a group of primitive, wormlike invertebrates; with soft-skinned bodies bearing slime-secreting papillae, imperfectly joined legs with 2 claws, and respiration by unbranched trachea; also called *velvet worm;* see also **Onychophora.**

PERIODIC TABLE OF THE ELEMENTS

GROUPS (vertical columns; Roman numerals): The main groups (A) generally have clear metallic or nonmetallic properties. Metals form positive ions in solution and their oxides or hydroxides are bases. Nonmetals form negative ions in solution and their oxides form acids in water. The subgroups (B) are transition elements, metals with varying degrees of nonmetallic properties. Valence tends to be the same for all elements in a group and its subgroup.

PERIODS (horizontal rows; Arabic numerals): Within each period, elements (a) range from active metals on the left to active nonmetals on the right, ending in an inert gas; (b) have increased valence through the A groups, which is repeated in the B's; and (c) acquire enough electrons to complete or stabilize an electron shell or energy level.

BLUE—light metals

GREEN—heavy metals; the transition elements, with decreasing tendency to form bases

YELLOW—nonmetals

WHITE—metalloids: look like metals but form acids or bases, depending on conditions

RED—inert gases of zero valence; some can be made to form compounds under very special conditions

†mass number of most stable isotope

Key:
- Atomic number
- Chemical symbol
- Atomic weight (carbon-12=12.000)
- Number of electrons in each shell, or energy level—from nucleus— K, L, M, N, O, P, Q

IA — Alkali metals; valence +1	H 1, Li 3, Na 11, K 19, Rb 37, Cs 55, Fr 87
IIA — Alkaline earths; valence +2	Be 4, Mg 12, Ca 20, Sr 38, Ba 56, Ra 88
IIIA — Boron family; valence +3	B 5, Al 13, Ga 31, In 49, Tl 81
IVA — Semiconductors; valence +4	C 6, Si 14, Ge 32, Sn 50, Pb 82
VA — Nitrogen family; valence −3	N 7, P 15, As 33, Sb 51, Bi 83
VIA — Oxygen family; valence −2	O 8, S 16, Se 34, Te 52, Po 84
VIIA — Halogens; valence −1	H 1, F 9, Cl 17, Br 35, I 53, At 85
O — Inert gases	He 2, Ne 10, Ar 18, Kr 36, Xe 54, Rn 86

VIII — Principal transition elements; generally allotropic

Transition elements (Groups IIIB–IIB):
Sc 21, Ti 22, V 23, Cr 24, Mn 25, Fe 26, Co 27, Ni 28, Cu 29, Zn 30
Y 39, Zr 40, Nb 41, Mo 42, Tc 43, Ru 44, Rh 45, Pd 46, Ag 47, Cd 48
Lanthanide rare-earth series, Hf 72, Ta 73, W 74, Re 75, Os 76, Ir 77, Pt 78, Au 79, Hg 80
Actinide series

Lanthanide (rare-earth) series:
La 57 138.91, Ce 58 140.12, Pr 59 140.907, Nd 60 144.24, Pm 61 147†, Sm 62 150.35, Eu 63 151.96, Gd 64 157.25, Tb 65 158.92·4, Dy 66 162.50, Ho 67 164.93·0, Er 68 167.26, Tm 69 168.93·4, Yb 70 173.04, Lu 71 174.97

Actinide series:
Ac 89 227†, Th 90 232.038, Pa 91 231†, U 92 238.03, Np 93 237†, Pu 94 242†, Am 95 243†, Cm 96 247†, Bk 97 249†, Cf 98 251†, Es 99 254†, Fm 100 253†, Md 101 256†, No 102 254†, Lw 103 257†

Atomic weights (selected):
H 1.00797, He 4.0026, Li 6.939, Be 9.0122, B 10.811, C 12.011–15, N 14.0067, O 15.999·4, F 18.998·4, Ne 20.183, Na 22.9898, Mg 24.312, Al 26.9815, Si 28.086, P 30.97·38, S 32.064, Cl 35.453, Ar 39.948, K 39.102, Ca 40.08, Sc 44.956, Ti 47.90, V 50.942, Cr 51.996, Mn 54.938–0, Fe 55.847, Co 58.933·2, Ni 58.71, Cu 63.54, Zn 65.37, Ga 69.72, Ge 72.59, As 74.9216, Se 78.96, Br 79.909, Kr 83.80, Rb 85.47, Sr 87.62, Y 88.905, Zr 91.22, Nb 92.906, Mo 95.94, Tc 99†, Ru 101.07, Rh 102.905, Pd 106.4, Ag 107.87–0, Cd 112.40, In 114.82, Sn 118.69, Sb 121.75, Te 127.60, I 126.90·44, Xe 131.30, Cs 132.905, Ba 137.34, La 138.91, Hf 178.49, Ta 180.948, W 183.85, Re 186.2, Os 190.2, Ir 192.2, Pt 195.09, Au 196.967, Hg 200.59, Tl 204.37, Pb 207.19, Bi 208.980, Po 210†, At 210†, Rn 222†, Fr 223†, Ra 226†

Kurchatovium, element number 104, was discovered in 1964. Its atomic weight is 260.

Hahnium, element number 105, was discovered in 1967. Its atomic weight is 260.

peripheral (puh-RIF-uh-ruhl), *adj.* found in the direction of the surface or away from the center, as in *peripheral* vision, the seeing of objects that are not in the straight line or field of vision. *n.* **periphery.**

peripheral nervous system, part of the nervous system made up of paired cranial and spinal nerves running to and from the brain and spinal cord; contrast with **central nervous system.**

periscope (PAIR-i-skohp), *n.* an optical device for viewing objects that are not in the viewer's straight line of sight, usually because of ob-

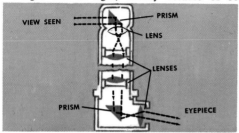

structions; consisting of a tube with 2 mirrors set at angles so that light from the object being viewed changes its direction; much used in submarines for viewing the water surface.

permanganate (puhr-MAN-guh-nayt), *n.* any compound containing the permanganate radical, MnO_4^-.

permeability (puhr-mee-uh-BIL-uh-tee), *n.* **1.** the degree to which a substance passes or absorbs liquids or gases, as certain cell membranes show permeability to water; see also **semipermeable membrane. 2.** in magnetism, the degree to which a substance takes on magnetism within a magnetic field. *adj.* **permeable.**

Permian (PUHR-mee-uhn), *n.* the latest geologic period of the Paleozoic era, beginning about 210 million years ago and lasting about 10 million years; marked by much volcanic action, appearance of the earliest reptiles, and extensive glaciation in what is now the Southern Hemisphere; see also **geologic time table.**

pernicious anemia (puhr-NISH-uhs uh-NEE-mee-uh), a type of anemia resulting from incomplete development of red blood cells; symptoms include yellowish skin, digestive disturbances, and weakness and paralysis of the legs; cause is unknown; see also **anemia.**

peroxide (puhr-AHK-syd), *n.* any compound containing an O_2 group with the 2 oxygen atoms joined to each other by a single bond; see **hydrogen peroxide.**

BRAZILIAN TAPIR
Tapirus terrestris

BONES OF HOOF; HORSE HAS ONLY ONE BIG TOE REMAINING

HORSE, *Equus caballus*
BREED—AMERICAN QUARTER HORSE

HEEL

VESTIGIAL TOE

WILD MONGOLIAN HORSE
Equus przewalski

WHITE RHINOCEROS
Rhinoceros simus

ELONGATED MIDDLE TOE

METATARSAL BONES

COMMON MOUNTAIN ZEBRA *Equus chapmani*

Perissodactyla (puh-ris-uh-DAK-tuh-luh), *n.* an order of mammals with odd-toed hoofs and teeth modified for chewing; *perissodactyls* include horses, rhinoceroses, tapirs, and zebras.

peristalsis (pair-uh-STAWL-sis), *n.* the regular muscular contractions of the alimentary canal; involuntary movements that result in the gradual but continuous passage of food through the digestive system.

peritoneum (pair-uh-tuh-NEE-uhm), *n.* a thin layer of tissue (membrane) consisting of flat cells that cover the organs of the abdomen and line the abdominal cavity in many animals; develops from the mesoderm. *adj.* **peritoneal.**

peritonitis (pair-uh-tuh-NY-tuhs), *n.* infection or inflammation of the peritoneal membrane; may be a serious complication of many pelvic and abdominal diseases and abdominal surgery.

permafrost (PUHR-muh-frawst), *n.* in the arctic regions, the permanently frozen layer of soil (sometimes bedrock) on the surface of the earth; see also **tundra.**

permanent tooth, in vertebrates, especially man, any of the second and final set of 32 teeth; contrast with **milk tooth;** see also **tooth.**

perpetual motion (puhr-PETCH-uh-wuhl), motion of a body that, once started, never slows down but keeps moving without change; *perpetual motion machines,* long looked for, have been proved to be impossible because all motion involves some energy loss due to friction.

Perseid (PUHR-see-id), *n.* any meteorite seen about August 10-11 in the constellation Perseus; there is an annual meteorite shower called the *Perseids* at this time.

Perseus (PUHR-see-uhs), *n.* a brilliant northern constellation seen during December and January, containing Algol, a bright star.

persimmon (puhr-SIM-uhn), see **Ebenales.**

persistence of vision (puhr-SIS-tuhns), the retention of an image by the human eye after the light causing the image has disappeared; this persistence explains why a rapid sequence of separate still pictures is seen as moving pictures; the images overlap and the motion appears to be continuous.

perspiration (puhr-spi-RAY-shuhn), *n.* moisture excreted by skin pores; consists of water containing dissolved salts and urea; evaporating perspiration from the skin aids in regulation of body temperature; also called *sweat;* see also **skin, sweat gland.** *v.* **perspire.**

perturbation (puhr-tuhr-BAY-shuhn), *n.* in astronomy, an irregularity in the regular orbit of a heavenly body; caused by some unusual force, as in the irregular orbit of Uranus, affected by gravitational forces of Neptune.

pertussis (puhr-TUS-uhs), the medical term for **whooping cough.**

pesticide (PES-ti-syd), *n.* any substance or process that is toxic to a pest, either plant or animal, and used to rid buildings, fields, crops, etc., of the pest; includes *insecticides, rodenticides, herbicides.* *adj.* **pesticidal.**

pestle (PEHS-uhl), *n.* a device used to grind a solid substance into smaller particles; usually used with a mortar; see **mortar.**

petal (PET-uhl), *n.* one of the often brightly colored sections of the corolla of a flower.

petiole (PET-ee-ohl), *n.* the slender stalk which attaches a leaf blade to a main stem; a *leaf stem.*

Petri dish (PEE-tree), a circular, low, flat glass dish consisting of 2 parts that fit together like the top and bottom of a box; used extensively for culturing bacteria and in work with other microorganisms; named for Julius Petri, German bacteriologist.

petrifaction (pet-ruh-FAK-shuhn), *n.* the process in which bodily remains of organisms change partly or completely to stone by the exchange of minerals (from those dissolved in water) for organic parts; also called *petrification.* *v.* **petrify.**

petrology (puh-TRAHL-uh-gee), *n.* the science that studies the origin, composition, and changes of the rocks in the earth's crust.

PGAL, abbreviation for *phosphoglyceraldehyde,* a sugar containing 3 carbons; the end product of photosynthesis; see **photosynthesis.**

pH, *n.* a symbol indicating the acidity or basicity (alkalinity) of a substance; a neutral substance (neither acid nor basic), such as pure water, has a pH of 7.0. Acidic substances have a pH less than 7; basic substances have a pH greater than 7. Numerically, pH is defined as the negative common logarithm of the hydrogen-ion concentration, in moles per liter.

Phaeophyta (fee-AHF-uh-tuh), *n.* a division of thallophyte plants containing the brown algae; *phaeophytes* vary in size and complexity from small filament to huge body with specialized tissue; reproduces asexually and sexually; chlorophyll is masked by brown pigment; includes giant, brown kelp and fucus or rockweed; see also **alga, Thallophyta.**

phage (FAYJ), shortened term for **bacteriophage.**

phagocyte (FAG-uh-syt), *n.* **1.** a blood cell of higher animals capable of ingesting and destroying bacteria and particles of dead tissues or cells. **2.** in sponges and certain other invertebrates, any cell which takes in (ingests) foreign materials, carrying on digestion in this way.

phagocytosis (fag-uh-sy-TOH-sis), *n.* the ingestion of bacteria and other foreign particles by phagocytes in the bodies of complex animals. *v.* **phagocytose.**

PETROLEUM AND ITS PRINCIPAL CHEMICALS		
WORD PARTS USED IN NAMING ORGANIC PETROCHEMICALS	**ALIPHATIC COMPOUNDS** (open chain—straight or branched) **AND SAMPLE PRODUCTS**	**CYCLIC COMPOUNDS** (ring-shaped) **AND SAMPLE PRODUCTS**
-ane—saturated hydrocarbon; single bond -ene—unsaturated hydrocarbon; alternating single and double bonds -yne—triple bond iso- —straight chain isomer with a branch cyclo- —ring-shaped	methane, CH_4 ethane, C_2H_6 (CH_3CH_3) acetylene cracked to ethylene, ammonia C_2H_4 ($CH_2=CH_2$) carbon black ethyl alcohol chlormethane ethylene glycol hydrogen cyanide polyethylene methyl alcohol styrene	benzene, C_6H_6 cyclohexane (adipic acid) ethylene phenols styrene
meth- —methyl group, CH_3 tridec- —13 eth- —ethyl group, C_2H_5 tetradec- —14 prop- —propyl group, C_3H_7 pentadec- —15 but- —butyl group C_5H_9 hexadec- —16 pent- —5 (carbon atoms) heptadec- —17 hex- —6 octadec- —18 hept- —7 nonadec- —19 oct- —8 eicos- —20 non- —9 triacont- —30 dec- —10 tetracont- —40 hendec- —11 pentacont- —50 dodec- —12 hexacont- —60	propane, butane, C_4H_{10} C_3H_8 ($CH_3CH_2CH_3$) cracked to butylene, cracked to propylene, C_4H_8 ($CH_2=$ C_3H_6 ($CH_3CH=CH_2$) $CHCH_2CH_3$) acetone butadiene glycerol butyl alcohol isopropyl alcohol butyl rubber hydrogen peroxide gasoline, phenols high-octane polypropylene	toluene, C_7H_8 gasoline solvents TNT xylene, C_8H_{10} gasoline phthalic anhydride

petrochemical (pet-roh-KEM-i-kuhl), *n.* any one of a series of chemicals derived from crude oil or natural gas; all are hydrocarbons. *adj.* **petrochemical.**

petroleum (puh-TROH-lee-uhm), *n.* a yellowish to black, thick, heavy liquid occurring naturally in certain geological formations; formed from decayed organic matter; composed of a complex variety of hydrocarbons; used as a source of natural gas, naphtha, gasoline, kerosene, various fuel oils, lubricating oils, asphalt, coke, and organic chemicals used for synthesis.

phalanges (fuh-LAN-jeez), *pl. n.* (*sing.* **-lanx**) the bones of the fingers and toes in vertebrate animals; see **skeletal system.**

pharmacology (fahr-muh-KAHL-uh-jee), *n.* the study of drugs, including their preparation, physiological properties, and medicinal uses.

Pharmacopeia (fahr-muh-kuh-PEE-uh), *n.* the official guide for pharmacists, revised every 5 years and containing instructions and standards pertaining to the composition, purity, potency, preparation, and dispensing of drugs; also spelled **Pharmacopoeia.**

pharynx (FAIR-inks), *n.* **1.** in invertebrates, a muscular portion of the alimentary tract between the mouth and esophagus. **2.** in vertebrates, the passage connecting the mouth and nasal cavities with the esophagus; see **digestive system.** *adj.* **pharyngeal.**

phase (FAYZ), *n.* **1.** any specific stage in a cycle, as a phase in the lunar cycle or a phase in the development of an organism. **2.** a portion of matter distinguishable from other portions, as a liquid or gas phase. **3.** in electricity, the state of a wave when compared with another as a reference.

pheasant (FEZ-uhnt), see **Galliformes.**

phenobarbital (fee-nuh-BAHR-buh-tawl), *n.* a poisonous, white, crystalline powder; used as a sedative in medicines; formula, $C_{12}H_{12}N_2O_3$.

phenol (FEE-nohl), *n.* **1.** a poisonous, white, crystalline, solid organic compound that readily absorbs water from the air; used to make resins for plastics, weed killers, and as a solvent and organic intermediate; formula, C_6H_5OH; also called *carbolic acid.* **2.** any of a class of aromatic compounds characterized by one or more hydroxyl ($^-$OH) groups attached directly to the benzene ring, as *phenol* (above) and *resorcinol,* $C_6H_4(OH)_2$.

phenolphthalein (fee-nohl-THAY-leen), *n.* a yellowish, crystalline powder used as an acid-base indicator and in dyes and medicines; in solution it turns reddish-purple for some basic substances, and is otherwise colorless.

phenomenon (fuh-NAHM-uh-nahn), *n., pl.* **-mena.** any fact, characteristic, action, etc., that is seen to occur.

phenotype (FEE-nuh-typ), *n.* as a group, the many inheritable features by which a specific organism is recognized. Skin color, blood types, body shape, and eye color are examples of features which make up a phenotype; contrast with **genotype.**

phlebitis (fluh-BY-tis), *n.* infection or inflammation of the wall of a vein.

phlegm (FLEM), *n.* the thick mucus secreted during a respiratory infection, especially that occurring in the lungs and throat and discharged by coughing.

phloem (FLOH-uhm), *n.* a complex plant tissue consisting of various types of cells, such as sieve

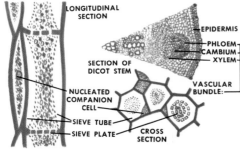

LONGITUDINAL SECTION

EPIDERMIS

PHLOEM
CAMBIUM
XYLEM

SECTION OF DICOT STEM

VASCULAR BUNDLE:

NUCLEATED COMPANION CELL

SIEVE TUBE
SIEVE PLATE
CROSS SECTION

tubes, and functioning as a means of food conduction from leaves downward to portions of the stem and roots.

phlogiston (floh-JIS-tuhn), *n.* the substance which, an 18th-century theory held, escaped from a burning or rusting substance. Later proof of oxidation disproved existence of phlogiston.

phlox family (FLAHKS), see **Polemoniales.**

Pholidota (fahl-uh-DOH-tuh), *n.* an order of mammals with a covering of overlapping horny scales developing from fused bundles of hair; they eat ants and are related to edentates; includes only pangolins; also called *scaly anteaters.*

Giant pangolin, or scaly anteater, *Manis gigantea,* of western Africa; about 5 feet long

phon (FAHN), *n.* the unit of loudness of a scale in which zero equals the quietest sound that is audible.

phon-, phono-, a word part meaning *sound.*

phonograph (FOH-nuh-graf), *n.* a sound-reproducing device; specifically, an instrument composed of a rotating, circular table, a needle, an amplifier, and a loudspeaker. Impressions marked in grooves on a *record* (a flat, plastic disk) vibrate the needle which produces a modulated electrical impulse. This electrical signal is amplified by the amplifier and changed into an audio sound by the loudspeaker.

phosphate (FAHS-fayt), *n.* any compound containing the phosphate ion, PO_4^{-3}; many of these, as calcium phosphate, are useful for fertilizers; several are important as basic parts of the nucleic acid molecules.

phosphoprotein (fahs-foh-PROH-teen), *n.* any of certain proteins (except nucleic acids and lecithin, an organic, waxy solid) composed of molecules of proteins and a phosphorus compound, as casein, a milk protein.

phosphor (FAHS-fohr), *n.* a material that emits light when exposed to electromagnetic or particle irradiation; color of light emitted depends upon the material chosen. TV picture tube screens are coated with a phosphor.

phosphorescence (fahs-foh-RES-uhnts), *n.* **1.** the state of continued emission of light after the exciting radiation (electrons, X-rays, etc.) has stopped. **2.** light emitted without production of heat, as by phosphorus or living organisms, such as glow worms. *adj.* **phosphorescent.**

phosphoric acid (fahs-FOHR-ik), any of many acids of phosphorus; specifically, *orthophosphoric acid,* occurring as a colorless liquid or crystals; used for fertilizers, soft drinks, pharmaceuticals, and inorganic synthesis; formula, H_3PO_4.

phosphorous (FAHS-fuhr-uhs), *adj.* pertaining to phosphorus with a valence of 3 or compounds containing phosphorus in this valence state, as phosphorous acid, H_3PO_3.

phosphorus (FAHS-fuhr-uhs), *n.* a chemical element necessary for growth of animals and plants; occurs in several forms, commonly as poisonous, yellow crystals; used in fertilizers, animal feeds, and medicine; symbol P; *at. no.,* 15; *at. wt.,* 30.9738; first identified by Brand in 1669.

photo-, a word part meaning *light.*

photochemistry (foh-toh-KEM-uhs-tree), *n.* the branch of chemistry that studies the effects of light or radiation on chemical reactions.

photoelectric cell (foh-toh-ee-LEK-tric), a device (may be electron tube instead of cell) with a cathode that emits electrons when struck by a light beam and an anode that collects the electrons; the current generated may activate other equipment; automatic devices operated by such cells are often called *electric eyes.*

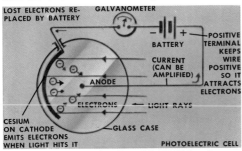

LOST ELECTRONS REPLACED BY BATTERY
GALVANOMETER
BATTERY
POSITIVE TERMINAL
KEEPS WIRE POSITIVE SO IT ATTRACTS ELECTRONS
CURRENT (CAN BE AMPLIFIED)
ANODE
ELECTRONS — LIGHT RAYS
CESIUM ON CATHODE EMITS ELECTRONS WHEN LIGHT HITS IT
GLASS CASE
PHOTOELECTRIC CELL

photoelectricity (foh-toh-ee-lek-TRIS-i-tee), n. **1.** the study of electric effects (especially currents) induced in matter by the action of light. **2.** the electricity induced by light. *adj.* **photoelectric.**

photoemission, n. the process in which electrons are emitted from the surface of a photosensitive material when light or other electromagnetic radiation falls upon the surface.

photography (foh-TAHG-ruh-fee), n. the art or science of reproducing images on sensitive surfaces by use of a camera or related instrument; see also **camera.**

photometer (foh-TAHM-uh-tuhr), n. a device that measures light intensity or brightness, especially by comparison of different intensities; a *light meter.*

photomicrograph (foh-toh-MY-kroh-graf), n. a photograph taken through a microscope eyepiece. The camera is placed where the viewer's eye would be; also called *microphotograph.*

photomorphogenesis (foh-toh-mohr-foh-JEN-uh-sis), n. the effect of visible light on the growth and development of a plant, particularly on the shape of the cells, unrelated to photosynthesis; see also **tropism.**

photon (FOH-tahn), n. a quantum of electromagnetic energy, usually light.

photosensitive (foh-toh-SEN-si-tiv), *adj.* influenced by, or reacting to, light or other similar radiations. n. **photosensitivity.**

photosphere (FOH-tuh-sfeer), n. the white-hot layer of vapor that surrounds the sun; it is believed to contain a considerable amount of metals; see **sun.**

photosynthesis (foh-toh-SIN-thuh-sis), n. the production, by green plants, of simple sugar from carbon dioxide and water, releasing oxygen and water; occurs only in the chloroplasts of green plant cells and in the presence of light. The actual end product of photosynthesis is PGAL (*phosphoglyceraldehyde*), an unstable, 3-carbon sugar used by plants for energy at the site but converted to other types of food for storage.

photothermic (foh-toh-THUHR-mik), *adj.* pertaining to changes or chemical reactions that give off both light and heat, as burning lithium.

phototropism (foh-TAHT-ruh-pizm), n. growth movements of plants induced by a light stimulus.

phototube, n. a tube in which the emission of electrons from the cathode is controlled by the electromagnetic radiation falling on the cathode, rather than by heat.

phthalic anhydride (THAL-ik), the anhydride of any of 3 phthalic acids with formula $C_6H_4(COOH)_2$, made by oxidation of orthoxylene or petroleum products; important in manufacture of many synthetic resins.

phycology (fy-KAHL-uh-jee), n. the study of algae, a branch of botany.

Phycomycetes (fy-koh-my-SEET-eez), n. a class of plants containing the alga-like fungi; *phycomycetes* have a filamentous plant body containing

(Left) Bread mold, *Rhizopus nigricans,* showing enlarged spore cases; (right) disease-producing potato-blight fungus, *Phytophthora infestans*

more than one nucleus; many species reproduce by algal-like flagellated spores; examples are bread mold and water mold; see **Eumycophyta.**

phyla (FY-luh), plural of **phylum.**

phylogeny (fy-LAHJ-uh-nee), n. the ancestral history and evolutionary relationships of a group of plants or animals; contrast with **ontogeny.** *adj.* **phylogenetic.**

phylum (FY-luhm), n., pl. **phyla.** one of the major groups into which the animal kingdom is divided; consists of one or more classes. In modern classification of plants, the term *division* is often used instead of *phylum.*

physical change, a change in state (gas, liquid, or solid) of matter without any change in basic chemical makeup; usually occurs through variations in heat or pressure; evaporation and freezing are examples; contrast with **chemical change.**

physical science, any of the sciences dealing with nonliving phenomena, as physics, chemistry, geology, astronomy, mineralogy, etc.; part of natural science.

physician (fi-ZISH-uhn), n. a person licensed to practice the art of medicine, regardless of his field of specialization.

physics (FIZ-iks), n. the science that deals with matter and energy, and particularly the relationship between them. *Physicists* deal with: structure of matter, mechanics, electricity and magnetism, heat, optics, acoustics. *Nuclear* (atomic) *physics* is concerned with the structure of matter. *adj.* **physical.**

physiology (fiz-ee-AHL-uh-jee), n. **1.** the chemical and physical functions and activities of a living organism. **2.** a branch of botany or zoology concerned with studying these functions. *adj.* **physiological.**

phytochrome (FY-toh-krohm), n. a soluble protein found in all green plants; it is stable in darkness but changes when irradiated with red light; involved in photomorphogenesis.

pia mater (py-uh MAY-tuhr), see the **meninges.**

Piciformes (pis-i-FAWR-meez), *n.* an order of birds with long, sharp bills, sharp, clawed toes for climbing, and long tongues for sucking up insects; includes woodpeckers, toucans, and others.

pickling, *n.* **1.** in metal processing, acid treatment of metal (as steel) to remove oxide scale from its surface. **2.** in food preservation, treatment of food with a brine solution. *v.* **pickle.**

picric acid (PIK-rik), a poisonous, explosive, yellow, crystalline organic acid; used in explosives, medicines, and dyes; formula, $C_6H_2(NO_2)_3OH$.

piezoelectricity (py-EE-zoh-uh-lek-TRIS-uh-tee), *n.* the electrical charges of some crystals, such as quartz, resulting from pressure: the crystal expands in one direction and contracts along another. *adj.* **piezoelectric.**

pigeon (PIJ-uhn), see **Columbiformes.**

pigment (PIG-muhnt), *n.* **1.** a substance that gives color to the tissues of living organisms, as chlorophyll in plants. **2.** any of many substances, both inorganic and organic, used to color materials, as carbon black is used for black coloring.

pika, see **Lagomorpha.**

pileus (PY-lee-uhs), *n., pl.* **pilei.** the cap of a mushroom, usually shaped like an upside-down bowl; produces spores.

pi-meson (py-MEZ-ahn), *n.* a nuclear particle with a mass equal to 263 to 273 electron mass units; positive, negative, or neutral charge. Positive and negative pi-mesons decay into neutrinos and mu-mesons; neutral pi-mesons decay into light quanta; also called *pion.*

pimple (PIM-puhl), *n.* **1.** a small, inflamed and raised area on the skin often containing pus and associated with acne. **2.** a pustule.

pincer (PIN-chuhr), *n.* a grasping or pinching tool or organ, such as a claw on a lobster.

pine, *n.* any of the family *Pinae* of coniferous evergreen trees or shrubs, varying greatly in size, with long, thin leaves (needles) and naked seeds borne in cones; many species found throughout the world; see **conifer.**

pineal body (PIN-ee-uhl, PY-nee-uhl), an endocrine gland in the brain with uncertain function; thought to secrete a hormone affecting sex; see **endocrine gland.**

pineapple family, see **Farinales.**

pinfeather, *n.* a young feather, before the web portions have expanded.

pinion (PIN-yuhn), *n.* **1.** the narrowed, end part of a bird's wing. **2.** a cogwheel with numerous small teeth.

pinkeye, a common name for **conjunctivitis.**

pink family, see **Centrospermales.**

pinna (PIN-uh), *n.* **1.** one of the leaflets of a fern leaf. **2.** a feather. **3.** the external ear.

pinnate (PIN-ayt), *adj.* with a featherlike shape, as *pinnate* compound leaves that have leaflets arranged opposite to each other on either side of a central axis, as a locust leaf.

pinnate venation, a type of netted venation in a leaf in which one main vein comes from the base of the leaf; smaller veins branch off the main vein.

Piperales (pip-uh-RAY-leez), *n.* an order of primitive dicot plants, usually herbs, having sim-

ple alternate leaves, joined stems, and tiny flowers in spikes without perianth. Of the 3 families, only the tropical pepper family (*Piperaceae*) has value as a source of pepper, cubebs (used in drugs), and betel nuts.

pipette (py-PET), *n.* an accurately calibrated (for volume), narrow glass tube with a very small opening, used to measure liquids; a simple type is used to suction up liquid to measure and transfer it to another vessel.

Pisces (PYS-eez), *n.* **1.** the *Fish,* a faint constellation of the zodiac seen in the northern sky during November and December. **2.** formerly, a class of vertebrates including all of the jawed fishes; now considered to be 2 separate classes; see **Chondrichthyes, Osteichthyes.**

piscine (PY-seen), *adj.* relating to fishes.

pistil (PIS-tuhl), *n.* the female floral organ, a flask-shaped structure in flowers, including the stigma, style, and ovary. *adj.* **pistillate.**

piston (PIS-tuhn), *n.* a closely fitted, sliding piece, usually cylindrical in shape, which is moved or moves against the pressure of a liquid or a gas without allowing the escape of the fluid. The piston in an automobile engine compresses the fuel-air mixture.

pitch, *n.* **1.** in sound, the number of vibrations per second, giving a distinct musical note. **2.** in a machine screw, the distance measured parallel to the screw axis from a point on one thread to the corresponding point on the next thread. **3.** on a propeller, the angle at which it is set. **4.** a dark, thick, sticking substance occurring both naturally and as a residue of coal tar; used for waterproofing and road paving.

pitchblende, *n.* the chief ore of uranium; a brown-black mineral containing uranite; U_3O_8.

pitcher-plant family, see **Sarriceniales.**

pith, **1.** *n.* tissue in the center of a stem, inside the area occupied by vascular bundles, and most often composed of parenchymal cells. **2.** *v.* to destroy the action of the central nervous system of an animal (especially a frog) by putting a needle into the spinal canal.

Pithecanthropus (pith-i-KAN-thruh-puhs), scientific name for **Java man.**

Pitot tube (PEE-toh), in aviation, a device for measuring air speed and atmospheric pressure; consists of a tube (with open end pointed into the wind) to measure impact wind pressure, and a second tube (closed at the ends, but with perforations in the side) to register static pressure. The difference in pressures is considered the relative air speed; named for Henri Pitot, French physicist (1695–1771).

pitting, *n.* **1.** corrosion due to air in metals that do not rust or tarnish, particularly in aluminum. **2.** formation of pits on a surface of a crystal when put in a dissolving chemical; caused by more rapid dissolving along line defects (dislocations) within the crystal; see **dislocation.**

pituitary gland (pi-TYOO-uh-tair-ee), a small, 3-lobed, ductless gland located at the base of the brain; secretes numerous hormones important to fundamental physiological functions; often called "master gland" of the body; see **endocrine gland.**

Pituitrin (pi-TOO-uh-trin), *n.* an extract made of hormones from the posterior lobe of the pituitary gland; causes contraction of uterine muscles; a tradename for an extract from cattle.

pivot joint (PIV-uht), a skeletal joint permitting rotation, such as the joint permitting the head to rotate from side to side.

placenta (pluh-SEN-tuh), *n.* in most mammals, a tissue attaching the unborn embryo to the wall of the mother's uterus, thus providing nourishment for the embryo; formed from the chorion; ejected from the uterus after birth.

placental mammal, any mammal carrying young in a placenta.

plagioclase (PLAY-jee-uh-klayz), *n.* any of a mineral group of triclinic feldspars, including albite, labradorite, and semiprecious moonstone.

plague (PLAYG), *n.* an infectious disease caused by a rod-shaped bacterium and carried to man by fleas that have fed on infected rats.

plain, *n.* one of the main types of land formations; a large, flat area with the difference in elevation between local points within the area usually less than 500 feet.

planarian (pluh-NAIR-ee-uhn), see **Platyhelminthes.**

Planck's theory, see **quantum theory.**

plane, *n.* **1.** a flat surface, having length and width but no depth. Every point on a straight line joining 2 points on a plane lies completely within the surface. **2.** any flat surface (usually imaginary) on or through a 3-dimensional object. **3.** short term for **airplane.**

planet, *n.* **1.** any of the 9 opaque bodies, each revolving around the sun in its own orbit and also rotating on its own axis; shines by reflected light; see table on page 219. **2.** such a body revolving around any star.

plant, *n.* **1.** any living organism having chlorophyll or having descended from chlorophyll-bearing ancestors; a member of kingdom *Plantae.* Most plants have unlimited growth, cellulose in the cell walls, and can manufacture their own food. **2.** the apparatus or building for a specific task, as a *power plant.* **3.** *v.* to place a plant or seed where it can grow, as into soil.

plantigrade (PLAN-ti-grayd), *adj.* walking upon the whole bottom surface, or sole, of the foot, as does a man; contrast with **digitigrade.**

planula (PLAN-yuh-luh), *n.* the larva of a coelenterate, covered with short hairs and consisting of a solid mass of cells, of outer ectoderm and inner endoderm; freely swimming; see **larva.**

-plasm, a word part meaning *shaped material; cytoplasm* is the material shaped into a cell.

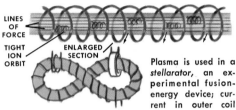

Plasma is used in a stellarator, an experimental fusion-energy device; current in outer coil confines plasma to magnetic lines of force in an endless figure 8; the particles cannot lose energy by hitting tube sides, so a controllable current is produced

plasma (PLAZ-muh), *n.* **1.** the liquid part of the blood that carries the corpuscles; includes the dissolved fibrinogen and the serum. **2.** in physics, a balanced mixture of free positive gaseous ions and free electrons; unlike regular gas, it is

POSITIONS AND ORBITS OF THE SUN'S PLANETS
(not to scale)

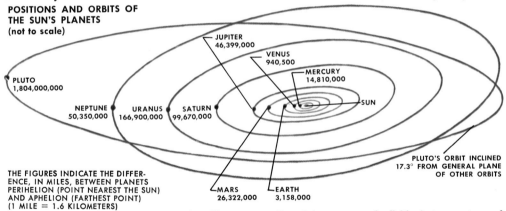

JUPITER 46,399,000
VENUS 940,500
MERCURY 14,810,000
PLUTO 1,804,000,000
NEPTUNE 50,350,000
URANUS 166,900,000
SATURN 99,670,000
SUN
PLUTO'S ORBIT INCLINED 17.3° FROM GENERAL PLANE OF OTHER ORBITS
THE FIGURES INDICATE THE DIFFERENCE, IN MILES, BETWEEN PLANETS PERIHELION (POINT NEAREST THE SUN) AND APHELION (FARTHEST POINT) (1 MILE = 1.6 KILOMETERS)
MARS 26,322,000
EARTH 3,158,000

planetary, *adj.* referring to or moving like a planet, as the *planetary* movement of electrons around the nucleus of an atom.

planetesimal hypothesis (plan-i-TES-i-muhl), a proposed set of ideas holding that the planets formed from tiny, scattered bits of matter called *planetesimals* that may have formed early in the life of the solar system.

planetoid (plan-uh-toyd), *n.* a minor planet; an **asteroid.**

plankton (PLANK-tuhn), *n.* collectively, the small plant and animal organisms in water that drift with water currents and have little locomotive ability of their own, especially those at or near the surface; contrast with **nekton.**

affected by a magnetic field. A temperature of thousands of degrees gives the particles the necessary energy to remain in this condition. Such temperatures are found in stars, plasma engines, and the center of fusion reactors.

plasma pinch engine, a reaction engine, developed for spacecraft, in which plasma is first heavily compressed, then forced out of a nozzle.

plasmodium (plaz-MOH-dee-uhm), *n.* **1.** the continuous, multinuclear sheet of protoplasm formed by fusion of slime molds or other ameboid organisms. **2.** a parasitic protozoan; see **malaria.**

plasmolysis (plaz-MAHL-uh-sis), *n.* shrinking of the protoplasm in a cell because of water loss through osmosis.

plastic, 1. *n.* any substance that can be molded; especially the man-made organic materials that are shaped while soft; 2 main types: *thermoplastic,* which can be melted and remolded, and *thermosetting,* which cannot be melted once it has set.

plasticity (plas-TI-si-tee), *n.* the ability of a material to assume a new shape when heated, put under pressure, etc., and keep its shape when stress is removed; contrast with **elastic.** *adj.* **plastic.**

plastid, *n.* any of various structures in certain cells that contain the pigments in plants and are involved in food synthesis and storage; see **leucoplast, chloroplast, chromoplast.**

plastron (PLAS-trahn), *n.* the bottom or ventral covering of bony plates that, with the carapace, makes up a turtle's shell.

plate, *n.* **1.** any of the flat disks or sections of bony or horny material making up an animal's protective covering, as on an armadillo. **2.** any flat, often round, piece of metal, glass, or other hard material. **3.** a grid filled with electrolyte in a storage battery. **4.** a flat anode in an electron tube. **5.** *v.* to put a thin metal film on a surface, see **electroplating.**

plateau (plat-OH), *n.* any flat area elevated above the land surrounding it.

platelet, *n.* a minute cellular particle found in the blood of mammals, produced by certain large cells in the bone marrow through fragmentation; concerned with blood clotting; known technically as *thrombocyte.*

plate tectonics (playt-tek-TON-ikz), an area of geology that deals with the nature of movement in the Earth's crust. It is used to explain the current placement of continents and oceans.

platinum (PLAT-i-nuhm), *n.* a precious, silvery-white, metallic chemical element; ductile, malleable, and nontarnishing; used as a catalyst and alloy for jewelry and electronic equipment: symbol Pt; *at. no.* 78; *at. wt.,* 195.09; isolated by Scaliger in 1557.

Platyhelminthes (plat-ee-hel-MINTH-eez), *n.* a phylum of invertebrates called *flatworms,* with a

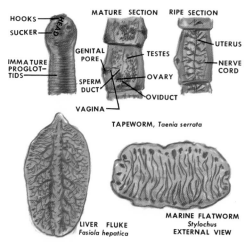

HOOKS
SUCKER
HEAD
IMMATURE PROGLOTTIDS
GENITAL PORE
SPERM DUCT
VAGINA

MATURE SECTION
TESTES
OVARY
OVIDUCT

RIPE SECTION
UTERUS
NERVE CORD

TAPEWORM, *Taenia serrata*

LIVER FLUKE
Fasiola hepatica

MARINE FLATWORM
Stylochus
EXTERNAL VIEW

soft, solid, usually flattened body showing bilateral symmetry; includes free-living planaria and parasitic flukes and tapeworms, with life cycles that include one or more hosts.

platypus (PLAT-uh-puhs), see **Monotremata.**

Pleiades (PLEE-uh-deez), *n.* a group of stars, 6 of which are visible to the naked eye, in the constellation Taurus, forming a small dipper.

Pleistocene (PLYS-tuh-seen), *n.* the most recent geological epoch, lasting about one million years, distinguished by 4 ice ages separated by warm periods; also called *Glacial.*

pleura (PLOO-ruh), *n., pl.* **-rae** or **-ras.** either of 2 thin membranes, each of which covers one lung and forms half a closed sac lining the chest wall in mammals. *adj.* **pleural.**

pleurisy (PLOO-ruh-see), *n.* infection or inflammation of the pleura.

Plexiglas (PLEKS-uh-glas), *n.* tradename for a lightweight, strong, unbreakable material made from acrylic resins (polymerized methyl methacrylate); used for glass and lenses.

plexus (PLEK-suhs), *n.* a structure of interlaced nerves or blood vessels in various parts of the body, as the *solar plexus* in the abdomen.

Pliocene (PLEE-uh-seen), *n.* an epoch of the Cenozoic Era, starting about 12 million years ago and lasting 11 million; a time of great volcanic activity and mountain building.

plumbic (PLUM-bik), *adj.* referring to lead with a valence of 4, and compounds containing lead in this valence state, as PbO_2.

plumbism (PLUHM-bizm), an alternate term for **lead poisoning.**

plume, *n.* a feather or group of feathers that is often soft, showy, and ornamental.

plumule (PLOOM-yuhl), *n.* **1.** a down feather of birds. **2.** a main bud of a plant embryo containing leaves and an epicotyl.

Pluto (PLOO-toh), *n.* ninth planet away from the sun, at an average distance of over 3½ billion miles; thought to be the last planet in our solar system, but different in composition from other planets and has an eccentric orbit; solar year equals 248 of our years.

pluton (PLOO-tahn), *n.* any body formed by the cooling and solidification of igneous rock deep below the earths' surface; an igneous intrusion.

plutonium (ploo-TOH-nee-uhm), *n.* a silvery-white, metallic, man-made, radioactive chemical element in the actinide series; used for nuclear fuel and research; symbol Pu; *at. no.,* 94; mass number of most stable isotope, 242; made by Seaborg, Kennedy, McMillan, and Wahl in 1940.

Pm, symbol for **promethium.**

P.M., p.m., abbreviation for the period of time between noon and midnight; from Latin, *post meridiem,* meaning *after noon.*

pneumatic (noo-MAT-ik), *adj.* relating to air, or depending on it for operation: a *pneumatic* hammer is operated by compressed air.

pneumonia (noo-MOHN-yuh), *n.* a usually acute infection of the lungs caused by several different bacteria and viruses; the several types have varying symptoms, and may involve different parts of the lungs.

Po, symbol for **polonium**

pod, alternate term for **legume.**

Podicipediformes (poh-di-si-ped-i-FAWR-meez), *n.* an order of aquatic diving birds commonly found in ponds overgrown with rushes and cattails in which nests are built; have lobed toes and sharp beaks; includes grebes and hell-divers.

poikilotherm (PWAH-ki-loh-thuhrm), *n.* an animal that is cold-blooded. *adj.* **poikilothermous** or **-thermic.**

Pointers, *n.* the 2 stars in the bowl of the Big Dipper farthest from the handle that form a line pointing to Polaris, the North Star.

poison (POY-zuhn), *n.* any substance which, when taken into the body (or applied to its surface), unfavorably affects health or even causes death; antidotes should be available and ready for any common poison that may be taken accidentally; see also **universal antidote.** *adj.* **poisonous.**

polar (POH-luhr), *adj.* **1.** of or near the North or South Pole. **2.** of or at opposite ends of any object, as of the poles of a magnet, which are opposite in charge.

polar body, one of the several small, nonfunctional cells produced by unequal meiotic divisions of the oocyte in forming the mature ovum; see **meiosis.**

polar front, the area separating cold, easterly winds from the North Pole from warm, southwesterly winds from the tropics.

Polaris (poh-LAR-is), see **North Star.**

polarity (poh-LAIR-i-tee), *n.* **1.** the property of having a definite tendency or strength along one end of an axis, opposite to that along the other. **2.** in mathematics, having either a plus or minus sign. **3.** in electricity, having a positive or a negative charge. **4.** in magnetism, having either a north or south pole.

polarization, *n.* **1.** in chemistry, the formation of bubbles of nonconducting gas on the electrodes of a voltaic or other primary cell, decreasing the current output. **2.** the transmission of an electromagnetic wave either vertically or horizontally. **3.** in optics, the transmission of light through a lens or sheet in one direction. *v.* **polarize.**

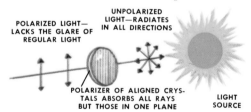

POLARIZED LIGHT— LACKS THE GLARE OF REGULAR LIGHT

UNPOLARIZED LIGHT—RADIATES IN ALL DIRECTIONS

POLARIZER OF ALIGNED CRYSTALS ABSORBS ALL RAYS BUT THOSE IN ONE PLANE

LIGHT SOURCE

polaroid (POH-luh-royd), *n.* **1.** commonly, the camera or special film developed by Edwin Land for taking pictures and developing them in the camera. **2.** a material which has the property of polarizing light.

polar projection, a map projection made by extending the points on the earth's sphere onto a plane surface centered on the North (or South) Pole.

pole, *n.* **1.** either the northern or the southern end of the axis of the earth's rotation. **2.** the extension of the earth's North (or South) Pole onto the celestial sphere. **3.** either end of a magnet, battery, etc., with an electrical charge opposite that of the other end.

Polemoniales (poh-li-mohn-ee-AY-leez), *n.* a large order of dicot plants, mostly herbs, with flower parts usually in groups of 4, commonly a compound ovary, and stamens fused to petals. The 19 families of food and ornamental plants include: the mint family (*Labiatae*)—catnip, lavender, peppermint, sage, spearmint, coleus; the morning-glory family (*Convolvulaceae*)—morning-glory,

sweet potato; the nightshade family (*Solanaceae*)—belladonna, eggplant, petunia, potato, tobacco, tomato; the phlox family (*Polemoniaceae*); the borage family (*Boraginaceae*)—forget-me-not; the figwort family (*Scrophulariaceae*)—foxglove, snapdragon; the gesneria family (*Gesneriaceae*)—Afri-

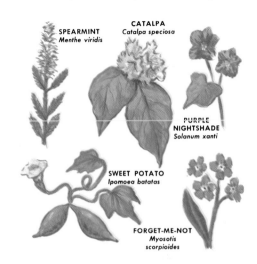

SPEARMINT
Menthe viridis

CATALPA
Catalpa speciosa

PURPLE NIGHTSHADE
Solanum xanti

SWEET POTATO
Ipomoea batatas

FORGET-ME-NOT
Myosotis scorpioides

can violet, gloxinia; the bignonia family (*Bignoniaceae*)—catalpa; and the insect-eating bladderwort family (*Lentibulariaceae*); order also called *Tubiflorales.*

poliomyelitis (poh-lee-oh-my-uh-LY-tis), *n.* an infectious disease of the central nervous system characterized by inflammation and destruction of nerve cells in the gray matter of the spinal cord; may result in a motor paralysis followed by muscular atrophy; caused by several viruses; also called *polio* and *infantile paralysis.*

pollen (PAHL-uhn), *n.* a fine dust, often yellow, produced and discharged by the stamens in a flower, and consisting of many microscopic spores which fertilize the ovules.

pollination (pahl-uh-NAY-shuhn), *n.* the transfer of pollen from the stamen of one flower to the stigma of the same or another flower; usually accomplished by wind and insects. *v.* **pollinate.**

polliwog (PAHL-i-wahg), *n.* the small tadpole, or larva, of a frog.

pollution (puh-LOO-shuhn), *n.* the state of being contaminated by bacteria, industrial waste, human waste, radioactive material, etc.; commonly applied to water supplies, streams, and rivers, but also applies to the atmosphere.

pollution potential, the degree to which the air at a particular place can become polluted; affected by average wind speed.

Pollux (PAHL-uhks), *n.* the brightest star in constellation Gemini, the 18th brightest star in the sky in visual magnitude.

polonium (puh-LOH-nee-uhm), *n.* a soft, metallic, radioactive chemical element; used as a neutron source in nuclear research; symbol Po; *at. no.,* 84; mass number of most stable isotope, 210; isolated by Curie in 1898.

poly-, a word part meaning *many.*

polycarbonate (pahl-ee-KAR-buh-nayt), *n.* **1.** a substance containing more than one carbonate group. **2.** a thermoplastic, high-strength, transparent plastic.

polycotyledon (pahl-ee-kaht-uh-LEE-duhn), *n.* any plant with more than 2 cotyledons in the embryo of a seed, as the pine tree.

polyester (pahl-ee-ES-tuhr), *n.* a man-made thermosetting substance, formed by polymerizing a glycol with a carboxylic acid: Dacron fiber is a polyester.

polyethylene (pahl-ee-ETH-uh-leen), *n.* a lightweight, odorless, corrosion-resistant polymer of ethylene; a thermoplastic resin used for packaging films and various molded products.

Polygonales (puh-lyg-uh-NAY-leez), *n.* an order of dicot plants, mostly herbs and shrubs of the north, often having stems with swollen nodes,

(Left) Dock, *Rumex crispus;* (center) buckwheat, *Fagopyrum sagittatum;* (right) rhubarb, *Rheum rhaponticum*

fruit as triangle or lens-shaped achene, and seeds with much mealy endosperm. The one family, the buckwheat family (*Polygonaceae*), has many weeds, but does supply buckwheat and rhubarb.

polymer (PAHL-uh-muhr), *n.* a substance consisting of very large molecules and with a high molecular weight; formed when simple molecules, called *monomers,* unite with each other. Rubber and most plastics are polymers; see also **monomer.**

the hydra has a polyp form; see also **medusa.** **2.** a smooth-coated tumor projecting from a mucous surface; commonly found in the nose, bladder, rectum, and large intestine.

polysaccharide (pahl-ee-SAK-uh-ryd), *n.* a sweet substance formed by the joining of molecules of many different simple sugars; contrast with **disaccharide, monosaccharide.**

polyunsaturate (pahl-ee-un-SATCH-uh-rayt), *n.* an unsaturated fatty acid; one, or sometimes 2, carbon atoms near the middle of the long molecule do not have their full complement of hydrogen atoms, thus the fat is unsaturated.

polyurethane (pahl-ee-YUHR-uh-thayn), *n.* one of a series of thermosetting plastics derived from a benzene derivative; these plastics can be pumped into hard-to-reach places and then made to foam.

polyvalent (pahl-ee-VAY-luhnt), *adj.* having more than one unit of electrical charge per atom or group of atoms being considered.

pome (POHM), *n.* a type of accessory fruit with seeds enclosed in a capsule, surrounded by a thick, fleshy layer, as an apple; see **fruit** picture.

pomegranate family (PAHM-gran-uht), see **Myrtales.**

pondweed family, see **Naiadales.**

pons (PAHNZ), *n.* a band of nerve fibers in the brain connecting the lobes of the cerebellum, and carrying impulses between them; see **brain.**

poppy family, see **Papaverales.**

pore, *n.* any very small opening such as is found in sponges and the epidermis of leaves.

Porifera (paw-RIF-uh-ruh), *n.* the animal phylum including the sponges, the most primitive of all metazoan animals; characterized by a body wall penetrated by many pores, a primitive skeleton, and no means of locomotion in adult life; includes 3 main groups based on presence of calcareous, siliceous, or spongin skeletons.

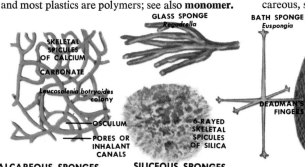

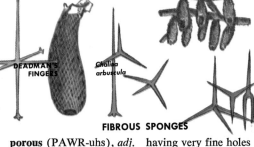

CALCAREOUS SPONGES   SILICEOUS SPONGES   FIBROUS SPONGES

GLASS SPONGE *Regadrella*   BATH SPONGE *Euspongia*   ENLARGED NETWORK OF SPONGIN FIBERS FORMING FIBROUS SKELETON

SKELETAL SPICULES OF CALCIUM CARBONATE

Leucosolenia botryoides colony

OSCULUM — PORES OR INHALANT CANALS   6-RAYED SKELETAL SPICULES OF SILICA   DEADMAN'S FINGERS   *Chalina arbuscula*

polymerization (puh-lim-uhr-uh-ZAY-shuhn), *n.* the process of uniting simple molecules (monomers) to form large, complex molecules (polymers), as ethylene can be converted into polyethylene. *v.* **polymerize.**

polymorphism, *n.* **1.** the presence in a species, as in some coelenterates, of more than one type of individual, often differing from the general type in function as well as form; see **medusa, polyp. 2.** in chemistry, the existence of a specific substance in different crystalline forms.

polyp (PAHL-uhp), *n.* **1.** one of the 2 body forms occurring in the coelenterates, characterized by an elongated cylindrical body with a ring of tentacles surrounding a mouth opening at one end and attachment of the other end to the substratum;

porous (PAWR-uhs), *adj.* having very fine holes (*pores*) through which substances, as water, air, etc., can pass: unglazed porcelain, for example, is *porous* to viruses.

porphyry (PAWR-fuhr-ee), *n.* an igneous rock containing large crystals of one or more minerals imbedded in a fine-grained matrix; has a polka-dotted appearance.

porpoise (PAWR-puhs), see **Cetacea.**

Portuguese man-of-war, see **Hydrozoa.**

positive charge, 1. a lack of electrons, or presence of excess protons. **2.** the type of static charge obtained by rubbing a glass rod with silk.

positron (PAHZ-uh-trahn), *n.* an unstable nuclear particle identical with an electron but with a positive rather than a negative charge.

posterior (pahs-teer-ee-uhr), *adj.* toward the rear, farther back than other parts, used especially in anatomy; contrast with **anterior.**

potash (PAHT-ash), *n.* common name for potassium carbonate, formula, K_2CO_3; originally obtained from wood ashes; used in making soaps and glass, and to remove water from organic liquids.

potassium (poh-TAS-see-uhm), *n.* a soft, silvery-white, metallic chemical element of low density; an alkali metal; used in making fertilizers and chemical compounds; symbol K; *at. no.,* 19; *at. wt.,* 39.102; isolated by Davy in 1807.

potassium-argon dating, a method for accurate dating of very old rocks, fossils, and artifacts; based on the fact that argon occurs in rock only by radioactive decay of potassium-40 (K^{40}) to argon-40 (Ar^{40}); the half-life of K^{40} is about 1.3×10^9 years; from analysis of K^{40} to Ar^{40} ratio, the duration of potassium decay is calculated.

potassium nitrate, a colorless or white crystalline inorganic salt, soluble in water; used in fireworks, explosives, matches, and fertilizers, and as a reagent in analytical chemistry; formula, KNO_3; also called *saltpeter* or *niter.*

potential (puh-TEN-shuhl), *n.* **1.** any stored quantity available for possible future use. **2.** the electrical pressure, expressed in volts, between 2 points in a circuit, or between 2 charged bodies. *adj.* **3.** able to be brought into being.

potential energy, stored-up energy in any substance; energy due to position; contrast with **kinetic energy.**

pouch, *n.* a bag- or pocketlike structure found in certain animals such as the abdominal pocket of female marsupials and the saclike cheeks of certain gophers; see **Marsupialia.**

poultry (POHL-tree), *n.* collectively, the domestic fowls including chickens, ducks, geese, turkeys, guinea fowls, and some game birds.

pound, *n.* **1.** a unit of force in the fps system; in the United States, 453.6 grams. **2.** commonly, a unit of weight equal to 16 ounces.

poundal, *n.* the basic unit of force in the fps system; equal to the force which will accelerate a one-pound mass one foot per second per second.

power, *n.* **1.** work done in unit time, often expressed in units such as kilowatts or foot-pounds per second; energy used divided by the time it was used. **2.** the magnification of an optical instrument: a lens with a *power* of 10 (written 10X) magnifies 10 times the diameter of the object being observed.

power plant, any installation for energy generation, including buildings, boilers, turbines, and other equipment needed for energy production; also the engine in a vehicle.

pox (PAHKS), *pl. n.* (used as singular), **1.** a small, round skin eruption, resembling a blister, containing pus; characteristic of several diseases such as smallpox and syphilis. **2.** any disease characterized by these skin eruptions.

Pr, symbol for **praseodymium.**

praseodymium (pray-see-oh-DIM-ee-uhm), *n.* a metallic chemical element in the lanthanide series; its salts are used for coloring glass and glazes; symbol Pr; *at. no.,* 59; *at. wt.,* 140.907; isolated by Welsbach in 1885.

Precambrian (pree-KAM-bree-uhn), *n.* the earliest era of geologic time, beginning about 4 billion years ago and lasting about a billion years; only algae and very simple marine animals were then living; see **geologic time table.**

precession (pree-SESH-uhn), *n.* a motion of the axis about which a spherical body rotates; precession of the earth in its rotation around its axis causes the equinoxes to fall at changing rela-

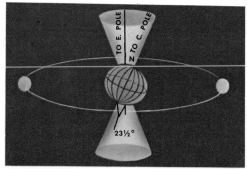

Precession of the equinoxes: gradual westerly movement of Earth's axis, extended to the celestial (C.) pole, around the ecliptic (E.) pole, creates changing equinoxes; a circle is made about once every 26,000 years

tions to the constellations; another result is that in about 12,000 years the star Vega will replace Polaris as the North Polar Star.

precious stone, a gem; a rare mineral, as a diamond, or a rare stone of animal origin, as pearl.

precipitate (pree-SIP-uh-tayt), *n.* any substance, usually solid, which settles out of a solution due to a chemical change such as electrolysis or the addition of another chemical to the solution.

precipitation, *n.* **1.** the act of causing a precipitate to form. **2.** moisture condensed from the air, as rain, snow, sleet, dew, etc. *v.* **precipitate.**

predator (PRED-uh-tuhr), *n.* any animal which preys upon other animals for food. *adj.* **predatory, predaceous.**

prediction, *n.* a forecast of coming events based on accurate observations and a systematic interpretation of the observations.

pre-emergence, *adj.* generally, before something comes out; specifically, referring to a weed-killer, such as Chlordane, that kills only weed seeds that have not yet germinated, not the growing grass.

preformation (pree-fawr-MAY-shuhn), *n.* an obsolete biological theory which considered the complete adult of any organism to be present in miniature in the embryo, and even in the egg; according to this theory, development was merely the enlargement of already existing tiny parts.

pregnancy (PREG-nuhn-see), *n.* the period of time during which a female mammal is carrying one or more embryos, beginning with conception and ending with birth. *adj.* **pregnant.**

prehensile (pree-HEN-suhl), *adj.* adapted for gripping, seizing, or holding on by encircling or partly encircling an object, as the tail of the opossum or spider monkey.

prehistoric (pree-his-TAWR-ik), *adj.* pertaining to events, organisms, and the like that occurred before man started writing or otherwise recording them; known from fossil or geologic evidence.

prenatal (pree-NAY-tuhl), *adj.* before birth.

BLACK HOWLING MONKEY, *Alouatta belzebul,* NEW WORLD, ARBOREAL

ANUBIS BAB *Papio doguera* OLD WORLD, TERRESTRIAL

TARSIER *Tarsius* FAR EAST, ARBOREAL

GOLDEN LION MARMOSET *Callithrix chrysoleuca* NEW WORLD, ARBOREAL

SIFAKA LEMUR *Propithecus* MADAGASCAR, ARBOREAL

ORANGUTAN *Pongo pygmaeus* FAR EAST, ARBOREAL

MIRIKI SPIDER MONKEY *Ateles hypoxanthus* NEW WORLD, ARBOREAL BUT CAN WALK ERECT

JAVA MAN *Pithecanthropus* 500,000 YEARS AGO IN FAR EAST

CRO-MAGNON MAN *Homo sapiens* 30,000 YEARS AGO IN EUROPE

GIANT GORILLA *Gorilla gorilla* AFRICA, LARGELY TERRESTRIAL

MODERN MAN *Homo sapiens*

prepuce, see **glans.**

presbyopia (pres-bee-OH-pee-uh), *n.* a condition of the eyes in which near objects are seen with difficulty; occurs frequently in people of advanced age; due to decreased elasticity of the lens.

prescription (pree-SKRIP-shuhn), *n.* a written order by a licensed physician, stating that the patient named in the order needs specified drugs and is authorized to obtain them; the order is filled by a pharmacist. *v.* **prescribe.**

preservative, *n.* any natural or man-made chemical that is added to a second substance to slow down decaying or spoiling: calcium propionate is added to bread to prevent spoiling.

pressure, *n.* the force (push) on an area, normally expressed as the force per unit area; expressed in pounds per square inch, grams per square centimeter, dynes per square centimeter, etc. Pressure of air at sea level is 14.7 pounds per square inch (psi).

pressurize, *v.* to keep the air pressure inside something at a higher level than the outside environment: the cabin of a high-altitude aircraft may be *pressurized* to near-normal (ground) levels for the comfort and safety of passengers.

prevailing wind, in any geographic area, a wind which blows predominantly from one direction at any one season; prevailing winds may change with the season.

prey, *n.* any living creature hunted for food by another. *v.* **prey.**

prickle, *n.* a spiny outgrowth from the epidermis of a stem, as on a rose.

prickly heat, an itchy skin condition caused by inflammation of the skin around the pores of the sweat glands.

primary color, one of the 3 colors from which all other colors can be obtained by mixing in the proper proportion; for light, the primaries are red, green, and blue; for pigments, yellow, crimson, and blue-green. When the 3 primaries are mixed in the same amounts (balanced), white light, or white pigment, is obtained; see **color.**

Primates (PRY-mayts), *n.* an order of mammals with highly developed brains, generally 5 fingers and toes covered by flat nails; limbs usually at the front, with opposable thumbs for grasping; includes man, apes, Old and New World monkeys, lemurs, tarsiers, and others.

prime meridian, the meridian indicated as 0°, from which longitude east and west is figured; passes through Greenwich, England.

primrose family, see **Primulales.**

Primulales (prim-yoo-LAY-leez), *n.* a small order of dicot plants with flower parts usually in groups of 5 including 5 stamens and petals joined at least at the base, with brightly colored petal-like

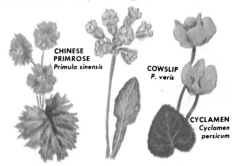

CHINESE PRIMROSE *Primula sinensis*

COWSLIP *P. veris*

CYCLAMEN *Cyclamen persicum*

calyx; fruit is a capsule. One of the 3 ornamental families is the primrose family (*Primulaceae*) of cyclamen, pimpernel, and cowslip.

principle (PRIN-si-puhl), *n.* **1.** a statement derived from one of the laws of mechanics, such as Archimedes' principle. **2.** in pharmacology, the substance giving a drug certain properties.

printed circuit, an electrical or electronic circuit printed onto an insulated flat sheet or card, usually by use of conducting, metallic inks; adapted for mass production of identical circuits and for miniaturization, since such circuits are in effect thin and compact.

prism (PRIZM), *n.* **1.** a wedge-shaped piece of transparent material, frequently glass, that refracts white light passing through it to give a continuous

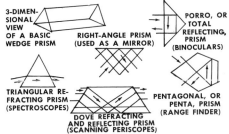

3-DIMENSIONAL VIEW OF A BASIC WEDGE PRISM

RIGHT-ANGLE PRISM (USED AS A MIRROR)

PORRO, OR TOTAL REFLECTING, PRISM (BINOCULARS)

TRIANGULAR REFRACTING PRISM (SPECTROSCOPES)

PENTAGONAL, OR PENTA, PRISM (RANGE FINDER)

DOVE REFRACTING AND REFLECTING PRISM (SCANNING PERISCOPES)

spectrum. **2.** such a piece with one surface silvered so that all light is reflected from it and not refracted, used in periscopes. *adj.* **prismatic.**

probe (PROHB), *n.* in general, any device for examining ordinarily unreachable spaces, especially: **1.** a surgical instrument for dissection or locating foreign bodies (such as bullets) in the flesh. **2.** an exploratory satellite or space vehicle for gathering information. *v.* **probe.**

Proboscidea (proh-buh-SID-ee-uh), *n.* an order of mammals with long snouts called *trunks,* large heads and ears, upper incisor teeth extended to form tusks, and hair confined to tip of tail; living examples include only the elephants, the largest living land animals.

proboscis (pruh-BAHS-uhs), *n.* any flexible, elongated, protruding structure in animals associated with the mouth, as an elephant's trunk and the feeding organ of insects.

Procellariiformes (proh-sel-air-ee-uh-FAWR-meez), *n.* an order of swimming birds with a tube-shaped nose; includes petrels, albatrosses—the largest flying birds—and others.

Proconsul (proh-KAHN-suhl), *n.* a genus of prehistoric African anthropoid apes, regarded as possible ancestors of the present anthropoids and of man.

Procyon (PROH-see-ahn), *n.* a star in the constellation Canis Minor, eighth brightest in the sky in visual magnitude; it and its companion Sirius are known as the "dog stars."

producer organism, in an ecological community, chiefly a green plant, the only kind of organism that can make its own food from simple, inorganic materials.

progesterone (proh-JES-tuh-rohn), *n.* the female hormone produced by the corpus luteum (tissue formed from a Graafian follicle) which continues the preparation of the uterine wall for receiving and nourishing a fertilized egg; following fertilization, progesterone maintains the thickened uterine wall and stimulates growth in the mammary glands; in later pregnancy, most of the progesterone is secreted by the placenta; a steroid, formula, $C_{31}H_{30}O_2$.

proglottid (proh-GLAHT-uhd), *n.* any of the segments of a tapeworm; each segment carries reproductive organs of both sexes.

prognosis (prahg-NOH-sis), *n.* an estimate of the probable course and termination of a disease.

program, *n.* a step-by-step series of operations for carrying out some task; especially such a series for operation of a computer. *v.* **program.**

projectile (proh-JEK-til), *n.* any body set in motion by external forces, and kept in motion by inertia; see **ballistics, missile.**

projection (proh-JEK-shuhn), *n.* in cartography, the extension of the earth's features onto a geometrical surface which can then be converted into a plane; any technique for representing the features of a spherical body on a plane.

projector (proh-JEK-tuhr), *n.* an optical device that displays an image on an external surface, such as a screen; most transmit a bright beam of light through a transparent source onto the screen, but an *opaque projector* reflects light from the source object to the screen.

prolactin, *n.* a hormone, commonly called LTH (*lactogenic hormone*), secreted by the anterior lobe of the pituitary gland; stimulates growth of the corpus luteum and production of milk in mammary glands after the female has given birth.

proliferation (proh-lif-uhr-AY-shuhn), *n.* an increase, often rapid, in the number of cells in an organism, part, or embryo, by cell division. *v.* **proliferate.**

promethium (proh-MEE-thee-uhm), *n.* a man-made radioactive chemical element in the lanthanide series; used as a tracer element in nuclear research; symbol Pm; *at., no.,* 61; mass number of most stable isotope, 147; identified by Marinsky, Glendenin, and Coryell in 1945.

pronator (proh-NAY-tuhr), *n.* a muscle that rotates the hand and lower arm (or foot and leg), so that the palm faces backward and the bones of the forearm are crossed; contrast with **supinator.**

propagate (PRAHP-uh-gayt), *v.* to bring about production of an organism; to reproduce; in horticulture, to bud or otherwise start a new plant; physicists often use the term for generating wave motion or chain reactions. *n.* **propagation.**

Fossil and living examples of Proboscidea

EXTINCT WOOLLY MAMMOTH
Elephas primigenius

EXTINCT MASTODON
Mammut americanus

AFRICAN ELEPHANT
Loxodonta africana

propane (PROH-payn), *n.* **1.** a colorless gas, used as a fuel, and from which other hydrocarbons are derived; formula, C_3H_8. **2.** more generally, any of the isomers of simple propane.

propellant (proh-PEL-uhnt), *n.* any evenly burning explosive, especially the fuel and fuel oxidizer for a missile or a space vehicle.

propeller (proh-PEL-uhr), *n.* any device for propelling a vehicle through a gas or liquid; usually consists of a hub with several blades, the hub being driven by an engine shaft; blades are set at an angle, so that rapid rotation causes function as an airscrew or water screw. *abbr.* **prop.**

property (PRAH-puhr-tee), *n.* **1.** in physical science, a definite, describable quality, action, or structural feature of a particular form of matter or energy: certain crystals have piezoelectric *properties.* **2.** in biology, an alternate term for **characteristic.**

prophase (PROH-fayz), see **mitosis.**

propolis (PRAHP-uh-lis), *n.* a reddish, gummy substance secreted by tree buds and collected by worker bees to use in repairing hives.

proprioceptor (proh-pree-uh-SEP-tuhr), *n.* the sensory structure at the end of muscles, tendons, and joints, the activities of which act as internal stimuli; see also **receptor.**

prop root, a root that develops from stem joints at or above the soil and grows downward into the soil providing support for the plant; the banyan tree and corn plant have prop roots; also called *adventitious roots;* see **root.**

propulsion (proh-PUL-shuhn), *n.* any action that moves an object; the propulsion of an airplane depends on engines and propellers or jet operation of a reaction engine. *v.* **propel.**

propyl alcohol (PROH-puhl), a colorless liquid with a characteristic alcohol odor; used as an organic intermediate; formula, $CH_3CH_2CH_2OH$.

propylene (PROH-puh-leen), *n.* a colorless, flammable, gaseous hydrocarbon; used as an organic intermediate (especially for isopropyl alcohol, polypropylene, and isoprene); formula, $CH_3CH:CH_2$.

prostate gland (PRAHS-tayt), a gland in male mammals that secretes fluid forming part of the seminal fluid; located between the bladder and urethra in mammals; various modifications occur in the more primitive animals.

prosthesis (prahs-THEE-sis), *n.* any artificial or man-made body part, used to replace a missing part, as an artificial limb. *adj.* **prosthetic.**

protactinium (proh-tak-TIN-ee-uhm), *n.* a radioactive chemical element in the actinide series; decays into actinium; symbol Pa; *at. no.,* 91; mass number of most stable isotope, 231; discovered by Hahn and Meitner, and separately by Soddy and Cranston, in 1917; also spelled **protoactinium.**

protease (PROH-tee-ays), *n.* any enzyme that breaks down proteins by hydrolysis, such as proteinase and peptidase.

protein (PROH-teen, -tee-uhn), *n.* any of a group of complex organic compounds which are the most important constituents of protoplasm; composed of amino acids combined in a large molecule; proteins contain carbon, hydrogen, oxygen, nitrogen, and usually sulfur.

proteinase (PROH-ti-nayz), *n.* any enzyme capable of breaking down proteins to peptides by hydrolysis, such as pepsin and trypsin that are secreted by the stomach and pancreas in inactive forms.

Proterozoic (proh-tuhr-uh-ZOH-ik), *n.* formerly, a geological epoch of volcanic activity and glacial ages; now referred to as the Precambrian; see also **geologic time table.**

prothorax, *n.* the first or most anterior section of the 3 sections of an insect's thorax.

proto-, a word part meaning *first* or *earliest: protozoans* are the simplest organized animals.

protoactinium, former spelling of **protactinium.**

protochordate (proh-toh-KAWR-dayt), *n.* any animal in the 3 lower subphyla of phylum *Chordata;* includes **Urochordata, Hemichordata, Cephalochordata.**

proton (PROH-tahn), *n.* a nuclear particle with a single positive charge; has mass number 1 and mass 1836 times the mass of an electron (slightly less than that of a neutron); see **electron, neutron.**

proton collision, collision of a nuclear particle, such as a pi-meson, with a proton; new particles formed in the collision leave observable tracks in a cloud or bubble chamber.

proton-proton reaction, the reaction believed to be the source of stellar energy; 4 protons combine to give one helium nucleus, giving off great amounts of energy in the process.

protoplasm (PROH-tuh-plazm), *n.* a grayish translucent living substance of which all plant and animal cells and tissues are composed; regarded as fundamental life, having the properties of metabolism and reproduction.

protoplast (PROH-tuh-plast), *n.* the organized living unit of protoplasm and other parts contained within a single cell.

protostar (PROH-toh-star), *n.* a mass of interstellar gas formed into a compact, dark cloud by radiation pressure from distant stars; when massive enough, it breaks up to form star systems.

prototype (PROH-toh-typ), *n.* **1.** the first model for a machine or other constructed object; often a hand-constructed operating machine used as a model for later automatically manufactured products. **2.** in biology, a term for **archetype.**

Protozoa (proh-toh-ZOH-uh), *n.* a phylum of one-celled animals and colonies made of like or

Representative protozoans: (1) *Euglena,* often considered an alga; (2) *Trypanosoma,* that causes African sleeping sickness; (3) *Gonyaulax;* (4) *Chrysameba,* the flagellate form; (5) *Codosiga,* a collar flagellate; (6) *Arcella,* and (7) *Foraminifera,* shelled protozoans; (8) *Opalina,* a frog parasite; (9) *Stentor;* (10) *Vorticella;* (11) *Balantidium coli,* that causes a human dysentery; (12) colonial *Volvox*

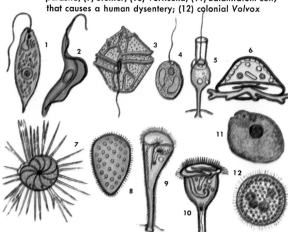

similar cells; the most primitive animals, often considered a subkingdom comparable to Metazoa; some *protozoans* are considered by botanists to be algae; includes 5 classes: see **Rhizopoda, Mastigophora, Ciliata, Sporozoa, Suctoria.**

protuberance (proh-TOO-buh-ruhns), *n.* any bulge from a surface: a sunspot is a *protuberance* on the sun's surface.

proximal (PRAHK-suh-muhl), *adj.* closest to the point of origin: the *proximal* part of the arm is that closest to the shoulder; contrast with **distal.**

prussic acid, an alternate term for **hydrocyanic acid.**

pseudopodium (soo-duh-POH-dee-uhm), *n., pl.* **-podia. 1.** a blunt, fingerlike, retractable projection found in certain plant and animal cells, as a leucocyte, and used for securing food and for locomotion; see **ameba. 2.** a leafless, stemlike structure occurring in the peat mosses, bearing the capsule and a short stalk.

psi, p.s.i., abbreviation for *pounds per square inch;* see **pressure.**

Psilopsida (sy-LAHF-suh-duh), *n.* a subdivision of tracheophyte plants known mainly from fossils;

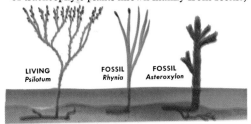

LIVING
Psilotum

FOSSIL
Rhynia

FOSSIL
Asteroxylon

psilopsids occur now in only 2 living genera; important as the most primitive vascular plants; simple plant body with underground stem and scale-like leaves.

Psittaciformes (sit-uh-si-FAWR-meez), *n.* an order of tropical birds with brilliant coloring, hooded heads, and 2 toes of the foot pointing forward and 2 backward; includes all parrots and parakeets.

psittacosis (sit-uh-KOH-sis), *n.* a very contagious disease characterized by high fever, delirium, and a pneumonia-like lung condition; caused by a virus occurring in parrots and easily transmitted to humans; also called *parrot fever.*

psychiatry (sy-KY-uh-tree), *n.* the branch of medicine that deals with the diagnosis and treatment of mental disorders and diseases. *adj.* **psychiatric.**

psychology (sy-KAHL-uh-jee), *n.* the science concerned with the study of the mind, mental processes, and behavior in man and animals *adj.* **pyschological.**

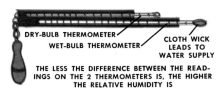

DRY-BULB THERMOMETER
WET-BULB THERMOMETER
CLOTH WICK LEADS TO WATER SUPPLY

THE LESS THE DIFFERENCE BETWEEN THE READINGS ON THE 2 THERMOMETERS IS, THE HIGHER THE RELATIVE HUMIDITY IS

psychrometer (sy-KRAHM-uh-tuhr), *n.* a handheld instrument measuring moisture content of air by comparing the readings on a wet bulb and a dry bulb thermometer; evaporation from the wet

bulb results in a lower temperature reading; the difference in readings indicates the humidity of the air; also called *wet-and-dry bulb hygrometer.*

Pt, symbol for **platinum.**

pteridophyte (tuh-RID-uh-fyt), *n.* in classification no longer used, any of a phylum of plants comprising the ferns, club mosses, and horsetails; characterized by lack of true seeds; see **Pteropsida, Lycopsida, Sphenopsida.**

pterodactyl (ter-uh-DAK-til), *n.* any animal of an extinct order of flying reptiles ranging greatly in size, characterized by an elongated outside digit of the forelimb supporting a wing of leatherlike skin; died out during the Mesozoic.

Pteropsida (tuh-RAHP-suh-duh), *n.* a subdivision of tracheophyte plants containing the ferns and all seed plants; the sporophyte generation of *pteropsids* is dominant; see also **Filicineae, angiosperm, gymnosperm.**

Ptolemaic system (tahl-uh-MAY-ik), a theory propounded by the ancient astronomer Ptolemy, who thought that the sun and the planets revolved around Earth; contrast with **Copernican system.**

ptomaine (TOH-mayn), *n.* **1.** any of a group of amine bases formed by bacterial action, frequently on decaying organic matter. **2.** commonly but inaccurately, illness brought on by eating rotten food, also called *ptomaine poisoning.*

ptyalin (TY-uh-luhn), *n.* a salivary enzyme that starts the digestive process by splitting starch into dextrose and maltose.

Pu, symbol for **plutonium.**

puberty (PYOO-buhr-tee), *n.* the period of life when human reproductive organs reach maturity and are capable of procreating offspring; accompanied by development of secondary sexual characteristics in male and female.

pubis (PYOO-bis), *n.* any of the 3 fused bones making up the bowl-shaped pelvic girdle; see **skeletal system.**

puerperal fever (pyoo-UHR-puh-ruhl), an acute infection of the genital tract that used to frequently occur following childbirth, caused by certain bacteria; also called *childbed fever.*

puffball, see **Basidiomycetes.**

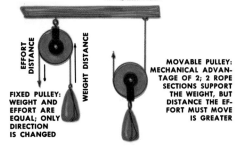

EFFORT DISTANCE

WEIGHT DISTANCE

FIXED PULLEY: WEIGHT AND EFFORT ARE EQUAL; ONLY DIRECTION IS CHANGED

MOVABLE PULLEY: MECHANICAL ADVANTAGE OF 2; 2 ROPE SECTIONS SUPPORT THE WEIGHT, BUT DISTANCE THE EFFORT MUST MOVE IS GREATER

pulley (PUHL-ee), *n.* a grooved wheel, one of the 6 simple machines; its function is to change the direction of effort with a minimum of friction, and in groups, to reduce effort force; see also **block and tackle.**

pulmonary (PUHL-muh-nair-ee), *adj.* referring to the lungs, lunglike organs, or blood vessels serving the lungs.

pulmotor (PUHL-moh-tuhr), *n.* apparatus for forcing air or oxygen into the lungs and withdrawing it, as an aid to restarting normal breathing.

pulp, *n.* soft portion of any plant or animal tissue, as of plant stems or fruits; in teeth, the soft, central portion containing nerves and blood vessels; see **tooth.**

pulsar, *n.* pulsating radio stars discovered in 1967. Identified as rotating neutron stars.

pulse, *n.* **1.** any regular wave-like rise and fall, as in the modulation of electricity. *v.* **pulsate. 2.** the rhythmic beat caused by expansion of the arteries after each contraction of the heart muscle; can be felt wherever an artery is near the skin. **3.** the edible seed of a legume.

pulse jet, a jet propulsion engine depending on a series of separate explosions of fuel to produce thrust.

pumice (PUHM-is), *n.* a porous, volcanic, igneous rock with high glass content; can float on water because of low density; used as an abrasive.

pump, *n.* a device for moving fluids (liquid or gas) by either vacuum or pressure; a *vacuum pump* is frequently called a *suction* or *force pump;* some of the devices for removing liquid by centrifuge are also classed as pumps; see **force pump.**

pupa (PYOO-puh), *n., pl.* **-pae, -pas.** an insect in the nonfeeding, usually immobile stage, of

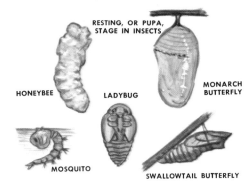

RESTING, OR PUPA, STAGE IN INSECTS

HONEYBEE   LADYBUG   MONARCH BUTTERFLY

MOSQUITO   SWALLOWTAIL BUTTERFLY

metamorphosis; between the larval and adult forms. *v.* **pupate.**

pupil, *n.* the circular, expanding and contracting opening in the center of the iris of the eye, through which light passes through the lens to the retina; see **eye.**

purebred, *adj.* referring to an animal with ancestors that are all of the same standard breed; for example, a *purebred* poodle comes from ancestral stock in which only poodle genes are carried.

pure culture, a single, isolated bacterium or other microorganism and its descendants, grown on an artificial nutrient medium such as agar.

purine (PYOO-reen), *n.* **1.** a nitrogen-containing organic base related to uric acid; formula, $C_5H_4N_4$. **2.** any of a series of chemical compounds related to this, including caffeine, uric acid, and others of physiological importance, as in DNA.

purslane family (PURS-lihn), see **Centrospermales.**

pus, *n.* a yellowish, oozy discharge from the site of an infection, consisting of dead microorganisms and leucocytes, lymph, and other debris.

pustule (PUS-chuhl), *n.* a blisterlike swelling of the skin containing pus.

putrefaction (pyoo-truh-FAK-shuhn), *n.* the decay or breakdown of organic material, especially

protein, by the action of microorganisms, often with an accompanying foul odor.

pycnometer (pik-NAHM-uh-tuhr), *n.* an instrument used for determining the specific gravity of a liquid; often called a *specific gravity bottle;* also spelled **pyknometer.**

pylorus (py-LOH-ruhs), *n.* the narrow, muscular opening between the stomach and the first section of the small intestine; controls the passage of food. *adj.* **pyloric.**

pyorrhea (py-uh-REE-uh), *n.* an infection of the tissues surrounding teeth, characterized by breakdown of the gums and bones, often resulting in loss of teeth.

pyrargyrite (py-RAHR-juh-ryt), *n.* a deep-red to black, lustrous, crystalline mineral with hardness 2½; composed of silver and antimony, Ag_3SbS_3; used as a source of silver metal.

pyridine (PEER-uh-deen), *n.* a flammable, yellowish liquid with a penetrating odor; an organic base; used to synthesize vitamins, drugs, rubber chemicals, and as a solvent; formula, C_5H_5N.

pyridoxine (peer-uh-DAHK-seen), *n.* vitamin B_6; a pyridine derivative; formula, $C_8H_{11}NO_3$.

pyrimidine (py-RIM-uh-deen), *n.* an organic compound containing nitrogen; formula, $C_4H_4N_2$ is the simplest pyrimidine; vitamins B_1 and B_2 contain pyrimidines.

pyrite (PY-ryt), *n.* a mineral containing sulfur and iron, formula, FeS_2; used in the manufacture of sulfuric acid; also called *fool's gold,* because of its yellowish, metallic color.

pyroelectric (py-roh-ee-LEK-trik), *adj.* developing electrical charge (as in a crystal) as a result of change in temperature.

pyromagnetic (py-roh-mag-NET-ik), *adj.* referring to the joint effects of heat and magnetism, working as a unified force.

pyrometer (py-RAHM-uh-tuhr), *n.* a device for measuring high temperatures; usually either *optical* (depending on color of radiation) or *electrical* (depending on current produced in a thermocouple); used for measuring temperatures above the range of regular thermometers.

pyrope (PY-rohp), see **garnet.**

pyroxene (py-RAHKS-een), *n.* any of a mineral group of silicates and oxides containing magnesium, calcium, iron, and/or aluminum, and occurring in igneous rocks; includes jadeite and diopside.

pyrrole (pih-ROHL), *n.* an organic compound with nitrogen and carbon in a ring structure similar to the benzene ring; basic to many biological compounds, such as chlorophyll; formula, C_4H_5N.

Pyrrophyta (peer-AHF-uh-tuh), *n.* a division of thallophyte plants including the yellow-green algae; *pyrrophytes* are usually motile, single-celled, and have 2 flagella; the cell wall is grooved with the cell appearing to have 2 sections; one of the 2 orders (Dinoflagellata) is seen in colorful, luminescent masses in the ocean; see also **alga, Thallophyta.**

pyruvic acid (py-ROO-vik), an organic acid occurring as an intermediate of protein and carbohydrate metabolism in living cells; a liquid with an odor similar to acetic acid; used in biochemical research; formula, $CH_3COCOOH$.

quadr-, quadri-, quadru-, a word part meaning *4,* as in *quadriceps,* the large, 4-part, thigh muscle.

quadrant (KWAH-druhnt), *n.* **1.** one-fourth of any generally circular area, as the lower-left *quadrant* of the abdomen. **2.** a device for measuring altitudes or elevations using a 90° measured arc and telescopic or other sights for viewing across the arc to the object; see also **sextant.**

quadruped (KWAHD-ruh-ped), *n.* any 4-footed animal; used especially in referring to mammals.

quadruplet (kwad-RUHP-luht), *n.* any of 4 offspring born at one time to a female mammal, especially human children; occurs once in about 700,000 births; the 4 cells formed in the first 2 cleavage divisions of a fertilized egg part and develop as separate embryos, or they may develop from more than one egg.

quake (KWAYK), *n.* a shaking motion; a tremor; commonly, short for **earthquake.**

qualitative analysis (KWAHL-i-tay-tiv uh-NAL-i-sis), chemical analysis of a substance to determine what materials are present in the substance, but not how much of each; contrast with **quantitative analysis.**

quanta (KWAHN-tuh), plural of **quantum.**

quantasome (KWAHN-tuh-sohm), *n.* one of the particles found in plant lamellae, shaped like flattened spheres, about 200 angstroms across and 100 angstroms thick, containing all the chlorophyll in the chloroplasts.

quantitative analysis (KWAHN-ti-tay-tiv), chemical analysis of a substance to determine how much of each specific element or compound makes up the particular substance; contrast with **qualitative analysis.**

quantum (KWAHN-tuhm), *n., pl.* **-ta. 1.** a particle or "bundle" carrying all the energy of an electromagnetic wave. **2.** the amount of energy carried by such a particle.

quantum mechanics, the science concerned with the theory of the interrelation and interaction of electromagnetic radiation and matter, and the mechanics of phenomena, especially subatomic, involving such interaction; deals with wave diffraction, effects of magnetic fields on waves, etc.; also called *wave mechanics.*

quantum theory, the theory, laid down largely by Max Planck, that energy travels through space as continuous waves but is emitted or absorbed as separate packets or bundles of minimum unit size (the units are called *quanta*); the theory has been much modified in recent years.

quarantine (KWAWR-uhn-teen), *n.* the isolation of an individual that has been exposed to a communicable disease, ordinarily for a period of time in which the disease will incubate, and intended to prevent further spreading.

quartz, *n.* a common mineral, consisting of silica, SiO_2; crystalline and colorless when pure. Traces of other minerals give it color and it is then known as amethyst, agate, opal, etc.; with silicates, the main mineral form in the earth.

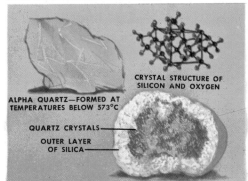

CRYSTAL STRUCTURE OF SILICON AND OXYGEN

ALPHA QUARTZ—FORMED AT TEMPERATURES BELOW 573°C

QUARTZ CRYSTALS

OUTER LAYER OF SILICA

quartzite (KWAWRT-syt) *n.* hard metamorphic rock with a granular, sugary appearance similar to sandstone; difficult to break; has a smooth, even texture; a metamorphic sandstone.

quasar (kway-sahr), *n.* a celestial object that is from 4 to 10 billion light-years distant that is a powerful source of radio energy; discovered in 1963.

Quaternary (KWAH-tuhr-ner-ee), *n.* the present period in the geologic time scale, estimated to have started about 6 million years ago when many of the present living organisms were in existence; man gradually emerged in this period; see **geologic time table.**

queen, *n.* fertile female of various insects such as ants and bees; does all the egg-laying for the colony; see also **Hymenoptera, Insecta.**

quicklime *n.* a common name for calcium oxide or unslaked lime; manufactured commercially by heating calcium carbonate and allowing carbon dioxide to escape; hisses when reacts with water.

quicksand, *n.* a moving bed of sand and water, usually over a clay layer; the water constantly wells upward and is unable to drain away: unlike regular sand, the sand grains are rounded and so have no tendency to adhere to each other; the surface of such an area is unstable and will not support objects of much weight.

quicksilver, a common term for **mercury.**

quill, *n.* **1.** the hard, tubelike portion of a feather without the slender lateral branches. **2.** a spine on a porcupine.

quinine (KWY-nyn), *n.* a white, crystalline, bitter powder obtained from bark of the cinchona, a tropical tree of the madder family; used in treatment of fevers, particularly in malaria; natural quinine is now commonly replaced by a synthetic; formula, $C_{20}H_{24}N_2O_2 + 3H_2O$.

quintuplet (kwin-TUHP-luht), *n.* any of 5 offspring born at one time, to a female mammal, especially humans; occurs once in about 60 million births; usually develop from 2 or more fertilized ova and so are rarely identical.

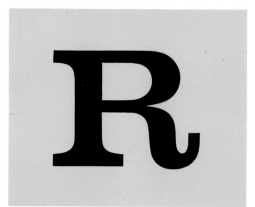

R, abbreviation for **Rankine.**

Ra, symbol for **radium.**

rabbit, see **Lagomorpha.**

rabies (RAY-beez), *n.* a virus-caused disease of the nervous system; spasms of the throat and larynx, extreme thirst and anxiety are characteristic symptoms; the Pasteur treatment prevents onset of the disease but there is no known cure once the disease has started; dogs, cats, wolves, and other mammals transmit rabies to man by biting; formerly called *hydrophobia. adj.* **rabid.**

raccoon (ruh-KOON), see **Carnivora.**

race, *n.* a subdivision of a species, with some characteristics distinguishing it from other groups in the species; such characteristics are inherited. Races are not genetically isolated as are species.

RAD, the standard unit of *radioactive dose,* suggested to replace the older and similar-sized roentgen unit; 100 ergs per gram of absorbing material; see **roentgen.**

Radar antenna is connected first to a microwave transmitter, then to a receiver which amplifies any echoes from objects, as aircraft, in the signal's path; a cathode-ray tube converts echoes to lights, or blips, on a screen that shows the object's position and direction

radar (RAY-dahr), *n.* a system for detecting and observing objects at a distance by means of ultra-high frequency radio waves that reflect from the objects and present images on a screen; short for *RA*dio *D*etecting *A*nd *R*anging.

radial symmetry (RAY-dee-uhl SIM-uh-tree), the arrangement of the parts of an organism in a wheel shape, forming 2 identical halves when divided in any plane passing through the center, as in a starfish.

radiant energy (RAY-dee-uhnt), energy in the form of electromagnetic waves or radiation; see also **electromagnetic spectrum.**

radiation (ray-dee-AY-shuhn), *n.* **1.** the travel of energy through space or through any medium (gas, liquid, solid) in the form of waves; electromagnetic waves of many different wavelengths, from radio waves to gamma rays, including all light waves, are forms of radiation; *radiant energy.* **2.** a spreading out from a surface or central point, as the radiation of arms in a starfish. *v.* **radiate.** *adj.* **radiant.**

radiation belt, see **Van Allen belt.**

radiator (RAY-dee-ay-tuhr), *n.* **1.** any device that emits radiant energy. **2.** a device for providing heat by radiation (convection and conduction) from a metal source of large surface area. **3.** a device for keeping automotive engines from overheating by circulating air over a large metal surface that removes the heat from a liquid coolant.

radical (RAD-i-kuhl), *n.* **1.** in chemistry, a combination of 2 or more atoms that stay together during chemical changes; in water solutions, radi-

REPRESENTATIVE CHEMICAL RADICALS			
Radical Name	Formula	Valence	Common Compound
Acetate	$C_2H_3O_2$	-1	lead acetate
Bicarbonate	HCO_3	-1	sodium bicarbonate
Carbonate	CO_3	-2	calcium carbonate
Chlorate	ClO_3	-1	potassium chlorate
Hydroxide	OH	-1	ammonium hydroxide
Nitrate	NO_3	-1	nitric acid
Nitrite	NO_2	-1	boron nitride
Peroxide	O_2	-2	hydrogen peroxide
Phosphate	PO_4	-3	sodium phosphate
Sulfate	SO_4	-2	sulfuric acid
Sulfite	SO_3	-2	sodium sulfite

cals usually become ions. **2.** in mathematics, the indicated root of a number, as the square root, cube root, etc.

radicle, *n.* that section in the embryo of a plant seed that is below the hypocotyl; upon germination of the seed, it becomes the primary root of the seedling; see **seed.**

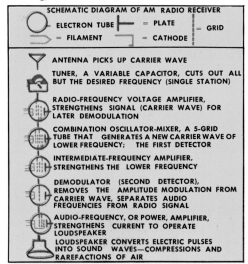

SCHEMATIC DIAGRAM OF AM RADIO RECEIVER

◯ = ELECTRON TUBE — = PLATE — = GRID

= FILAMENT — = CATHODE

ANTENNA PICKS UP CARRIER WAVE

TUNER, A VARIABLE CAPACITOR, CUTS OUT ALL BUT THE DESIRED FREQUENCY (SINGLE STATION)

RADIO-FREQUENCY VOLTAGE AMPLIFIER, STRENGTHENS SIGNAL (CARRIER WAVE) FOR LATER DEMODULATION

COMBINATION OSCILLATOR-MIXER, A 5-GRID TUBE THAT GENERATES A NEW CARRIER WAVE OF LOWER FREQUENCY; THE FIRST DETECTOR

INTERMEDIATE-FREQUENCY AMPLIFIER, STRENGTHENS THE LOWER FREQUENCY

DEMODULATOR (SECOND DETECTOR), REMOVES THE AMPLITUDE MODULATION FROM CARRIER WAVE, SEPARATES AUDIO FREQUENCIES FROM RADIO SIGNAL

AUDIO-FREQUENCY, OR POWER, AMPLIFIER, STRENGTHENS CURRENT TO OPERATE LOUDSPEAKER

LOUDSPEAKER CONVERTS ELECTRIC PULSES INTO SOUND WAVES—COMPRESSIONS AND RAREFACTIONS OF AIR

radio, *n.* a system for transmitting and receiving signals carried by electromagnetic waves that travel through space or through the air; such waves may have frequencies ranging from only 10 to 30 million kilocycles per second.

radio-, a word part meaning *radiation,* as in *radioactive* or *radiotelephone;* derived from Latin *radius,* a ray.

radioactive (ray-dee-oh-AK-tiv), *adj.* having radioactivity as a property.

radioactive isotope, an atom, or collection of atoms, which is able to give off one or more high energy particles or rays, such as alpha or beta particles and gamma rays, usually from the nucleus; also called *radioisotope.*

radioactive series, a series of elements that are produced by disintegration of a parent element; the uranium-radium series, the thorium series, and the actinium series occur in nature; the uranium-radium series is the most important.

radioactivity (ray-dee-oh-ak-TIV-i-tee), *n.* the spontaneous decay of the atoms of certain elements by the emission of alpha and beta particles and gamma rays; may also be induced by bombarding the nucleus. *adj.* **radioactive.**

radio astronomy, the branch of astronomy that uses radio telescopes to pick up electromagnetic (radio frequency) waves from stars, nebulae, and interstellar space, much as optical telescopes pick up light waves from distant stars.

radiocarbon dating, a process of dating organic fossil remains by measuring the amount of carbon-14 (radiocarbon) in a sample. C^{14} has a half-life of 5568 years; it decays to nitrogen-14.

radiochemistry, *n.* the branch of chemistry that studies the nature and quantity of chemical substances produced in materials during bombardment by high-energy particles and rays, and the mechanism of their production.

radio frequency, the frequency of electromagnetic waves in the ranges used for radio transmission.

radiograph (RAY-dee-oh-graf), *n.* an image of an opaque body formed on photographic film when X-rays are passed through the body; an X-ray picture; see **X-ray.**

radioisotope (ray-dee-oh-EY-soh-tohp), a short term for **radioactive isotope.**

radiolarian (ray-dee-oh-LAIR-ee-uhn), see **Rhizopoda.**

radiology (ray-dee-AHL-uh-jee), *n.* the study of radioactivity, and especially of its medical applications and hazards. A *radiologist* may help in diagnosis and treatment of many conditions.

radiometer (ray-dee-AHM-uh-tuhr), *n.* a device for demonstrating absorption of radiant energy, consisting of a set of vanes (usually 4) mounted on

Radiometer: within the near-vacuum of the chamber, small amounts of radiant energy are absorbed by the black surfaces which becomes hotter; air molecules bounce off with more push than on the silvered sides, causing the vanes to turn

a needle point. Looking down on it, each vane is blackened on the same side. It rotates because more energy is absorbed by the black than by the lighter surfaces.

radiosonde (RAY-de-oh-sahnd), *n.* a small radio transmitter that signals atmospheric and weather conditions from an unmanned balloon.

radio telescope, an electronic receiver used in radio astronomy to pick up radio waves from celestial bodies; basically a large, complex radio antenna that can be directed toward definite portions of the sky; signals are amplified and recorded.

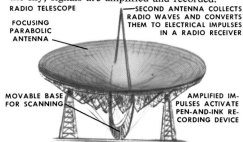

RADIO TELESCOPE — SECOND ANTENNA COLLECTS RADIO WAVES AND CONVERTS THEM TO ELECTRICAL IMPULSES IN A RADIO RECEIVER

FOCUSING PARABOLIC ANTENNA

MOVABLE BASE FOR SCANNING

AMPLIFIED IMPULSES ACTIVATE PEN-AND-INK RECORDING DEVICE

radiotherapy (ray-dee-oh-THER-uh-pee), *n.* treatment of disease by radioactive materials or by exposure to X-rays.

radio thermometer, a temperature-sensing device that uses the natural radio energy of a celestial body (planet or star) to indicate the temperature.

radio tube, any electron tube for use in radio transmitters or receivers.

radio wave, an electromagnetic wave that carries a radio (or TV) signal.

radium (RAY-dee-uhm), *n.* a brilliant white, radioactive, metallic chemical element in the actinide series; used principally in cancer therapy; symbol, Ra; *at. no.,* 88; mass number of most stable isotope, 226; separated from pitchblende in 1898 by the Curies, and isolated in pure form in 1911 by Madame Curie.

radius (RAY-dee-uhs), *n.* **1.** one of the 2 bones in the forearm; see **skeletal system. 2.** the distance from the center to the circumference of a circle; one-half the diameter.

radome (RAY-dohm), *n.* the protective housing (usually plastic) for a radar antenna, especially on aerospacecraft.

radon (RAY-dahn), *n.* a chemically inert, radioactive element given off as a colorless gas by radium; originally called *niton;* symbol Rn; *at. no.,* 86; mass number of most stable isotope, 222; first noted by Rutherford, who called it *radium emanation;* identified by Dorn in 1900.

radula (RAJ-uh-luh), *n.* in most mollusks, a tongue-like organ which can be extended from the mouth cavity; bearing numerous rows of minute horny teeth, it shaves off pieces of food.

rail, see **Gruiformes.**

rain, *n.* water that condenses from atmospheric water vapor when the proper conditions of humidity, temperature, air currents, and dust particles are present.

rainbow, *n.* a colored band of light in the sky, containing the colors of the spectrum from red to violet; caused by the light being refracted and reflected in rain drops.

rain forest, a dense, jungle-like plant community consisting of broad-leafed trees, woody vines and shrubs, and numerous kinds of epiphytes; found in tropical regions having a year-round warm and moist climate.

rain gauge, a device for indicating the volume of rainfall, usually during a certain time; consists of a funnel leading to a graduated water-collecting tube. It shows the rainfall in terms of depth, usually in inches or centimeters.

ram, *n.* **1.** any device for applying sudden impact, as a hydraulic ram for diving piles into earth. **2.** an adult male sheep.

ramjet engine, a jet engine so arranged that air intake is continuous, resulting in added compression for the air already admitted because of the forward motion of the engine.

ramus (RAY-muhs), *n., pl.* **rami.** a branch, or extended part, usually off the central body of something, as the *rami* of a spinal nerve.

Ranales (ruh-NAY-leez), *n.* an order of dicot herbs, shrubs, and trees with flower parts arranged in spirals, usually twice as many stamens as sepals, and pistils separated; leaves are usually alternate or opposite. The 16 families include magnolia (*Magnoliaceae*), nutmeg (*Myristicaceae*), water lily and lotus (*Nymphaeaceae*), bar-

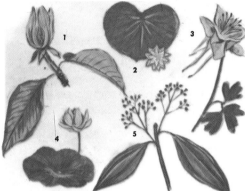

(1) Magnolia, *M. acuminata;* (2) fragrant water lily, *Nymphaea odorata;* (3) columbine, *Aquilegia vulgaris;* (4) Hindu lotus, *Nelumbium nelumbo;* (5) cinnamon, *Cinnamomum cassia*

berry (*Berberidaceae*), custard apple or pawpaw (*Annonaceae*), the valuable laurel family (*Lauraceae*)—avocado, camphor, cinnamon; and the crowfoot or buttercup family (*Ranunculaceae*)—aconite, delphinium, columbine, and peony.

Rankine (RAN-kuhn), *adj.* based on or pertaining to an absolute temperature scale, using degrees Fahrenheit from absolute zero rather than degrees Centigrade; freezing point of water is 491.7°; see also **Kelvin.** *abbr.* **R.**

raptures of the deep, a condition occurring among divers who use compressed air; it is believed that nitrogen in the air affects the brain, causing a sort of intoxication in which the diver has no desire to surface; *nitrogen narcosis.*

rare, *adj.* **1.** thin; containing very few molecules in a relatively large volume. **2.** unusual or seldom occurring: a *rare* gem is a very scarce one.

rare-earth element, an element within atomic numbers 58 through 71 (the lanthanide series) or atomic numbers 89 through 98 (actinide series); so-called because originally thought to be rare.

rarefaction (rair-uh-FAK-shuhn), *n.* the process of decreasing the density of a gas by removing most of the molecules in a volume. *v.* **rarefy.**

rare gas, one of the 6 *noble* gases (helium, neon, argon, krypton, xenon, and radon) which are chemically inert except under very special conditions of temperature and pressure.

rat, see **Rodentia.**

ratio (RAY-shoh), *n.* a proportion; the quotient of one physical measure divided by another of similar units; always a number with no dimensions: a percentage is a ratio.

rattlesnake, *n.* one of several poisonous snakes found primarily in Mexico and the United States. *Rattlers* have triangular heads, thick bodies, and several loosely attached horny rings at the tip of the tail, which make a rattling sound; see **snake.**

ray, *n.* **1.** in physics, any extremely narrow beam of radiant energy, or a particle that behaves much like such a beam, as *gamma rays.* **2.** in biology, any structure that radiates from a central point. **3.** see **Chondrichthyes.**

ray flower, one of the usually small flowers surrounding the central disk flowers in many composites; see **composite family.**

rayon (RAY-ahn), *n.* a synthetic fiber, normally made from cellulose, either by the viscose or the acetate process; acetate rayons are less likely to wrinkle as they have a specific gravity (1.3) close to that of silk (1.36) rather than the high specific gravity (1.5) of viscose.

Rb, symbol for **rubidium.**

Re, symbol for **rhenium.**

reactance (ree-AK-tuhnts), *n.* opposition to the flow of alternating current offered by inductance or capacitance. Although both are expressed in ohms, inductive and capacitive reactance have opposite effects in a circuit.

reaction (ree-AK-shuhn), *n.* **1.** in chemistry, the process in which one substance is transformed into another by the addition, or removal, of some chemical. **2.** in psychology, the mental or emotional state or other behavior caused by some situation. **3.** in physics, a force in the direction opposite to and caused by another force. *v.* **react.** *adj.* **reactive.**

reaction engine, an engine depending on thrust to create motion according to Newton's Third Law: an action in one direction causes reaction in the opposite direction; a jet engine.

reaction time, the time between receiving a stimulus and acting upon it; occasionally, time required for a chemical reaction to be completed.

reactor, see **nuclear reactor.**

reagent (ree-AY-juhnt), *n.* **1.** a chemical used to identify other chemicals present in a substance of unknown chemical composition. **2.** a chemical used to indicate the amount of other chemicals present in a substance.

realgar (ree-AL-gahr), *n.* a brownish-yellow, brittle mineral: the sulfide of arsenic, AsS.

real image, in optics, an image formed by an optical system that an observer sees outside the system; a motion picture projector forms a real image; contrast with **virtual image;** see **focus.**

receiver (ree-SEE-vuhr), *n.* any device for capturing and converting transmitted signals, as radio, television, and radar receivers.

Recent (REE-suhnt), *n.* the present epoch in the geologic time scale; still part of the Cenozoic era; generally regarded as starting 11,000 years ago.

receptacle (ree-SEP-tuh-kuhl), *n.* **1.** the end of a flower stalk from which the flower parts arise. **2.** an enlarged end of some brown algae containing the spore cases.

reception (ree-SEP-shuhn), *n.* **1.** the acceptance of transmitted signals by a receiver, as of radio, television, or radar signals. **2.** the quality of the received signals as converted to audible, visual, or other signals.

receptor (ree-SEP-tuhr), *n.* any sensory nerve ending that receives information and passes it to the central nervous system: *exteroceptors* are stimulated by environment outside the body; *proprioceptors,* by the position of the body or by movement (as in muscles); *interoceptors,* by impulses from the internal organs (viscera).

recessive (ree-SES-iv), *adj.* referring to a suppressed or partially masked hereditary character determined by a gene of lesser biochemical activity than its allele partner, the dominant gene; contrast with **dominant.**

reciprocal (ruh-SIP-ruh-kuhl), **1.** *adj.* pertaining to an opposite or inverse relationship between things, or to a reciprocating device (one that goes back and forth). **2.** *n.* a number consisting of 1 divided by any quantity: 1/15 is the reciprocal of 15; a mho is the reciprocal of the ohm.

reciprocating engine (ree-SIP-roh-kayt-ing), an engine operating by back-and-forward (or up-and-down) motion of a piston in a cylinder; the piston is linked to a connecting rod which in turn is linked to a drive shaft; gasoline and diesel engines and nonturbine steam engines are reciprocating.

Reciprocating engine in a propeller-driven aircraft

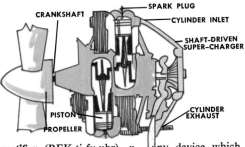

rectifier (REK-ti-fy-uhr), *n.* any device which electronically converts alternating current to direct current, such as electron tubes, selenium rectifiers, and germanium diodes. Motor-generator sets for converting AC to DC are called *converters.*

rectum (REK-tuhm), *n,* the last section of the large intestine, ending in the anus, in higher vertebrates; see **digestive system.**

recycle, *v.* to treat for further use.

red algae, see **Rhodophyta.**

red corpuscle (KAWR-puhs-uhl), an *erythrocyte,* a type of cell found in the blood of vertebrates; contains hemoglobin which readily combines with and releases oxygen, thus serving to transport oxygen; in mammals, normally has no nucleus.

red shift, the condition seen in a spectrum pattern coming from certain stars, galaxies, or other astronomical bodies, such that the color lines are all moved toward the long-wave (including the red-wave) ends of the usual spectrum pattern. Such a shift indicates that the body is moving away from the observer; see also **Doppler effect.**

reducing agent, any substance that supplies the electrons necessary in a reduction reaction and is oxidized during the reaction.

reduction (ree-DUK-shuhn), *n.* **1.** a chemical reaction in which a substance gains electrons. **2.** a chemical reaction in which a substance loses oxygen; contrast with **oxidation.**

reduction division, an alternate term for **meiosis.**

reef, *n.* a bar of rocks, coral, or sand at or just below the surface of the ocean, built up in layers from the ocean floor; see also **coral reef.**

reentry (ree-EN-tree), *n.* the return of a ballistic missile or other object into the atmosphere, which creates many problems, especially of heating due to friction with the molecules in the atmosphere; also spelled **re-entry.**

refine, *v.* **1.** to extract a pure product, as a metal or sugar, from its ore or other source by crushing, heating, adding chemicals, etc. **2.** to obtain end products such as diesel oil, fuel oil, gasoline, etc., from crude oil.

reflecting telescope, a telescope in which the major light focusing element is a curved mirror instead

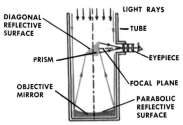

of a lens; the largest telescopes are reflectors, including the 200-inch reflector on Mount Palomar, in California.

reflection (ree-FLEK-shuhn), *n.* the turning back of a wave (as a light wave or sound wave) from a surface; see also **angle of reflection.** *v.* **reflect.** *adj.* **reflective.**

reflex (REE-fleks), *n.* the unvarying, involuntary response to a stimulus, frequently external, as laughter upon being tickled or the jerking of the leg when a sharp blow is delivered below the kneecap; can be a conditioned reaction.

reflex arc, the path of nerves along which a stimulus and the response travel in reflex action; in the simplest form, a stimulus at the *receptor* (sense organ) is carried along a nerve fiber to the central nervous system (adjustor neurons) and then back along another neuron to the *effector* (muscle or gland) which reacts.

refracting telescope, a telescope that uses lenses to focus the rays from the object being observed;

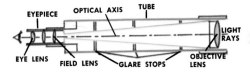

limited to about a 40-inch diameter; also called *Newtonian* after Isaac Newton, the first builder.

refraction (ree-FRAK-shuhn), *n.* the change in direction of propagation of light at any surface which it enters at an oblique angle in going from a medium of one index of refraction to that of another; caused by the difference in light velocity in the 2 media; see also **angle of refraction.** *v.* **refract.** *adj.* **refractive.**

refractory (ree-FRAK-tuh-ree), *n.* a ceramic material that is very resistant to high temperatures, as in the lining of a blast furnace. *adj.* **refractory.**

refractory period, the period immediately after a nerve responds to a stimulus, during which reduced irritability occurs and the nerve cannot respond; a period of electrochemical readjustment to prepare for another response.

refrigerant (ree-FRIJ-uh-ruhnt), *n.* a readily vaporized liquid or readily condensed vapor that may be used to absorb heat, as in a refrigeration system.

refrigeration (ree-frij-uh-RAY-shuhn), *n.* the process of reducing the temperature of any substance; often used for preservation of foods or other materials that decompose at higher temperatures. *v.* **refrigerate.**

regeneration (ree-jen-uh-RAY-shuhn), *n.* **1.** in biology, the growing of a new part to take the place of a lost or damaged one, as the starfish growing on a new ray or arm. **2.** in electronics, a system for feedback of energy to increase the input energy. **3.** in heat engineering, the transfer of heat from waste products to a useful process. *v.* **regenerate.**

regression, an alternate term for **atavism.**

regulator (REG-yuh-lay-tuhr), *n.* any device for controlling an operation, as: **1.** in engines, a governor. **2.** a device for adjusting the speed of clocks or watches. **3.** a device which will keep current or voltage at a desired value or within a desired range.

Regulus (REG-yuh-luhs), *n.* the bright star of the lion's head in the constellation Leo, 21st brightest star in visual magnitude in the sky.

reinforcement (ree-in-FAWRS-muhnt), *n.* in animal or human training, the act of strengthening the probability of a response to a stimulus occurring by rewarding the response.

relapse (ree-LAPS), *n.* the return of a disease or certain symptoms of a disease after partial or apparently complete recovery.

relative (REL-uh-tiv), *adj.* compared to something else, as to a standard: *relative* humidity is the moisture in the air compared to the amount the air could hold.

relativity (rel-uh-TIV-i-tee), *n.* those concepts in modern physics first stated in definite form by Albert Einstein: **1.** *special theory:* the laws of physics hold when given in terms of either of 2 observers, both inertial (at rest and remaining at rest); and velocity of light is independent of any motion of its source. From these he deduced: **a.** a particle, such as a proton, when moving has a larger mass than when the same particle is standing still (*relativistic increase of mass*), and, **b.** the energy of a mass at rest is equal to the mass times the square of the velocity of light, $E = mc^2$ (*the equivalence of energy and mass*). **2.** *general theory:* physical laws relating space, time, and gravity, stated in a form holding for any space-time relationship; led to deduction that light could be bent by gravitational attraction.

relax (ree-LAKS), *v.* to rest or lose tension; used in describing muscle action in which fibers that have contracted (shortened) resume their uncontracted state (become longer). *n.* **relaxation.**

relay (REE-lay), *n.* an electrical or electronic device for making changes in current in one circuit produce changes in a second circuit; voltage overloads on machines operate circuit breakers by means of relays; may be used in remote control.

rem, REM, *n.* in radiobiology, the unit of dose equivalent: the dose of radioactivity that is equivalent to a given standard dose (as X-rays) in terms of the effect produced; short for *R*oentgen *E*quivalent for *M*an.

renal (REE-nuhl), *adj.* referring to the kidneys or surrounding areas.

rendezvous orbit (RAHN-day-voo), the orbit in which a satellite must travel in order to meet with

Rendezvous maneuver around moon for Project Apollo: lunar excursion module meets command unit, astronauts change craft, modules separate, and command module returns to Earth

another satellite or other object at a planned time and place.

rennin (REN-in), *n.* an enzyme secreted by the stomach of mammals; one of 3 enzymes present in human gastric juice; curdles milk by converting casein to paracasein; obtained for commercial use (as in cheese making) from fourth stomach of calves; sometimes called *chymosin.*

repel (ree-PEL), *v.* to push away or to force apart: some chemicals repel mosquitoes; 2 like charges repel each other.

reproduction (ree-proh-DUK-shuhn), *n.* **1.** the production of a new living organism by an ancestor or by ancestors of the same species; may be *sexual,* usually requiring 2 parents of different sex; or *asexual,* involving only one ancestor. **2.** duplication; the making of copies; a photostat is a *reproduction* of an original. *v.* **reproduce.**

reproductive system, a gonad, together with other accessory organs that enable the plant or animal to produce its own kind.

Reptilia (rep-TIL-ee-uh), *n.* a class of cold-blooded vertebrates, usually covered with scales

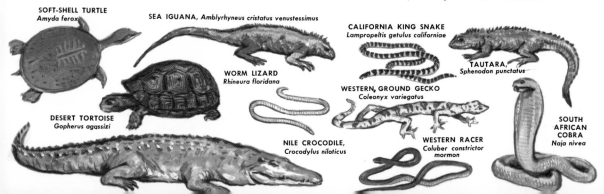

SOFT-SHELL TURTLE
Amyda ferox

SEA IGUANA, *Amblyrhyneus cristatus venustessimus*

CALIFORNIA KING SNAKE
Lampropeltis getulus californiae

WORM LIZARD
Rhineura floridana

TAUTARA,
Sphenodon punctatus

WESTERN, GROUND GECKO
Coleonyx variegatus

DESERT TORTOISE
Gopherus agassizi

NILE CROCODILE,
Crocodylus niloticus

WESTERN RACER
Coluber constrictor mormon

SOUTH AFRICAN COBRA
Naja nivea

and breathing throughout life by means of lungs. *Reptiles* include lizards, snakes, turtles, crocodiles, extinct dinosaurs, and related animals; see also **snake, turtle.** *adj.* **reptilian.**

repulsion (ree-PUHL-shuhn), *n.* the force with which electric currents, charged objects, or particles push away from each other.

research (ree-SUHRCH), *n.* any considered and organized study of a subject with the aim of discovering new facts or principles or of proving or disproving a theory or hypothesis; see **theory.**

residue (REZ-i-dyoo), *n.* **1.** a substance that remains after a physical or chemical change of the original substance. **2.** the individual units, not necessarily identical, that make up a polymer, such as the amino acid residue. *adj.* **residual.**

resilience (ree-ZIL-yuhns), *n.* elasticity, especially after compression.

resin (REZ-in) *n.* an organic solid or semisolid, natural or synthetic, usually with a typical luster and often transparent or translucent; natural resins are obtained from the sap of several coniferous trees. *adj.* **resinous.**

resistance, *n.* **1.** an opposing force, often classed as gravitational, molecular, frictional, or inertial. **2.** a property of any substance opposing the flow of electrical current, usually measured in ohms.

resistor (ree-ZIS-tuhr), *n.* a device offering resistance to the flow of electric current in a circuit; used to limit the amount of current reaching other circuit elements.

resonance (REZ-uh-nuhnts), *n.* **1.** increased duration or intensity of a wave vibration caused by a relatively slight vibration of the same frequency; especially common in music and other acoustic phenomena. **2.** equilibrium between 2 or more possible atomic or molecular structures of a chemical, differing only in electron configurations.

respiration (res-puh-RAY-shuhn), *n.* **1.** in land animals, the inhalation and exhalation of air, resulting in the absorption of oxygen by body tissues and the release of oxidation products, primarily carbon dioxide and water. **2.** in aquatic animals, the absorption of oxygen dissolved in water through gills or other specialized organs. **3.** in plants and animals, the process by which food materials are burned up or oxidized with the release of energy necessary for various cell activities.

respirator (RES-puh-ray-tuhr), *n.* **1.** any apparatus for providing artificial respiration, as a pulmotor or iron lung. **2.** a small mask worn over the mouth and nose to prevent inhalation of fumes, dust, etc.

respiratory system (RES-pi-ruh-toh-ree), the group of cells, organs, or other structures in an organism involved in bringing air or water into contact with body tissues for the exchange of gases.

response (ree-SPAHNS), *n.* **1.** an event happening after, and in relation to, a given experimental act; a *reaction.* **2.** in behavior, the reaction of an organism to a stimulus. *v.* **respond.**

resuscitate (ree-SUHS-i-tayt), *v.* to restore to life or to consciousness when apparently dead; air is forced into the lungs and heart action restored by massage of chest wall. *n.* **resuscitation.**

reticular (ruh-TIK-yuh-luhr), *adj.* **1.** forming a network; used especially to describe cells and fibers of the *reticular connective tissue* frame-

work of the spleen and lymph glands. **2.** referring to the *reticulum,* the second stomach of a ruminant. **3.** describing the networklike appearance of cytoplasm in some cells.

retina (RET-i-nuh), *n.* the innermost structure of the eyeball, consisting of 10 distinct layers; the layer of rods and cones (directly below the pigment layer) contains light-sensitive cells connected to the optic nerve; see **eye.**

retrograde (RET-ruh-grayd), *adj.* moving backward; especially, of satellites, moving in a direction opposite to most other such objects; thus, revolving around a planet from west to east.

retrogression (ret-ruh-GRESH-uhn), *n.* in biology, the change from a more developed or specialized to a less developed or specialized condition in an organism; see also **regression.**

retrorocket, *n.* a rocket that fires to produce thrust opposite to the motion of an object, slowing

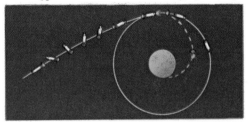

In the lunar landing of Project Apollo, retrorockets will be used to put the command module in a parking orbit, to slow up for separating the moon module, and to brake the moon module for its descent

it down or reversing its direction; especially, the rockets that slow a rocket for reentry into the atmosphere; see also **rendezvous orbit.**

reverberation (ree-vuhr-buh-RAY-shuhn), *n.* the reflection of radiated energy for some time after the energy source has been cut off; especially important in acoustics, as *echoes* in an auditorium.

revolution (rev-uh-LOO-shuhn), *n.* **1.** in astronomy, the action of a planet or other celestial body in making a complete orbit. In the solar system,

Major structures of the human respiratory system

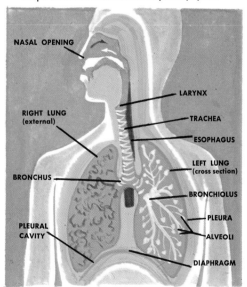

NASAL OPENING

LARYNX

RIGHT LUNG (external)

TRACHEA

ESOPHAGUS

LEFT LUNG (cross section)

BRONCHUS

BRONCHIOLUS

PLEURA

PLEURAL CAVITY

ALVEOLI

DIAPHRAGM

both sun and planet describe orbits around their common center of mass, but it is convenient to consider the smaller body, which always has the larger orbit, as revolving around the sun; contrast with **rotation.** **2.** in mechanics, the travel of a cylindrical, conical, or spherical object about its axis, often expressed in time units as *rpm, revolutions per minute.* *v.* **revolve.**

Rh, symbol for **rhodium.**

Rhamnales (ram-NAY-leez), *n.* a small order of dicot plants, mainly woody and climbing shrubs, with stamens in one whorl opposite the petals, and a disk surrounding the ovary. There are 2

CASCARA
Rhamnus purshiana

VIRGINIA CREEPER
Parthenocissus quinquefolia

CONCORD GRAPE
Vitis vinifera

families: the vine family (*Vitaceae*), including all varieties of grapes and the Virginia creeper; and the buckthorn family (*Rhamnaceae*), a source of cascara, a mild laxative.

rhea (REE-uh), see **Rheiformes.**

Rheiformes (ree-uh-FAWR-meez), *n.* an order of flightless birds with complete separation of the last vertebrae from the vertebral column, found in no other birds; an example is the rhea or American ostrich.

rhenium (REE-nee-uhm), *n.* a whitish, metallic chemical element; used in high-temperature thermocouples because of its high melting point; symbol **Re;** *at. no.,* 75; *at. wt.,* 186.2; isolated by Noddack, Tacke, and Berg in 1925.

rheostat (REE-uh-stat), *n.* a device for inserting and regulating resistance in an electrical circuit; can be adjusted to give more or less resistance: speed regulation of motors and light dimming in theaters depend on rheostats.

rheotropism (ree-AH-truh-pizm), *n.* growth movements of plants induced by their response to a flowing stream of water.

rheumatic fever (roo-MAT-ik), an acute disease, usually affecting children, marked by fever, inflammation of and pain in the muscles and joints; heart damage may occur; sometimes follows streptococcus infections in children.

rheumatism (ROO-muh-tizm), *n.* any of various painful disorders of the joints or muscles.

rheumatoid arthritis (ROO-muh-toyd ahr-THRY-tis), an acute or chronic disease of several forms, varying in severity but generally characterized by inflammation of the joints with degenerative changes resulting in crippling deformities.

Rh factor (ahr-aych), any of various substances, often present in human blood cells, that stimulate the production of antibodies; blood containing any such substance is classed as *Rh positive;* blood lacking it, as *Rh negative;* an inherited characteristic, Rh positive being dominant. The term *Rh* is from *Rhesus* monkey, in which similar substances were first identified.

rhinoceros (ry-NAHS-uh-ruhs), see **Perissodactyla.**

rhizoid (RY-zoyd), *n.* a rootlike multicellular organ that absorbs water and minerals from the soil and attaches the plant to the substratum; found most commonly in liverworts, mosses, and many fungi.

rhizome (RY-zohm), *n.* in certain plants, a true stem growing horizontally below ground, but with all the structure of a stem. Buds and leaves grow

Rhizome examples: slender, spreading rhizome of sugar cane, *Saccharum officinarum;* and pungent, fleshy rhizome of sweet flag, *Acorus calamus* (far right)

from the upper surface at the nodes and roots grow from the underside at the nodes.

Rhizopoda (ry-ZAHP-uh-duh), *n.* a class of protozoans that form pseudopodia for locomotion and food capture; mostly free living; some forms with shells (as *Foramenifera, Radiolaria*); some parasitic in man and other animals. Ameba is a *rhizopod* in subclass Sarcodina.

Rhodesian man (roh-DEE-zhuhn), a prehistoric man of Africa; only remains are a skull, indicating large but definitely human teeth; upright in walk; age uncertain, but probably late Pleistocene.

rhodium (ROH-dee-uhm), *n.* a hard, white, metallic chemical element; used to electroplate a hard shiny surface, to harden alloys, and as a catalyst; symbol Rh; *at. no.,* 45; *at. wt.,* 102.905; isolated by Wollaston in 1803.

rhodonite (ROH-duh-nyt), *n.* a pink-red ore of manganese; formula, $MnSiO_3$.

Rhodophyta (roh-DAH-fuh-tuh), *n.* a thallophyte division of plants containing the red algae; a *rhodophyte* may branch into a complex structure; chlorophyll is masked by red pigment; reproduces asexually and sexually; includes agar-agar and *Polysiphonia;* see **alga, Thallophyta.**

rhodopsin (roh-DAHP-sin), an alternate term for **visual purple.**

Rhoeadales (ree-uh-DAY-leez), an alternate name for **Papaverales.**

rib, *n.* any of several pairs of long, slender, curving bones attached to the spinal column of vertebrates and forming part of the bony cage of the thorax; see **skeletal system.**

riboflavin (ry-buh-FLAY-vin), *n.* vitamin B_2, the heat-stable and water-soluble fraction of the vitamin B group, first isolated from milk; deficiency in humans leads to sores on the mouth; found in milk and organ meats; formula, $C_{17}H_{20}N_4O_6$.

ribonucleic acid (RY-boh-noo-KLEE-ik), an organic substance composed of one molecule of

SCORIA

BASALT

GRANITE (RED)

PORPHYRY

OBSIDIAN

PUMICE

IGNEOUS ROCKS

TUFA

BOG IRON ORE

SANDSTONE

SHALE

LIMESTONE

CONGLOMERATE

SEDIMENTARY ROCKS ↑   ↓ METAMORPHIC ROCKS

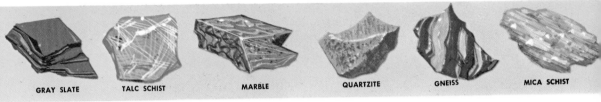
GRAY SLATE   TALC SCHIST   MARBLE   QUARTZITE   GNEISS   MICA SCHIST

phosphoric acid, one of ribose sugar, and one of a nitrogenous base (a purine or a pyrimidine). This substance, in polymer form, is believed to furnish the molecular pattern according to which proteins are synthesized in living cells and thus to affect embryonic growth; see also **deoxyribonucleic acid.** *abbr.* **RNA.**

ribose (RY-bohs), *n.* a suger found in the nucleic acid of yeast; formula, $CH_2OH(CHOH)_3CHO$.

Richter Scale (RIK-tuhr skayl), *n.* device used to measure earthquakes.

rickets (RIK-uhts), *n.* a disease characterized by softening of the bones during childhood due to lack of vitamin D and, sometimes, lack of calcium in diet; often causes limb deformities.

rickettsia (ri-KET-see-uh), *n. pl.* **-siae.** a parasitic organism on arthropods or rodents; diseases such as typhus fever are transmitted by arthropod carriers of rickettsiae.

ridge, *n.* **1.** long, narrow elevation of land; **2.** long, narrow upper edge, angle, or crest.

rift, *n.* a crevasse, geological fault.

Rigal (RY-juhl), *n.* a double star in the left foot of constellation Orion, seventh brightest star in the sky in visual magnitude.

rigid dirigible, a powered aerostat (dirigible) with a framework within the envelope to maintain form; contrast with **blimp.**

rigor mortis (RIG-uhr MAWR-tis) the stiffening of a dead body; affected by temperature; leaves the body after a certain time.

ringworm, *n.* any of certain contagious skin and scalp diseases characterized by patches of reddish, ring-shaped skin eruptions and loss of hair; caused by various fungi.

riptide, *n.* a swift, offshore current produced by the combination of breaking waves and shoreline currents.

river, *n.* a moving stream that drains a watershed and empties eventually into the ocean; a river is larger than the streams that feed into it.

Rn, symbol for **radon.**

RNA, abbreviation for **ribonucleic acid.**

roadable aircraft (ROHD-uh-buhl), experimental aircraft combining airplane and automobile: wings and tail can fold up or be removed.

robot (ROH-baht), *n.* machine made to look or act like a person; used to do mechanical, routine tasks on command.

rock, *n.* a naturally occurring hard mixture of minerals, frequently containing metal ore or gem crystals. Rocks are classified by the way they were formed: *igneous* rocks are hardened forms of magma; *sedimentary* rocks were formed from compressed mineral or organic sediments and pieces of earlier rocks; *metamorphic* rocks were earlier igneous or sedimentary rocks that changed (*metamorphosed*) by heat, pressure, or chemicals; see also **intrusion, mineral.**

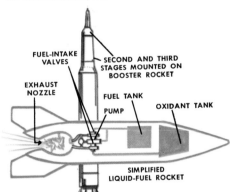

FUEL-INTAKE VALVES   SECOND AND THIRD STAGES MOUNTED ON BOOSTER ROCKET
EXHAUST NOZZLE
FUEL TANK
PUMP   OXIDANT TANK
SIMPLIFIED LIQUID-FUEL ROCKET

rock crystal, a transparent and colorless quartz; often cut and polished as a gem.

rocket (RAHK-uht), *n.* a self-propelling vehicle that operates by ejecting part of its own mass, the fuel; the ejection device is a *rocket engine,* a completely self-contained reaction engine capable of working in outer space; see also **missile.**

rocket sled, a device for testing equipment and organisms at high speed, rapid acceleration and deceleration, and similar phenomena; an instrument platform propelled by rockets.

rockweed, see **Phaeophyta.**

rod, *n.* **1.** any body in a layer of elongated sensory bodies found with cones in the retina of the eye; contains visual purple and transmits colorless sensations in dim light: see also **cone. 2.** a unit of length equal to 16½ feet.

169

Rodentia

Rodentia (roh-DEN-shuh), *n.* an order of gnawing mammals with no more than one pair of continually growing, chisel-like incisor teeth in each jaw; canine teeth are absent. *Rodents* include

MARMOT
Marmota caligata

BEAVER
Castor canadensis

EASTERN GRAY SQUIRREL
Sciurus carolinensis

CHINCHILLA
Chinchilla laniger

HOUSE MOUSE
Mus musculus

BROWN RAT
Rattus norvegiens

CHEEK TEETH

CONTINUALLY GROWING INCISORS

BEAVER SKULL

POCKET GOPHER
Rhomomys bottae

LEAST CHIPMUNK
Eutamias minimus

CAVY OR GUINEA PIG
Cavia cobaya

PORCUPINE
Erithizon dorsatum

beavers, rats, mice, squirrels, flying squirrels, agoutis, and others.

roe (roh), *n.* **1.** the spawn or mass of eggs in the ovary of a female fish, known as *hard roe.* **2.** the milt or sperm of a male fish, known as *soft roe.* **3.** the unfertilized eggs of a crustacean, such as of the lobster.

roentgen (RENT-guhn), *n.* a unit for measuring the radiation of X-rays or gamma rays; the amount producing, in one cubic centimeter of dry air (at 0°C and 760 mm pressure), positive or negative ionization equivalent to one electrostatic unit of charge; named for W. K. Roentgen, German physicist. *abbr.* **r.**

Roentgen ray, an alternate term for **X-ray.**

rolling friction, friction between bodies that are in rolling, rather than sliding, contact; the resistance between a road and automobile tires, and the resistance offered to a roller bearing are examples.

root, *n.* **1.** that portion of a vascular plant that usually grows downward into the soil serving for anchorage, absorption, transportation, and often

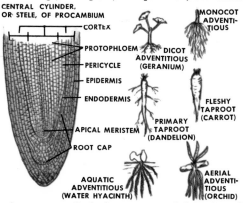

CENTRAL CYLINDER, OR STELE, OF PROCAMBIUM

CORTEX

PROTOPHLOEM

PERICYCLE

EPIDERMIS

ENDODERMIS

APICAL MERISTEM

ROOT CAP

MONOCOT ADVENTITIOUS

DICOT ADVENTITIOUS (GERANIUM)

FLESHY TAPROOT (CARROT)

PRIMARY TAPROOT (DANDELION)

AQUATIC ADVENTITIOUS (WATER HYACINTH)

AERIAL ADVENTITIOUS (ORCHID)

for storage. **2.** the base or concealed portion of many different portions of an organism, as hair roots, tooth roots. **3.** the surface between threads at the smaller end of a screw.

root canal, see **tooth.**

root hair, a minute, threadlike extension of an epidermal cell near the tip of a plant root, increases the surface exposed to soil for water and mineral absorption.

root tip, the end of a root, with a *root cap* for protection of the growing or *meristematic region,* and

the *elongation area,* which matures into the root hair section for increased absorption.

Rosales (roh-ZAY-leez), *n.* a large and varied order of dicot trees, shrubs, and herbs, usually with flower parts in a circle in groups of 5 and with a complete perianth. The largest of the 11 families is the legume or pea family (*Leguminosae*). Others are the rose family (*Rosaceae*); the orpine family (*Crassulaceae*), with succulent sedum; the plane-tree or sycamore family (*Platanaceae*); the saxifrage family (*Saxifragaceae*) of currant, gooseberry, and hydrangea; and the witch-hazel family (*Hamamelidaceae*); see **pea family, rose family.**

(1) American red raspberry, *Rubus strigosus;* (2) spiraea, *S. latifolia;* (3) Bartlett pear, *Pyrus communis;* (4) sycamore, *Platanus occidentalis;* (5) sour cherry, *Prunus cerasus;* (6) cultivated hybrid rose, *Rosa,* var. Mary Margaret McBride

rose family, a large and economically important family (*Rosaceae*) of fruit trees, shrubs and herbs; plants have alternate leaves, regular flowers with 5 petals and many stamens; fruits are dry (pomes, drupes, berries, etc.). The family includes such trees as almond, apricot, apple, cherry, peach; shrubs as raspberry, bridal wreath, blackberry, rose; and herbs as strawberry; see **Rosales.**

roseola (roh-ZEE-uh-luh), *n.* a rose-colored rash, especially German measles.

rosette (roh-ZET), *n.* a cluster of leaves growing around a short internode.

rosin (RAHZ-in), *n.* the residue of the resin obtained from pine trees after the steam-volatile portion (gum turpentine) has been driven off.

rot, *n.* **1.** a breakdown in plant cells; decay often caused by fungi, bacteria, or unfavorable weather conditions. **2.** any of several diseases of plants or animals generally caused by parasites. *v.* **rot.**

rotation (roh-TAY-shuhn), *n.* the spinning of any cylindrical or spherical body about its own axis; the earth's rotation produces day and night; contrast with **revolution.** *v.* **rotate.**

Rotifera (roh-TIF-uh-ruh), *n.* a phylum of minute aquatic invertebrates with a complex, wormlike body structure characterized by a circlet of

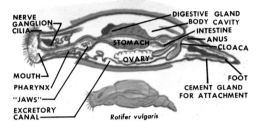

NERVE
GANGLION
CILIA
DIGESTIVE GLAND
BODY CAVITY
INTESTINE
ANUS
CLOACA
STOMACH
OVARY
MOUTH
PHARYNX
"JAWS"
EXCRETORY
CANAL
FOOT
CEMENT GLAND
FOR ATTACHMENT

Rotifer vulgaris

short, hairlike structures at one end and usually a forked, footlike appendage at the other.

rotor (ROH-tuhr), *n.* **1.** the rotating portion of an electrical engine or motor. **2.** the rotating portion of other machines, as the blades of a turbine or helicopter.

roundworm, see **Nematoda.**

royal jelly, a special protein substance secreted by food glands of a honeybee, which, if fed to a larva until pupation, causes the larva to develop into a queen instead of a worker.

rpm, abbreviation for *revolutions per minute,* used to designate engine speeds, etc.; actually indicates *rotations* per minute.

Ru, symbol for **ruthenium.**

rubber, *n.* **1.** an elastic, water-repellant substance obtained by removing the water from *latex,* the milky sap of the tropical tree, *Hevea brasiliensis.* Raw rubber may be formed from latex by smoking, coagulation, or spraying. **2.** any similar substance made synthetically, usually to obtain specific properties.

rubella (roo-BEL-uh), see **German measles.**

rubeola (roo-BEE-uh-luh), see **measles.**

Rubiales (roo-bee-AY-leez), *n.* an order of dicot trees, shrubs, and herbs with opposite or whorled leaves and flowers that usually appear in broad,

(1) Gardenia, *Gardenia jasminoides;* (2) cinchona, source of quinine, *Cinchona ledgeriana;* (3) goldflame honeysuckle, *Lonicera flava;* (4) Viburnum

flat-topped clusters with the petals and stamens of equal number and alternating. The largest of the 5 families is the madder family (*Rubiaceae*), a source of cinchona (quinine), gardenia, coffee, and madder (a dye). The honeysuckle family (*Caprifoliaceae*) includes elder, snowball, and viburnum.

rubidium (roo-BID-ee-uhm), *n.* a silvery-white, soft, chemical element, and alkali metal; used in electron tubes; symbol Rb; *at. no.,* 37; *at. wt.,* 85.47; isolated by Bunsen and Kirchoff in 1861.

ruby (ROO-bee), *n.* a deep red, precious mineral; an impure form of aluminum oxide, Al_2O_3; traces of chromium give it the red color; see **gem.**

rudder, *n.* **1.** an airfoil ordinarily mounted at the rear of a plane assembly, movable under the pilot's control to alter direction to the left or right. **2.** a movable vertical structure on a ship's stern that controls change in the ship's course.

rudimentary (rood-uh-MEN-tuh-ree), *adj.* **1.** not completely developed, especially used in referring to certain structures in organisms. **2.** not functioning. *n.* **rudiment.**

rue family (ROO), see **Geraniales.**

rumen (ROO-muhn), *n.* the first chamber in the stomach of a ruminant; food is mixed with saliva and passed to the rumen; it is later regurgitated as cuds and thoroughly chewed.

ruminant (ROO-mi-nuhnt), *n.* any mammal having a multi-chambered (usually 4) stomach, and

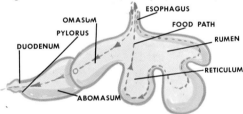

ESOPHAGUS
OMASUM
FOOD PATH
PYLORUS
RUMEN
DUODENUM
RETICULUM
ABOMASUM

Typical 4-chambered stomach of a ruminant

chewing a cud. Many artiodactyls are ruminants; see also **Artiodactyla.**

runner, *n.* a slender, trailing plant stem characteristic of some plants, such as strawberry, in which new plants are propagated by runners rooting and developing into new plants; also called *stolon.*

rupture (RUP-chuhr), *n.* **1.** any breaking or bursting from a container. **2.** alternate term for **hernia.** *v.* **rupture.**

rust, *n.* **1.** a reddish-brown film that covers iron or steel exposed to moist air; actually a complex mixture of ferric oxide, hydrated ferrous and ferric oxides, and basic ferrous and ferric carbonates. *v.* **rust. 2.** a fungus disease that attacks certain types of plants; may be part of a parasitic cycle.

ruthenium (roo-THEE-nee-uhm), *n.* a hard, white, metallic chemical element; used as a catalyst and to harden alloys; symbol Ru; *at. no.,* 44; *at. wt.,* 101.07; isolated by Klaus in 1844.

Rutherford theory (RUTH-uhr-fuhrd), the theory proposed by Ernest Rutherford in 1911 that the positive charge in an atom is concentrated in a small nucleus, surrounded by an equal negative charge (electrons) distributed through the rest of the atom; first statement of what is now considered a valid description of the structure of the atom; see also **Bohr theory.**

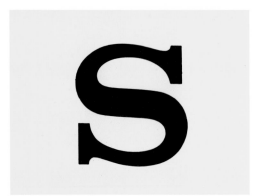

S, symbol for **sulfur.**

Sabin vaccine (SAY-buhn), a vaccine against poliomyelitis that uses the live polio virus in a weakened state; administered orally at 3 different times, frequently on lump sugar to disguise bitter taste; each of 3 types is specific for a type of polio; developed by Albert B. Sabin, Russian-American physician and virologist (1906-   ).

sac (SAK), *n.* a pouch or sacklike structure in an organism.

saccharide (SAK-uh-ryd), *n.* any carbohydrate, specifically, a monosaccharide (simple sugar), as glucose or fructose, $C_6H_{12}O_6$; see also **monosaccharide.**

saccharin (SAK-uh-ruhn), *n.* a crystalline compound of intensely sweet (but slightly bitter) taste; of low food-colorie content; used as a sugar substitute; formula, $C_7H_5NO_3S.$

sac fungus, see **Ascomycetes.**

sacrum (SAK-ruhm, SAY-kruhm), *n.* a group of vertebrae in the lower spinal column of primates; see **vertebra.**

safety glass, glass that will shatter but not fly to pieces when hit; may be made of 2 sheets of glass with a plastic sheet sandwiched between, or may have a fine wire mesh imbedded in it.

safety valve, a device for rapid release of excess pressure, as in steam boilers; if pressure rises above the amount regarded as safe for normal operation, it will force open a spring-closed valve until pressure is reduced to normal, when the valve will close again.

safrole (SAF-rohl), *n.* an oily ether extracted from the sassafras plant, poisonous in quantity; used in small amounts for flavor and perfumes; formula, $C_{10}H_{10}O_2$; also spelled **safrol.**

sagittal (SAJ-uh-tuhl), *adj.* **1.** on or within any vertical, longitudinal plane through the body including the median; see **section. 2.** referring to the 2 skull bones which form most of the top and upper sides of the skull.

Sagittarius (saj-uh-TAIR-ee-uhs), *n.* the *Archer,* a large constellation most clearly seen in the summer months; the farthest south of any zodiacal constellation, located chiefly within the Milky Way.

Saint Vitus' dance (VY-tuhs), *n.* a disease in which a variety of twitching movements occur; now known to be related to streptococcal infections and rheumatic fever; also called *chorea.*

salamander (SAL-uh-man-duhr), *n.* any of numerous lizardlike amphibians with short legs, a long tail, and moist skin lacking scales; some types remain aquatic throughout life; found in various moist habitats throughout the United States; see **Amphibia.**

Salicales (sal-i-KAY-leez), *n.* an order of dicot deciduous trees and shrubs, with dioecious flowers as catkins and seeds as samoras or drupes. The single family is the willow family *(Salicaceae)* and includes willow, poplar, aspen, and cottonwood.

(left) Cottonwood, *Populus deltoides;* (center) quaking aspen, *P. tremuloides;* (right) willow, *Salix nigra*

salicylic acid (sahl-uh-SIL-ik), a white, crystalline or powdered organic acid with a sweet followed by bitter taste; used to make medicines (as aspirin), preservatives, and dyes; formula, $C_6H_4(OH)(COOH)$; see also **acetylsalicylic acid.**

saline (SAY-leen), *adj.* referring to salt content, especially to common table salt, as a *saline* solution, or to the mineral salt content of sea water at any place or time. *n.* **salinity.**

saliva (suh-LY-vuh), *n.* the somewhat clear fluid produced in the mouth glands of vertebrates and containing, in man, certain digestive enzymes, as ptyalin; also lubricates in swallowing.

salivary gland (SAL-uh-vair-ee), one of the 3 pairs of glands that secrete and discharge saliva into the mouth through ducts; see **digestive system.**

salivate (SAL-uh-vayt), *v.* to produce saliva.

Salk vaccine (SAWK), a vaccine against poliomyelitis that uses 3 strains of killed polio virus in a fluid; a series of injections are required to produce immunity; developed by Jonas E. Salk, American physician and researcher (1914-   ).

sal soda, pure, crystalline, sodium carbonate, used for washing and bleaching cloth, and for general cleaning; see also **sodium carbonate.**

salt, *n.* **1.** commonly, ordinary table salt: sodium chloride, NaCl. **2.** a combination of 2 ions, one always a metallic ion; formed by substitution of hydrogen in an acid. **3.** a substance, often a crystalline mineral, that in solution is used as a medicinal cleaning or soaking fluid, as Epsom salts.

saltpeter, an alternate term for **potassium nitrate.**

saltwater, see **sea water.**

salve (SAV), *n.* a thick, sticky ointment applied to wounds as a healing agent or as a vehicle to hold medicine.

SAM, abbreviation for **surface-to-air missile.**

samara (SAM-uh-ruh), *n.* a dry, indehiscent fruit in a winged covering; can be easily dispersed by wind or water; usually one-seeded; see **fruit.**

samarium (suh-MAIR-ee-uhm), *n.* a metallic chemical element in the lanthanide series; used as a catalyst; symbol Sm; *at. no.,* 62; *at. wt.,* 150.35; identified by Boisbaudran in 1879.

sand, *n.* fine particles of rock, commonly found on beaches; most is silica, a compound of silicon, and is similar in composition to quartz.

172

sandalwood family, see **Santalales.**

sandstone, *n.* a porous sedimentary rock with a rough, gritty texture like sandpaper; formed by the cementing of particles of sand into layers.

sandworm, see **Annelida.**

Santalales (san-tuh-LAY-leez), *n.* an order of dicot trees, shrubs, vines, and herbs; many are parasitic or partly parasitic; fruit indehiscent, a drupe, nut, or berry. The 4 families include the sandalwood family *(Santalaceae)*—source of aromatic sandalwood; and the mistletoe family *(Loranthaceae).*

sap, *n.* the fluid containing water and dissolved minerals that circulates in vascular plant tissues; transports metabolism products throughout the plant; in some plants, as sugar maple, the sap has commercial value.

Sapindales (sap-uhn-DAY-leez), *n.* an order of dicot trees, shrubs and some herbs, having flowers with the stamens growing from a disk and the ovules hanging. The 16 families include the valuable maple family *(Aceraceae),* with box elder; the sumac or cashew family *(Anacardiaceae)* of edible mango and pistachio nut but also poison oak and poison ivy; the holly family *(Aquifoliaceae);* and the horse-chestnut family *(Hippocastanaceae).*

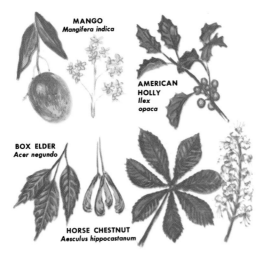

MANGO
Mangifera indica

AMERICAN HOLLY
Ilex opaca

BOX ELDER
Acer negundo

HORSE CHESTNUT
Aesculus hippocastanum

sapodilla family (sap-uh-DIL-uh), see **Ebenales.**

saponify (suh-PAHN-uh-fy), *v.* to change animal or vegetable fat by addition of an alkali and water: soap and glycerol are the end products of a *saponification* reaction; also used in refining of crude oil.

sapphire (SAF-eyr), *n.* a precious stone, usually blue; actually an impure form of aluminum oxide (Al_2O_3) with traces of carborundum in it; varies in color from very pale blue to almost black; cornflower blue stone, especially with a white star in it, is most precious.

saprolite (SAP-ruh-lyt), *n.* a mass of crumbled, soft rock that has not been moved from its place of disintegration.

saprophyte (SAP-ruh-fyt), *n.* any plant that derives its food from nonliving organic material, such as from decomposing organisms. *adj.* **saprophytic.**

sapwood, *n.* the wood just inside the bark of a tree which is still capable of conducting water, sap, and other fluids through the tree; contrast with **heartwood.**

Sarcodina (sahr-kuh-DY-nuh), see **Rhizopoda.**

sarcolemma (sahr-koh-LEM-uh), *n.* the delicate, noncellular membrane surrounding a striated muscle fiber or cell.

sarcoma (sahr-KOH-muh), *n.* any of various malignant tumors originating in connective tissues, especially in bone.

sargassum (sahr-GAS-uhm), *n.* rockweed, a brown alga; see **Phaeophyta.**

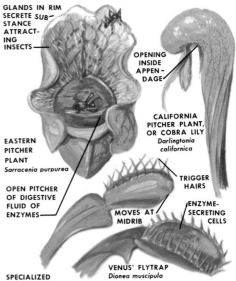

GLANDS IN RIM SECRETE SUBSTANCE ATTRACTING INSECTS

OPENING INSIDE APPENDAGE

CALIFORNIA PITCHER PLANT, OR COBRA LILY
Darlingtonia californica

EASTERN PITCHER PLANT
Sarracenia purpurea

OPEN PITCHER OF DIGESTIVE FLUID OF ENZYMES

TRIGGER HAIRS

MOVES AT MIDRIB

ENZYME-SECRETING CELLS

SPECIALIZED

VENUS' FLYTRAP
Dionea muscipula

Sarraceniales (sair-uh-sin-ee-AY-leez), *n.* an order of dicot insectivorous plants that trap insects by secretions in hollow leaves, or leaves covered with gland hairs, and digest them with enzymes. The families are the pitcher-plant families *(Nepenthaceae* and *Sarraceniaceae)* and the sundew family *(Droseraceae),* including Venus' flytrap.

satellite (SAT-uh-lyt), *n.* **1.** any heavenly body that revolves about a larger object, usually called the *primary,* of which the satellite is the *secondary.* **2.** especially, the satellite of a planet, also called a *moon.* **3.** a man-launched object that revolves around the earth, another planet, or the sun for scientific or military purposes.

saturate (SATCH-uh-rayt), *v.* to dissolve as much of a given chemical in a solute (such as water) as that solute will hold, at room temperature (20°C) or at other temperature stated.

saturated solution, a solution in which any additional amounts of the solute cannot be dissolved without conditions of temperature or pressure being changed.

saturation (satch-uh-RAY-shun), *n.* **1.** in chemistry, the point at which any more solute added to a solution cannot be dissolved. **2.** an organic compound in which only single covalent bonds exist. **3.** in meteorology, the point at which the atmosphere has absorbed all the water vapor it can hold at a particular temperature. **4.** in optics, the amount of freedom of a color from dilution by either white or black. **5.** in electricity, the point at which an increase in the force of the signal applied to a circuit does not increase the output. *v.* **saturate.**

Saturn (SAT-uhrn), *n.* **1.** a giant planet second only to Jupiter in size; average distance from the sun is about 895 million miles; diameter is about 3 times that of Earth; especially noted for the 3 rings surrounding it probably made of tiny separate particles covered with ice. **2.** any of an advanced series of space launch vehicles under development by the United States.

saurian (SAWR-ee-uhn), *adj.* referring to any of the lizardlike reptiles, especially the lizards and related forms of the present and the giant dinosaurs of the past. *n.* **saurian.**

Saurischia (saw-RIS-kee-uh), *n.* an order of dinosaurs with typical reptilian-type hips; examples are *Brontosaurus, Diplodocus, Tyrannosaurus;* see **dinosaur.**

savanna (suh-VAN-uh), *n.* a grassland plain with scattered tree growth and seasonal rainfall, occurring usually in subtropical or tropical regions.

saxifrage family (SAK-suh-frij), see **Rosales.**

Sb, symbol for **antimony** (from Latin, *stibium*).

Sc, symbol for **scandium.**

scab, *n.* **1.** the hard crust that forms over a sore when blood dries during healing. **2.** any of several plant diseases that form crustlike patches and are caused by fungi.

scalar (SKAY-luhr), *n.* a quantity having only magnitude, with no indication of direction; speed is a *scalar* quantity; contrast with **vector.**

scale, *n.* **1.** one of the flat, tiny, round plates covering the exterior of the body of many animals,

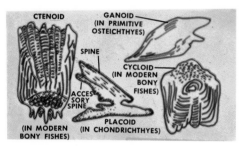

especially fishes and reptiles. *adj.* **scaly. 2.** a covering of somewhat similar appearance on the wings of butterflies and moths. **3.** a coating on a surface, especially a metal oxide coating produced on metal when heated. **4.** *proportion:* a model made to *scale* is one in which every detail is the same fraction of the full-size object. *v.* **scale. 5.** a device for weighing; see also **balance. 6.** any series of graduated units used as a reference in measuring or an instrument showing the series.

scalp, *n.* the soft tissues covering the skull of vertebrates; especially the skull covering that normally bears hair in humans.

scalpel (SKAL-puhl), *n.* a small, lightweight knife usually with a straight, very sharp blade; used in surgery and anatomical dissections.

scandium (SKAN-dee-uhm), *n.* a very rare metallic chemical element; symbol Sc; *at. no.,* 21; *at. wt.,* 44.956; isolated by Nilson in 1879.

scanning, *n.* **1.** the rapid travel of an electron beam back and forth over the surface of an image to transmit the light and dark areas as electron patterns for television or similar uses. **2.** a similar back and forth or circular, searching movement of a radar antenna. *v.* **scan.**

scapolite (SKAP-uh-lyt), *n.* a mineral; a mixture of sodium-aluminum-silicate and calcium-aluminum-silicate, in varying amounts; fairly hard; found in various colors.

scapula (SKAP-yuh-luh), *n.* the shoulder blade bone; see **skeletal system.**

scar, *n.* **1.** the mark or blemish of connective tissue formed when an injury has penetrated the skin. **2.** in plants, a mark indicating a former point of attachment, such as where a leaf petiole has fallen away from a stem.

scarlet fever, a contagious childhood disease, characterized by high fever and a fine, granular, reddish skin rash covering the entire body; the rash is caused by the toxin produced by a streptococcus bacterium.

scavenger (SKAV-uhn-juhr), *n.* any animal that feeds on dead organic matter (carrion).

Schiaparelli's canals (skyap-uh-REL-ee), streaks visible in the bright regions of the planet Mars, with structure not clearly known; named for Giovanni Schiaparelli, Italian astronomer (1835-1910) who discovered them.

Schick test (SHIK), a diphtheria immunity test consisting of a skin injection of a minute amount of toxin which causes redness and swelling in susceptible individuals; such individuals are then immunized.

schist (SHIST), *n.* a metamorphic rock, having the crystals of the various minerals lined up in thin layers; contains mica; see **rock.**

Schizomycophyta (skiz-oh-my-KAHF-uh-tuh), *n.* a division of plants containing the bacteria, often considered lower fungi; *schizomycophytes* lack chlorophyll, are unicellular and largely dependent on outside food sources, though a few make their own food by chemosynthesis or by photosynthesis using compounds other than chlorophyll; classified as coccus (round), bacillus (rod shaped) and spirillum (spirals); with blue-green algae, the oldest living organisms; see **bacterium.**

sciatica (sy-AT-uh-kuh), *n.* a painful inflammation of the large sciatic nerve in the lower back and back of the thigh, caused by injury or infection; when severe, may result in loss of leg control.

scintillation (sin-tuh-LAY-shuhn), *n.* a quick flash of light, as that produced in a phosphor when struck by a radioactive particle, or as the twinkling appearance of a star. *v.* **scintillate.**

scintillation counter, an alternate name for **Geiger counter.**

scion, alternate spelling of **cion.**

Scitaminales (sy-tam-i-NAY-leez), an alternate term for **Musales.**

sclera (SKLIR-uh), *n.* the tough, white, outer layer of the eyeball; opaque except for the cornea; see **eye.**

sclerenchyma (skluh-REN-kuh-muh), *n.* plant tissue with cells having thick secondary walls; nonliving at maturity; strengthens plant parts; includes fibers and stone cells, small pithy cells.

sclerosis (skluh-ROH-sis), *n.* **1.** hardening of tissue with tissue piling up layer on layer, as in *arteriosclerosis.* **2.** hardening of neural tissue with soft nerve cells replaced by hard supporting tissue, as in *multiple sclerosis.* **3.** hardening of plant cell walls, changing them to wood. *adj.* **sclerotic.**

scolex, (SKOH-leks), *n.* the head of larval and adult tapeworms, with suckers, hooks, or both, to hold to the host's intestinal wall; the segments grow from a small neck area behind the scolex.

scorpion (SKAWR-pee-uhn), see **Arachnida.**

Scorpius (SKAWR-pee-uhs), *n.* the *Scorpion,* a long constellation of the zodiac visible on summer nights; Antares is its heart and another first magnitude star, Shaula, is its stinger.

scree, an alternate term for **talus.**

screw, *n.* one of the simple machines: an inclined plane wrapped around a cone; used to hold objects

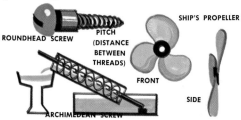

SHIP'S PROPELLER

ROUNDHEAD SCREW PITCH (DISTANCE BETWEEN THREADS)

FRONT

SIDE

ARCHIMEDEAN SCREW

together and to exert lifting force, as in automobile jacks; mechanical advantage depends on the length of the turn required to move the distance between threads.

screwpine family, see **Pandanales.**

scrotum (SKROH-tuhm), *n.* the external membranous pouch of most male mammals that contains the testes.

scurvy (SKUHR-vee), *n.* a dietary disease caused by vitamin C deficiency; symptoms include swollen joints, tiredness, and sore, bleeding gums.

Scyphozoa (sy-fuh-ZOH-uh), *n.* a class of coelenterates in which the bell-like, freely swimming medusa or jellyfish stage is well developed; polyp stage is reduced; see also **Coelenterata.**

Se, symbol for **selenium.**

sea, *n.* **1.** the expanse of saltwater that covers about three-quarters of the earth; an ocean. **2.** any of the smaller bodies of saltwater partly or completely enclosed by land. **3.** an ocean wave.

sea anemone (uh-NEM-uh-nee), see **Anthozoa.**

sea cow, see **Sirenia.**

sea cucumber, see **Echinodermata.**

sea horse, see **Osteichthyes.**

seal, see **Carnivora.**

season, *n.* **1.** any of the 4 periods into which the earth's year is divided, separated from each other by the equinoxes and solstices; temperatures are characteristic for each and are based largely on the amount of sunlight any portion of Earth receives. Seasons of the Northern Hemisphere are the reverse of those in the Southern Hemisphere: summer in the north is winter in the south. **2.** especially in tropical areas, periods of the year that are distinctive for a prevailing weather condition, as the dry or rainy season. *adj.* **seasonal.**

sea urchin, see **Echinodermata.**

sea water, the water found in the oceans; about 3.5% of the total water weight is a great variety of dissolved elements and minerals; mostly sodium chloride, with traces (usually as ions) of magnesium, potassium, iodine, copper, iron, gold, sulfates, carbonates, and many others; freezes several degrees below 32°F, exact temperature depending on salinity at any point; may be purified for drinking and recovering elements.

seaweed, *n.* **1.** any marine plant. **2.** a brown or red alga; brown algae usually found in cold seas, red in tropical seas; some contain iodine and algin. **3.** a common though incorrect name for pond plants, used in fresh-water aquariums.

sebaceous gland (see-BAY-shuhs), an oil gland in the skin of mammals, opening into a hair follicle; see **skin.**

sebum (SEE-buhm), *n.* the oily secretion of the sebaceous glands; lubricates hair and skin.

second (SEK-uhnd), *n.* **1.** a moment in time equal to 1/60 of a minute or 1/86,400 of a mean solar day. **2.** part of an arc that is 1/60 of a minute or 1/360 of a degree.

secondary (SEK-uhn-duhr-ee), *adj.* **1.** ranking second in importance or supplementing, as a *secondary cooling system.* **2.** produced at a point away from a main point of activity or development, or after a main period of activity, as *secondary meristem* tissue in a plant.

secondary sex characteristic, any trait of an animal not concerned directly with reproduction but somehow affecting it; usually develops or starts at puberty, as enlargement of the breasts in females or, in birds, the use of a specific call or song to attract a mate.

secretion (see-KREE-shuhn), *n.* **1.** a substance discharged from cells in plants and animals. **2.** the substance formed by animal epithelial cells from blood, such as mucus. **3.** the process of forming the substance. *v.* **secrete.**

section (SEK-shuhn), *n.* **1.** the plane surface seen when a slice is made through a 3-dimensional figure. **2.** the action of making such a slice, especially used in studying anatomy of organisms;

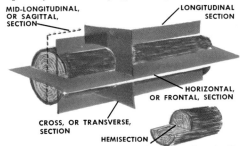

MID-LONGITUDINAL, OR SAGITTAL, SECTION

LONGITUDINAL SECTION

HORIZONTAL, OR FRONTAL, SECTION

CROSS, OR TRANSVERSE, SECTION

HEMISECTION

may use *cross section, medial* section, *longitudinal* section, etc. *v.* **section.** **3.** a subdivision of any taxonomic group of organisms.

sedative (SED-uh-tiv), **1.** *n.* a drug that reduces physical, emotional, or nervous excitement. **2.** *adj.* having the effect of reducing such excitement, as the *sedative* properties of a compound.

sedentary (SED-uhn-ter-ee), *adj.* **1.** of animal groups, staying in one locale without migrating. **2.** of an animal, not moving but remaining attached to some object, as barnacles to whales, piers, or ships; *sessile.*

sedge family, see **Graminales.**

sediment (SED-uh-muhnt), *n.* **1.** in geology, any rock debris carried by water, air, or other means and deposited in any place. **2.** in chemistry, the solid that settles to the bottom of a container of liquid, either because it is insoluble or because it has been deposited from solution.

sedimentary (sed-uh-MEN-tuh-ree), *adj.* formed by or pertaining to sediments; see **rock.**

Seebeck effect, the generation of an electromotive force (a voltage) in a closed circuit made of 2 different metals when the 2 junctions of the metals are held at different temperatures; discovered by T. J. Seebeck in 1826.

seed, *n.* the structure in any higher plants which contains the embryo, plus food and protective coverings, and develops into a mature plant; not encased in an ovary in gymnosperms; produced in an ovary in angiosperms; see also **fruit.**

seed leaf, a common term for **cotyledon.**

inside the cell. **2.** a characteristic of certain substances that absorb specific radiation wavelengths and not others.

selenite (SEL-i-nyt), *n.* colorless, translucent crystals of gypsum; formula, $CaSo_4 \cdot 2H_2O$.

selenium (suh-LEE-nee-uhm), *n.* a nonmetallic chemical element; exists in several different forms; used to harden alloys; one form conducts electricity when exposed to light and is used in photoelectric cells; symbol Se; *at. no.,* 34; *at. wt.,* 78.96; isolated by Berzelius in 1817.

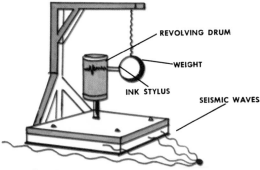

DORMANT SEED — COTYLEDONS — EMBRYO — INTEGUMENTS — HYPOCOTYL — MOISTURE-DRIVEN WILD OAT — COCKLEBUR CARRIED IN ANIMAL FUR — SPROUTING ROOT — POD ATTACHMENT — MICROPYLE — COTYLEDONS — MICROPYLE — WIND-BORNE SEED OF COTTONWOOD — DISPERSAL ADAPTATIONS — SHOOT SPROUTS — SECTION OF PEA OVULE — SECTION OF CASTOR BEAN — SINGLE COTYLEDON — STEM — ENDOSPERM — COTYLEDON — NAKED SEED — MICROSPORE OR POLLEN GRAIN — CAST-OFF SEED COVERING — ROOT — EPICOTYL — HYPOCOTYL — FEMALE PINE — MALE PINE — GERMINATION OF LETTUCE, A DICOTYLEDON — GERMINATION OF CORN, A MONOCOTYLEDON — CORN SECTION — GYMNOSPERM

segment, *n.* **1.** any part of a whole structure. **2.** one of a series of homologous sections, each somewhat similar to the others, such as the segments of earthworms; a *metamere.*

seiche (SAYSH), *n.* a series of tremors on the surface of a lake usually producing rapid tidelike waterwaves, and caused by sudden changes in atmospheric pressure.

seismic (SYZ-mik), *adj.* referring to, caused by, or like, a vibration or quake in the earth; a *seismic* wave travels at different speeds through different parts of the earth.

seismic sounding, a method of finding the depth of water by setting off an explosion under water and measuring the time echoes take to return.

seismograph (SYZ-muh-graf), *n.* a sensitive apparatus for recording (on *seismograms*) and measuring vibrations at or below the earth's surface; used especially for detecting earthquakes and underground nuclear explosions.

Simplified vertical seismograph in which the drum itself is moved up and down by earth tremors

REVOLVING DRUM

WEIGHT

INK STYLUS

SEISMIC WAVES

seismology (syz-MAHL-uh-jee), *n.* the study of earthquakes and other earth vibrations; also extended to include moonquakes.

selective absorption, **1.** the ability of a cell to absorb necessary chemicals even if there is already a greater concentration of these chemicals

selenology (sel-uhn-AHL-uh-jee), *n.* the astronomical study of the moon; derived from the Greek word for *moon.*

self-pollination, *n.* the transfer of pollen from one flower to another on the same plant, or from the stamen to the pistil in the same flower.

semen (SEE-muhn), *n.* a thick fluid from the male vertebrate genital tract, containing and protecting the spermatozoa before fertilization.

semi-, a word part meaning *half* or *partial:* a *semicircle* is half a circle; *semiconscious* is partially conscious.

semicircular canal, any of 3 looped structures at right angles to each other in the human ear concerned with equilibrium; filled with fluid; shifting fluid signals the brain to order body adjustment to maintain balance; see **labyrinth.**

semiconductor, *n.* a crystalline material with electrical conduction properties between those of metals and insulators; they may function as conductors only at certain temperatures or at certain voltages; germanium is a semiconductor.

semilunar valve, **1.** any of 3 crescent-shaped pouches projecting from the lining of the aorta near the left ventricle of the heart; prevents outgoing blood from returning into the heart. **2.** a crescent-shaped valve in a vein.

semimetallic, *adj.* having some, but not all, of the properties and characteristics of a metal, such as arsenic.

seminal fluid (SEM-uh-nuhl), an alternate term for **semen,** especially without spermatozoa.

semipermeable membrane (sem-ee-PUHR-mee-uh-buhl), a membrane through which small molecules, as those of water, can pass but which retains molecules of larger size; important in osmosis.

semiprecious, *adj.* describing a gemstone with some value but not as much as a precious stone; usually softer than a precious stone.

sense organ, any of a number of specialized organs that respond to stimuli by reporting to the nervous system what is happening, thus enabling the body to react; see also **receptor.**

sensor (SEN-suhr), *n.* a device that will respond to a stimulus by sending information to some regulating or controlling mechanism; important in missile control.

sensory (SEN-suh-ree), *adj.* **1.** carrying impulses from a receptor to a nerve center. **2.** pertaining to the senses or to a specific sense.

sensory nerve (SEN-sohr-ee), a nerve composed of sensory neurons or *affectors* that picks up impulses from receptors in the skin or sense organs and carries them to centers in the nervous system; contrast with **motor nerve.**

sepal (SEEP-uhl), *n.* any of the small, leaflike structures that form the calyx of a flower; serves as a guard for the delicate inner parts.

septic (SEP-tik), *adj.* pertaining to, or accompanied by, decomposing bacteria, as a *septic* tank; see also **asepsis.**

septum (SEP-tuhm), *n., pl.* **septa. 1.** a thin membrane or wall separating cells or tissues; the *nasal septum* separates the left and right passages of the nose; membranous *septa* divide the metameres of an annelid worm. **2.** a narrow layer of rock material separating larger features of a rock.

sequoia (see-KWOY-uh), *n.* any of several of the largest and oldest coniferous trees; see **conifer.**

series (SEER-eez), *n.* **1.** a group of objects, ideas, events, numbers, etc., that resemble one another or that are arranged one after the other, as a *series* of chemical elements with similar properties. **2.** *adj.* in electricity, describing a circuit in which all elements are connected one after the other, with voltage divided among the elements; see **circuit.**

serous membrane (SEE-ruhs), a thin layer of loose connective tissue and mesothelium lining or supporting organs in animal bodies; includes the pericardium, the pleura, and the peritoneum: as a group, called the *mesenteries.*

serpentine (SUHR-puhn-teen), *n.* a green mineral that may occur as a flaky or fibrous form; hardness 2.5; $Mg_6(Si_4O_{10}(OH)_8$. *Antigorite* is a form used for a decorative stone and *crysotile* is one type of asbestos.

serrate (SAIR-ayt), *adj.* having sawlike teeth, such as the edges of apple and basswood leaves. *n.* **serration.**

serum (SEER-uhm), *n.* **1.** the light-reddish, watery part of the blood, containing antibodies; like plasma but without fibrin. **2.** a preparation of animal blood containing bacteria, viruses, or toxins, given to produce passive immunity.

servomechanism (suhr-voh-MEK-uh-nizm), *n.* an automatic control system, as in a missile, in which a small amount of input power controls large amounts of output power in response to a signal; often the input power is merely the power required to close a circuit.

sessile (SES-uhl), *adj.* **1.** describing an organism that does not move about freely; permanently attached to a solid surface or to another organism, as an adult barnacle is sessile on a rock or crab shell. **2.** in plant anatomy, lacking a petiole.

seta (SEE-tuh), *n., pl.* **setae. 1.** a movable, bristle-like structure in certain annelid and other worms used for locomotion; usually found in pairs; see **Annelida. 2.** a stalklike structure with a spore case on the tip as in the moss.

sex (SEKS), *n.* the biological state distinguishing many organisms into one of 2 groups, *males* and *females;* males produce sperm and females produce eggs.

sex-linkage, *n.* a type of inheritance in which certain traits are passed on by the genes situated in the sex chromosome, such as color blindness and hemophilia carried by women but appearing only in men.

sextant, *n.* an instrument used in celestial navigation to measure the angle of stars appearing above

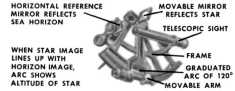

HORIZONTAL REFERENCE MIRROR REFLECTS SEA HORIZON
MOVABLE MIRROR REFLECTS STAR
TELESCOPIC SIGHT
WHEN STAR IMAGE LINES UP WITH HORIZON IMAGE, ARC SHOWS ALTITUDE OF STAR
FRAME
GRADUATED ARC OF 120°
MOVABLE ARM

the horizon, and in surveying to measure the angle of objects above plane level.

sexual (SEK-shuh-wuhl), *adj.* pertaining to organisms that have separate sexes and to reproduction of those organisms; contrast with **asexual.**

shadow, *n.* the dark region formed when an opaque material blocks the passage of light.

shale (SHAYL), a flaky sedimentary rock, formed by cemented particles of sand or clay; looks like slate but is softer and may be broken by the fingers; occurs in layers of thin plates.

shark, see **Chondrichthyes.**

shear, *n.* a stress produced in any object by forces tending to cause the sliding of one part along another. *v.* **shear.**

sheath, *n.* a saclike covering of any substance; in animals, often the covering of tendons, nerve axons, and other body parts.

sheelite (SHAY-lyt), *n.* one of the principal ores of tungsten, next in importance after wolframite; calcium tungstate; formula, $CaWO_4$.

shell, *n.* **1.** the hard, outside covering that protects various animals and plant fruits; an exo-

Shell examples from gastropod and pelecypod mollusks: (1) chocolate top, *Calliostoma javanicum;* (2) common Atlantic sundial, *Architectonica nobilis;* (3) West Indian fighting conch, *Strombus pugilis;* (4) triton, *Cymatium femorale;* (5) Venus murex, *M. Triremus;* (6) New England neptune, *Neptunea decemcostata;* (7) fig cone, *Conus figulinus;* (8) mantle scallop, *Gloripallium;* (9) growth rings (emphasized) on a clam shell

skeleton. **2.** the hard covering that protects the eggs of birds and reptiles, secreted within the female body; **3.** in an atom, one of the 7 regions in which the electrons move, known as (starting next to the nucleus) K, L, M, N, O, P, or Q shells. Each shell has a specific energy level, and electrons moving from one shell to another lose or gain energy; see **atom** picture.

shellfish, *n.* a common name given to shelled marine animals, although they are not true vertebrate fishes; generally refers specifically to crustaceans and mollusks.

shield, *n.* any protective device; a shield may be a sheet or screen that excludes unwanted interference or protects from excessive heat or glare; it may be a heavy wall of lead to guard against radioactivity.

shingles, *n.* an acute inflammatory disease caused by the chicken pox virus and affecting the sensory nerves; very painful; a usual symptom is temporary patches of tiny blisters.

shoal (SHOHL), *n.* **1.** a shallow spot in a body of water. **2.** a sandbar usually seen at low tide; contrast with **reef.**

shock, *n.* a condition in which blood collects in the large abdominal vessels or dilates the blood vessels on the surface of the body; accompanied by excessive perspiration and a feeling of warmth in the skin; may occur after receiving a severe burn, pain, or fright.

shock wave, **1.** a blast. **2.** a strong wave (in air or liquids) formed whenever an object or part of an object travels at a speed greater than the speed of sound in the same medium, as a sonic boom or a nuclear explosion.

shoot, *n.* an immature outgrowth from the stem of a plant.

shooting star, a common name for **meteor.**

short circuit, the formation of a circuit with relatively low resistance between points of a circuit with much higher resistance; may be accidental or controlled to prevent overloads.

short-takeoff-and-landing, any aircraft that employs exceptionally large lift to reduce its takeoff and landing distance. *abbr.* **STOL.**

short wave, a band of radio frequencies ranging from 1,700 to 30,000 kilocycles per second, especially useful for long-range radio communication.

shrew, see **Insectivora.**

shrub, *n.* a general name given to low, woody plants, usually possessing several stems.

shunt (SHUHNT), *n.* **1.** any electrical part placed across any other. **2.** a conductor placed across another or across an electrical part; in an ammeter, a conductor placed across the meter movement to carry a fixed part of the current around the movement and thus extend the range of the meter. *v.* **shunt.**

Si, symbol for **silicon.**

sial (SY-uhl), *n.* the less dense, upper portion of the earth's crust; mostly rocks containing much silicon and aluminum (Si + Al = sial); contrast with **sima.**

Siamese twins (SY-uh-meez), identical twins born joined together at such places as the hip, chest, or abdomen; sometimes are surgically separated; very rare; caused by incomplete division of a cell or cells early in cleavage.

sibling, *n.* one of 2 or more offspring of the same parents, but not necessarily born at the same time; a brother or sister.

sickle cell anemia, an inherited condition in which the red blood cells are sickle-shaped due to production of an abnormal type of hemoglobin; frequently studied in genetics.

sidereal (sy-DEER-ee-uhl), *adj.* related to the apparent motion of the stars; a *sidereal day* is the average value of the time between successive crossings of a fixed star over the meridian: 23 hours, 56 minutes, and 4.09 seconds of the mean solar day.

siderite (SID-uh-ryt), *n.* **1.** iron carbonate, $FeCO_3$, a mineral sometimes used as an iron ore; hardness 3½-4; light-gray; crystalline structure. **2.** a meteorite primarily of nickel and iron.

sieve tube (SIV), a phloem cell in plants, with perforated end walls used for conducting food.

sight, *n.* **1.** the sense of perception of light by the eye, including the ability to see objects and distinguish sizes, shapes, and distances; in some animals includes ability to distinguish wavelengths as color. **2.** a device on various instruments for optical adjustment or for measuring distances; as the *sight* on a sextant.

silica (SIL-uh-kuh), *n.* a colorless, crystalline or white, powdered chemical, occurring naturally in quartz, sand, agate, etc.; used to manufacture glass, ceramics, abrasives and, when powdered, as a filler for cosmetics, pharmaceuticals, and resin plasticizer; formula, SiO_2.

silicate (SIL-uh-kayt), *n.* any of a large group of compounds of silicon and oxygen combined with metals; found in many rocks as mica and in glass; one of the main mineral forms in the earth; see also **quartz.**

siliceous (si-LISH-uhs), *adj.* composed of, or pertaining to, silica or any of the silicates; sometimes spelled **silicious.**

silicon (SIL-ih-kuhn), *n.* a bluish-gray, nonmetallic chemical element; used to strengthen and harden alloys, to deoxidize steel and as a semiconductor; symbol Si; *at. no.,* 14; *at. wt.,* 28.086; isolated by Berzelius in 1823.

silicone (SIL-uh-kohn), *n.* one of a group of high-molecular weight compounds, usually synthetic; the long-chain molecules have alternating silicon and oxygen atoms, with various hydrocarbon groups bound to the silicon atoms; used in lubricants and electrical insulating materials, and instead of rubber.

silkworm, *n.* the larva of a moth (*Bombyx mori*); spins a cocoon from which silk is derived.

sill, *n.* a layer of solidified magma, usually in a sheetlike layer sandwiched in between exisiting rock; the surfaces of sills are usually parallel with the enclosing layers of rock; see **intrusion.**

silt, *n.* a sediment of earth or mineral particles smaller than particles of sand; commonly carried by streams and rivers and deposited at the river mouth; may form a delta.

Silurian (sy-LOO-ree-uhn), *n.* a period of the Paleozoic era of geologic time; noted for abundant coral-building activity and flourishing invertebrate marine life; see **geologic time table.**

silver (SIL-vuhr), *n.* a soft, pure white metallic element, having a brilliant luster; best conductor of heat and electricity known; both ductile and malleable; used in alloys for coins, jewelry, and tableware; symbol Ag; *at. no.,* 47; *at. wt.,* 107.870; known since ancient times.

silver bromide, a poisonous, pale yellow, crystalline salt; used for the light-sensitive area on photographic film; formula, AgBr.

silver iodide (EY-uh-dyd), a chemical used in seeding clouds in rainmaking; can be dropped from airplanes or carried upward from silver iodide generators on the ground; formula, AgI.

silver nitrate, a corrosive salt, the result of treating silver with nitric acid to get colorless rhombic crystals; used in medicine and hair dyes, as an analytical reagent, and for silvering mirrors; formula, $AgNO_3$

sima (SY-muh), *n,* the denser portion of the earth's crust, made up mostly of rocks containing much silicon and magnesium ($Si + Ma = sima$); contrast with **sial.**

simian (SIM-ee-uhn), *adj.* referring to or describing the monkeys and apes. *n.* **sĩmian.**

Simmond's disease, a pituitary gland disorder with disintegration of the gland, and wasting (atrophy) of the adrenal cortex; symptoms include retarded sexual development, dryness and wrinkling of the skin, and, when the onset is rapid, coma.

simple machine, one of 6 devices able to move a load through a distance, and a basic component of complex machines; the lever, wheel and axle, screw, wedge, pulley, and inclined plane are simple machines of which all other machines are made; see also **mechanical advantage.**

simple sugar, any **monosaccharide.**

Sinanthropus (suh-NAN-thruh-puhs), see **Peking man.**

sinew (SIN-yoo), a common term for **tendon.**

single flower, one flower growing on a stalk; contrast with **inflorescence.**

sinistral (SIN-uhs-truhl), *adj.* inclining to or referring to the left, as certain flatfishes; certain spiral shells coiled in reverse to the normal position are referred to as *sinistral* shells; contrast with **dextral.**

sink hole, a hole dissolved through rock by surface water draining into an underground channel.

sinter, 1. *n.* siliceous or calcareous material deposited by mineral springs. **2.** *v.* to transform into a solid mass, such as glass by heating the material without the material first melting.

sinus (SY-nuhs), *n.* **1.** any cavity in the skull of mammals, birds, and crocodiles; makes the head

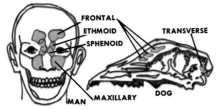

lighter in weight. **2.** an open channel in an animal body, as a blood channel in the open circulatory systems of arthropods.

siphon (SY-fuhn), *n.* an inverted, J-shaped tube that uses differences in air pressure to transfer a fluid standing at one level in a container to another container where it stands at a lower level.

Living sirenians: American manatee, *Trichechus manatus* (left), and Pacific dugong, *Dugong dugong*

Siphonaptera (sy-fuh-NAHP-tuh-ruh), *n.* an order of insects without wings; they have sucking mouth parts, complete metamorphosis, legs modified for leaping; includes the fleas.

Sirenia (sy-REE-nee-uh), *n.* an order of aquatic mammals with hair restricted to a few coarse bristles on the blunt muzzle, front limbs modified into flippers; hind limbs absent; broad, undivided tail with flukes; often called *sea cows;* includes manatees and dugongs.

Sirius (SEER-ee-uhs), *n.* the brightest star appearing in the sky; the nose of constellation Canis Major; known as the *Dog Star.*

size, *n.* the external surfaces and/or interior volume of an object.

skate, see **Chondrichthyes.**

skeletal system (SKEL-uh-tuhl), the bony framework that supports vertebrate bodies; serves as an attachment for muscles, protects vital organs, gives shape and form to body, houses blood-forming tissue; also called *skeleton.*

Skeletal system of the human body

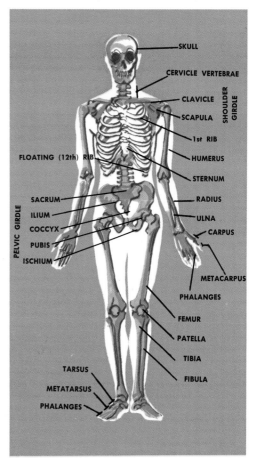

skin, *n.* the body covering of vertebrates; composed of 2 main layers, *epidermis* and *dermis;* serves as a secretory and excretory organ, as a defense against harmful organisms, and in mammals, as a heat-regulating organ; also called the *integument.*

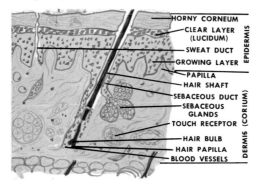

skin test, 1. a test made to determine the presence of an allergy by scratching the skin with a needle carrying the allergen. 2. a test made to determine whether a patient has been exposed to tuberculosis by scratching the skin with a needle carrying tuberculin.

skip-glide vehicle, a space vehicle that returns to Earth by skipping off the atmosphere and gliding gradually farther down into the atmosphere (as opposed to falling straight down), in a manner similar to a skipping stone on water.

skull, *n.* the bony structure forming the head and face of vertebrates; consists of a number of fused

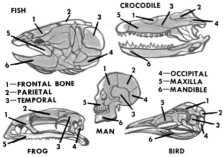

bones; in man, made up of 22 bones; see also **skeletal system.**

slag, *n.* the waste material from refining of minerals or separation of coal from its ore; usually dark gray or black in color; used in surfacing roads or mixed with concrete to make cinder blocks.

slaked lime, a commercial variety of lime; a fine, dry powder formed by treating lime with water; used for making paper sacks.

slate (SLAYT), *n.* a finely grained, metamorphic rock that breaks into thin sheets; generally gray, red, or black; used for roofing, blackboards, and construction, as in sidewalks.

sleeping sickness, *n.* 1. a serious disease of the nervous system, caused by the parasitic protozoans *Trypanosoma gambiense* or *T. rhodesiense,* both carried by the tsetse fly; occurs mainly in Africa; symptoms include headache, fever, and, eventually, coma. 2. a brain disease caused by an unknown agent, epidemic in the early 1920's.

slide, *n.* a rectangular piece of glass (sometimes plastic) upon which specially prepared sections of tissue or whole small animals and plants are mounted for study under a microscope.

sliding friction, resistance to motion caused by 2 bodies in contact with each other; directly proportional to the perpendicular pressure between the 2 surfaces; contrast with **rolling friction.**

slime mold, see **Myxomycophyta.**

slip, *n.* 1. a cutting from the stem or root of a plant used for grafting or to grow a new plant. 2. excessive movement in a mechanical device where such movement was not intended, thus lowering the mechanical efficiency. 3. in crystallography, a dislocation, a place where one plane of atoms can move past another because of a defect in the crystal structure. *v.* **slip.**

sloth (SLAWTH), see **Edentata.**

slug, see **Gastropoda.**

Sm, symbol for **samarium.**

smallpox, *n.* an often fatal, infectious virus disease; symptoms include fever and red spots starting on the face and wrists and spreading over the entire body, later changing into papules and then vesicles (small blisters); scabs over the vesicles fall off, leaving *pock* marks; now largely prevented by vaccination.

smog, *n.* a suspension of smoke, fog, and dust in air, particularly from industrial processes and automobile exhausts; see **air pollution.**

smoke, *n.* a suspension of tiny particles in a gas; the term is commonly used for unburned carbon particles from wood, oil, etc., but smoke can consist of particles of any solid.

smooth muscle, nonstriated contractile tissue not voluntarily controlled; composed of spindle-shaped cells each with one oval nucleus and many cytoplasmic fibrils; see **voluntary muscle.**

Sn, symbol for **tin** (from Latin, *stannum*).

snail, see **Gastropoda.**

snake, *n.* any animal of order *Squamata,* a large group of scaled, limbless reptiles; has a long backbone with numerous vertebrae; moves by crawling; widely distributed. Only 4 kinds of snakes in the

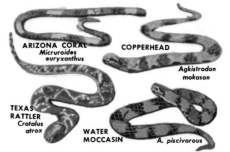

Examples of poisonous snakes in the continental U.S.

continental U.S. are poisonous: **copperhead, coral snake, cottenmouth** (water moccasin), and **rattlesnake;** see also **Reptilia.**

SNAP, a compact nuclear (isotopic) reactor, designed for space vehicles and ocean buoys; uses decay heat from plutonium-238 to produce electricity. The name is short for *Systems for Nuclear Auxiliary Power.*

snow, *n.* 1. water vapor that has condensed out of the air into ice crystals; falls as snow as long as the air temperature remains at or below the freezing point of water. **2.** the random white dots or lines that appear on a TV screen.

soap, *n.* a cleaning agent made from animal or vegetable fat by the addition of alkali and water.

soapstone, *n.* a soft rock with soapy consistency, composed of much talc, with serpentine and carbonates, such as magnesite, dolomite, or calcite.

social insect, any of the insects in a group where each insect has a well-defined role in the activities of the community; some are involved in reproduction, some hunt, and some guard the group; termites, ants, and certain bees and wasps are social insects; see **Hymenoptera.**

sociobiology, *n.* study of behavior that combines sociological and biological factors.

soda (SOH-duh), *n.* loosely, any of various forms of sodium carbonate or bicarbonate.

sodium (SOH-dee-uhm), *n.* a soft, silvery-white chemical element; an alkali metal; very reactive; used to make tetraethyl lead and sodium compounds, to reduce animal fats and oils, and to reduce metals from their ores; symbol Na; *at. no.,* 11; *at. wt.,* 22.9898; isolated by Davy in 1807.

sodium bicarbonate, a white crystalline powder; soluble in water; used in making baking powder and carbonated beverages, and as a reagent in analytic chemistry; formula, $NaHCO_3$; also called *baking soda.*

sodium carbonate, a white, powdered salt, soluble in water; used for glass, ceramics, soap, detergents, water-softeners, and chemical synthesis; formula, Na_2CO_3; also called *washing soda* and *soda ash.*

sodium chloride, a colorless or white crystalline salt; characteristically salty in taste; used as a food additive and chemical intermediate; formula, NaCl; also called *table salt.*

sodium hydroxide, a corrosive, lumpy, white inorganic base that absorbs water and carbon dioxide from the air; used as a chemical intermediate; formula, NaOH; also called *caustic soda.*

sodium nitrate, a colorless, odorless, crystalline salt; *Chile saltpeter* is an impure form; used as a chemical intermediate, oxidizing agent, and for fertilizers, dyes, fireworks, and matches; formula, $NaNO_3$; also called *soda niter.*

sodium pentothal (PEN-tuh-thahl), a tradename for thiopental sodium, a derivative of barbituric acid; also known as *truth serum;* has ultra-fast acting anesthetic properties.

sodium-vapor lamp, a kind of electric light source in which an electric arc between 2 electrodes causes sodium vapor to glow; used in street lights.

soft palate, the nonbony part of the roof of the mouth near the uvula; see **palate.**

softwood, *n.* a name given to the wood of coniferous trees which is lacking in vessels or typical xylem conducting tubes and has mostly tracheids for support and conduction; contains long fibers useful in paper; contrast with **hardwood.**

soil, *n.* any mixture of dirt, minerals, organic matter, and rock particles that will support plant life; includes *topsoil* and *subsoil.*

sol (SAHL), *n.* a colloidal solution; particles are intermediate in size between those of a true solution and those of a suspension and are carried in a liquid medium, usually water; carry an electric charge, and are not easily removed by filtration.

solar (SOH-luhr), *adj.* of or pertaining to the sun: a *solar year* is the period it takes a planet to complete one revolution around the sun.

solar cell, a photoelectric device that changes solar light energy into electricity; most often containing a silicon crystal with an electric-field barrier

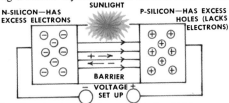

that breaks down when struck by light energy, allowing electrons to move; particularly useful in satellites as a source of energy.

solar cycle, the cyclic variation in disturbances and sunspot activity on the sun; points of maximum activity occur about 11½ years apart and show in the changing shape of the corona. The next period of maximum activity will be 1979

solar eclipse, an astronomical event occurring when the moon passes between the sun and the earth, and the moon's shadow falls on the surface of the earth; a *total eclipse* occurs when the moon covers the entire solar area; a *partial eclipse,* when only part of the sun is obscured; see **eclipse.**

solar energy, the thermonuclear energy radiated from the sun as light rays, infrared rays, ultraviolet rays, radio waves, X-rays, and cosmic rays. Most energy on Earth comes directly or indirectly from solar energy.

solar plexus (PLEK-suhs), a large system of nerves in the abdomen; controls the abdominal organs; a hard blow to the area can cause unconsciousness; part of the sympathetic nervous system.

solar prominence (PRAHM-i-nuhnts), a mass of flowing gases ejected from the solar chromosphere thousands of miles into space. It does not extend as far as a streamer and is much hotter than a sunspot; a solar *protuberance.*

solar system, the sun and all bodies related to it; includes 9 planets, thousands of asteroids, comets, and meteors; part of the Milky Way galaxy; see also **planet.**

solar wind, a cloud of fast-moving ionized atoms from the sun; may be part of the sun's corona.

solenoid (SOH-luh-noyd), *n.* **1.** any long coil of wire wound as a cylinder. **2.** an electromagnet with an additional iron armature, usually movable; frequently used to open or close contacts when electric current flows through coil.

solid (SAHL-id), *n.* **1.** one of the 3 states, or phases, of matter; has less molecular motion than a gas or liquid. **2.** any substance with a definite shape and volume. **3.** any 3-dimensional figure, such as a cube, sphere, etc.

solid fuel, a type of rocket fuel in the form of a powder or grain, often with an adhesive mixed in so the fuel is caked on the inside of the engine; forms hot gases when ignited. A mixture of nitroglycerin and cellulose nitrate is a typical solid fuel.

solidify (suh-LID-uh-fy), *v.* to convert into the solid state of matter from the liquid state (occasionally, directly from the gaseous state) by lowering temperature, pressure, etc., as in freezing water to form ice. *n.* **solidification.**

solid-state physics, the branch of physics dealing with characteristics of solid materials, especially *semiconductors;* transistors, silicon solar cells, and ruby lasers are *solid-state* devices.

Solo man, a prehistoric man who lived about 50,000 years ago; remains include several skull-caps and 2 leg bones found near the Solo River in Java; thought to be contemporary with Neanderthal and Rhodesian men.

solstice (SOHL-stis, SAHL-), *n.* **1.** either of 2 points on the sun's eliptic when the sun is farthest north or farthest south of the equator; at 23½° *north* latitude, it is summer solstice (about June 22); at 23½° *south* latitude, it is winter solstice (about December 22). **2.** the date on which one of these points is reached.

soluble (SAHL-yuh-buhl), *adj.* able to be dissolved in another substance, usually liquid or gas.

solute (SAHL-oot), *n.* that substance that is dissolved in another substance (the solvent), resulting in a solution; always present in smaller quantity than the solvent.

solution (suh-LOO-shuhn), *n* **1.** in chemistry, a mixture in which the atoms or molecules of one substance mix uniformly with the atoms of molecules of another substance, with no chemical reaction occurring. **2.** in mathematics, the procedure that must be followed to solve a problem.

solvent, *n.* that substance, frequently a liquid, in which another substance can be dissolved, resulting in a solution; always present in larger quantity than the solute.

somatic (soh-MAT-ik), *adj.* **1.** of, or about, the body. **2.** of, or about, the body cells; contrast with **germ cell. 3.** of, or about, the whole body, as opposed to specific organs.

somite (SOH-myt), *n.* any of a repeating series of similar external or internal body parts in annelids, arthropods, and embryonic chordates; chordate somites give rise to vertebrae, almost all muscles, blood vessels, and the underlying layer of the skin.

sonar (SOH-nahr), *n.* apparatus used to generate high-frequency sound waves and record the time of their reflections; used for underwater communications, locating schools of fish, and locating submarines; abbreviation for *SO*und *N*avigation *A*nd *R*anging.

sonic boom, an explosive sound created by a diving aircraft in supersonic flight: the shock wave generated by the dive continues in the same plane although the craft has pulled out of the dive; the noise occurs when the wave reaches earth.

soporific (sahp-uh-RIF-ik), **1.** *adj.* pertaining to sleep. **2.** *n.* a sleep-producing drug.

sound, *n.* **1.** a vibrating form of energy that moves through a medium in longitudinal waves; not transmitted through a vacuum, its velocity depends on the degree to which the medium in which it travels can be compressed and rarefied and on the medium's temperature. The velocity of sound through dry air at 32°F is 1087 ft/sec; in water at 8°C, 4708 ft/sec; in steel (20°C), 16,400 ft/sec; see **wave. 2.** the sensation an animal hears in response to sound waves.

sound barrier, the greatly increased drag to which an aircraft is subjected when the craft's speed nears the speed of sound (760 mph); a shock wave is created along the nose of the aircraft.

sounding, 1. *adj.* used for measurement or data collection; a *sounding* rocket carries measuring instruments into the upper atmosphere. **2.** *n.* see **depth sounding.**

sound wave, a longitudinal wave characterized by compressions and rarefactions of the medium through which it travels; produced by a vibrating object; not necessarily audible.

Southern Hemisphere, the southern half of the earth, below the equator.

southern sky, that portion of the sky, and the stars in it, visible only from below the equator; see **constellation** picture.

South Pole, the south geographic pole, in Antarctica, first crossed in December, 1911, by Roald Amundsen; the south end of the imaginary axis on which the earth rotates.

space, *n.* all the area beyond the outer limits of Earth's atmosphere.

space capsule, 1. a small, self-contained instrument package separated from a spacecraft or spaceship. **2.** a small, manned space vehicle, such as *Mercury, Vostok,* or *Gemini.*

spacecraft, *n.* an instrumented space vehicle used for reconnaissance and exploration.

space medicine, the science of maintaining life in space; especially, protecting human life from adverse effects of acceleration, weightlessness, radiation, etc.

spaceship, *n.* a large, interorbital space vehicle, used for flights to the moon and to the planets; manned or unmanned.

space station, an artificial satellite with an internal environment that will sustain human life; orbits the earth indefinitely.

space suit, a pressurized outer covering that creates a personal, artificial environment suitable for sustaining human life in space.

space vehicle, any nonstationary vehicle system that can operate in orbit, as well as take off and land on the surface of a celestial body.

spar, *n.* any shiny, crystalline mineral, such as mica and fluorspar, that flakes easily or cleaves into chips.

spark, *n.* a visible flash of light caused by an electrical discharge, or arc, between 2 unlike electric poles.

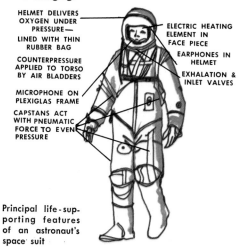

HELMET DELIVERS OXYGEN UNDER PRESSURE—LINED WITH THIN RUBBER BAG

COUNTERPRESSURE APPLIED TO TORSO BY AIR BLADDERS

MICROPHONE ON PLEXIGLAS FRAME

CAPSTANS ACT WITH PNEUMATIC FORCE TO EVEN PRESSURE

ELECTRIC HEATING ELEMENT IN FACE PIECE

EARPHONES IN HELMET

EXHALATION & INLET VALVES

Principal life-supporting features of an astronaut's space suit

spark plug, in an internal-combustion engine, the electrical device that produces a spark in the cylinder, thus causing the air-fuel mixture to ignite.

spasm (SPAZM), *n.* a violent muscular contraction, usually occurring as one of a rapid series. *adj.* **spastic.**

spathe (SPAYTH), *n.* a specialized leaf (bract), often large and colored, enclosing a fleshy spike, or *spadix,* bearing minute and inconspicuous flowers; may be mistaken for a true flower, as in jack-in-the-pulpit.

spatial (SPAY-shuhl), *adj.* referring to or happening in space.

spawn, 1. *n.* the eggs of certain invertebrates and vertebrates living in water as shellfish, frogs, and fishes. **2.** *v.* in fishes, to lay eggs, usually in a particular place called a *spawning ground.*

species (SPEE-sheez, -seez), *n., pl.* **species.** the basic unit of plant or animal classification; members of a species share characteristics that distinguish them from those of other groups, have a more or less definite geographical range, and can breed with each other (but usually not with other species) and produce fertile offspring.

specific gravity (spuh-SIF-ik), the density of a substance compared to the density of water; gold has a specific gravity of about 19 compared to 1 for water.

specific heat, 1. the number of calories required to raise the temperature of one gram of a substance one degree centigrade. **2.** the ratio of that number of calories to the number required to raise the temperature of one gram of water one degree centigrade.

specimen (SPES-uh-muhn), *n., pl.* **-mens.** an object taken apart or collected for close study and observation, often under a microscope.

spectra (SPEK-trah), plural of **spectrum.**

spectral class (SPEK-truhl), any of 8 main categories into which stars can be grouped according to their spectra and the light and dark bands that show; within each group (indicated by a letter) are subdivisions of various gradations (indicated by a number); classes O, B, A, F, G, K, and M include the main-sequence stars; the system in use today is the *Draper Classification,* developed at Harvard University and named for Henry Draper, first astronomer to photograph a stellar spectrum; see also **main-sequence star, star table.**

spectrograph (SPEK-truh-graf), *n.* an optical instrument that separates light radiation into a spectrum and records the spectrum on a photographic plate; see also **mass spectrograph.**

spectrometer (spek-TRAHM-uh-tuhr), *n.* an instrument used to measure the wavelength and index of refraction of various radiations.

spectroscope (SPEK-troh-skohp), *n.* an instrument using a prism or diffraction grating to study color lines of the visible spectrum.

spectrum (SPEK-truhm), *n., pl.* **-tra. 1.** the colored bands of light produced by passing white or other complex light through a prism or diffraction grating, progressing from the longest visible wavelength (red) to the shortest (violet); may reveal different absorption lines. **2.** the **electromagnetic spectrum.** *adj.* **spectral.**

speed, *n.* a rate of motion: $s = d/t$, where s is the average speed of a body, d the distance covered, and t the given time; contrast with **velocity.**

speleology (spee-lee-AHL-uh-jee), *n.* the science of exploring caves; an explorer of caves is a *speleologist,* or, if he does it for sport, a *spelunker.*

sperm, *n., pl.* **sperm, sperms.** a mature male gamete, especially an animal spermatozoon.

spermatocyte (sphur-MAT-uh-syt), *n.* a male sex cell undergoing meiotic division; a *primary* spermatocyte has a diploid number (2n) of chromosomes, the *secondary* has a haploid number (n).

spermatophyte (spuhr-MAT-uh-fyt), *n.* in classification no longer used, any of a large phylum including the seed plants.

spermatozoon (spuhr-muh-toh-ZOH-uhn), *n., pl.* **-zoa.** a mature male sex cell, or sperm in ani-

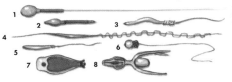

Magnified examples of spermatozoa; (1) man, (2) enlarged head of man's, (3) fowl, (4) salamander, (5) frog, (6) amphioxus, (7) ascaris, (8) crustacean

mals; capable of fertilizing the female sex cell; has power of locomotion, using a long flagellum.

sphagnum (SFAG-nuhm), *n.* any of numerous species of mosses that form the spongy base of bogs; also called *peat moss;* see **Musci.**

sphalerite (SFAL-uh-ryt), *n.* a white or yellow to dark brown mineral ore of zinc; occurs as isometric crystals with hardness 3½-4; formula, ZnS.

Spheniciformes (sfuh-nis-uh-FAWR-meez), *n.* an order of aquatic, flightless birds with short legs, webbed feet, flippers, and erect walking position; includes the penguins.

Sphenopsida (sfee-NAHP-suh-duh), *n.* a subdivision of tracheophyte plants containing the horsetails; *sphenopsids* are perennial, herbaceous, and reedlike with hollow, jointed stems impregnated with silica; spores are borne on terminal, club-shaped structures; also called *scouring rushes.*

sphere (SFEER), *n.* **1.** a 3-dimensional object bounded by a surface consisting of points all of which are an equal distance from one point, called the *origin,* and all points contained within this surface. *adj.* **spherical. 2.** any celestial object with a somewhat spherical shape.

MAIN SPECTRAL CLASSES OF STARS				
Class	Color	Surface Temperature	Line Features In Spectrum	Example
O	blue	35,000° K- up	Hydrogen; ionized helium	Lambda Cephei (O6)
B	bluish	20,000° K	Hydrogen; neutral helium	Rigel (B8)
A	white	10,000° K	Less hydrogen; some metals	Sirius-main star (A1)
F	yellowish-white	6,800° K	Weaker hydrogen; strong ionized calcium	Procyon (F5)
G	yellow	5,300° K	Very weak hydrogen; strong metals, as potassium	Sun (G2)
K	orange	4,500° K	Weak ionized calcium; strong metals	Arcturus (K2)
M	deep orange-red	3,000° K	Strong neutral calcium; titanium oxide	Betelguese (M2)
C	red	2,500° K- down	Carbon & its compounds	giants or supergiants

sphincter

sphincter (SFINK-tuhr), *n.* a ring-shaped muscle that opens and closes a passageway by contracting and relaxing; the pyloric valve at the end of the stomach is a sphincter.

sphygmomanometer (sfig-moh-muh-NAHM-uh-tuhr), *n.* an instrument used to measure arterial blood pressure; consists of a bladder that is

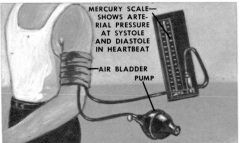

MERCURY SCALE—SHOWS ARTERIAL PRESSURE AT SYSTOLE AND DIASTOLE IN HEARTBEAT

AIR BLADDER PUMP

wrapped around the patient's arm, a graduated column of mercury, and an airtight tube with a valve and bulb at the end; see **blood pressure.**

Spica (SPY-kuh), *n.* a first-magnitude binary star in constellation Virgo; the 16th brightest star in visual magnitude.

spicule (SPIK-yool), *n.* a hard, needle-like, limy or siliceous structure commonly found in most sponges; serves to support softer tissues; see also **Porifera.**

spider, see **Arachnida.**

spike, *n.* an inflorescence with many flowers (*spikelets*) growing along and closely attached to one central stem, as in grain plants; see **flower.**

spinal (SPY-nuhl), *adj.* **1.** pertaining to the vertebrate backbone, or vertebral column. **2.** pertaining to any biological or medical process that involves the spine, as *spinal* anesthesia.

spinal column, the backbone of a vertebrate; composed of a variable number of vertebrae enclosing the spinal cord; see **vertebra.**

spinal cord, the large dorsal, tubular nerve trunk in vertebrates that connects to the medulla oblongata of the brain; located within the top ⅔ of

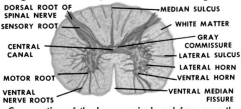

DORSAL ROOT OF SPINAL NERVE
MEDIAN SULCUS
SENSORY ROOT
WHITE MATTER
GRAY COMMISSURE
CENTRAL CANAL
LATERAL SULCUS
LATERAL HORN
MOTOR ROOT
VENTRAL HORN
VENTRAL NERVE ROOTS
VENTRAL MEDIAN FISSURE

Cross section of the human spinal cord from near the center of the chest region

the spinal column; covered by meninges and cerebrospinal fluid; see also **nervous system.**

spinal nerve, any of 31 pairs of sensory and motor nerves that enter and leave the spinal cord between vertebrae; contrast with **cranial nerve.**

spinal tap, the withdrawal of cerebrospinal fluid with a hollow needle inserted between certain vertebrae; used to examine the spinal fluid for evidence of disease or analysis of its substance.

spine, *n.* **1.** the backbone of vertebrates. **2.** any of the sharp projections on the surface of certain animals. **3.** a sharp, woody projection growing just below a shoot or bud on certain plants, such as barberry; a modified leaf part; also called *thorn.*

spinneret, *n.* one of several pairs of spinning organs of spiders, composed of many microscopic tubes connected to silk glands that produce a protein liquid which passes through these tubes to the outside and hardens into web filaments.

spiracle (SPY-ruh-kuhl), *n.* any of the external openings in the bodies of arachnids, insects, and sharks; leads to the respiratory systems.

spirillum (spy-RIL-uhm), *n., pl.* **-rilla. 1.** any of a genus of slender, coiled bacteria. **2.** any coil-shaped bacterium.

spirit (SPEER-uht), *n.* **1.** a liquid produced by distillation of certain organic compounds; usually volatile. **2.** ethyl alcohol.

spirochete (SPY-ruh-keet), *n.* any of numerous species of an order of disease-causing, coiled bacteria that move by an undulating movement; cause numerous tropical fevers and syphilis.

spirogyra (spy-ruh-JY-ruh), see **Chlorophyta.**

spirometer (spy-RAHM-uh-tuhr), *n.* a device for the measurement of *lung capacity,* the volume of air a person's lungs can hold.

spit, *n.* in geology, a long, thin point of land extending outward into a body of water; sometimes formed by deposits of rock and silt carried by the water.

spleen, *n.* an organ in most vertebrates which acts as a blood reservoir, regulates the volume of blood in various body regions, produces white corpuscles, and destroys old red corpuscles.

sponge (SPUHNJ), see **Porifera.**

spongin (SPUHN-juhn), *n.* a chemically inert protein; the network of flexible fibers that composes the body of most sponges; see **Porifera.**

spontaneous combustion (spahn-TAY-nee-uhs), combustion (rapid oxidation) occurring without external application of heat; internal heat is generated by chemical action.

spontaneous generation, an alternate term for **abiogenesis.**

sporangium (spoh-RAN-jee-uhm), *n., pl.* **-gia.** a structure in certain plants, as ferns, that produces and encases spores.

spore (SPAWR), *n.* an asexual reproductive cell, usually single and haploid (n); separates from parent and undergoes cell division, forming a new plant; produced in a sporangium.

sporophyte (SPAWR-uh-fyt), *n.* a plant in the asexual phase of alternation of generations; reproduction is accomplished through spores; contrast with **gametophyte.**

Sporozoa (spawr-uh-ZOH-uh), *n.* a class of protozoans without structures for locomotion; reproduction is sexual or multiple asexual fission; all are internal parasites in other animals; *Plasmodium* is a *sporozoan.*

sprain, *n.* an injury to the ligaments at a joint when the joint is wrenched; accompanied by rapid swelling of the joint, heat, and great pain; treated with hot or cold compresses.

spring, *n.* **1.** water bubbling up from an underground river or stream, often with large mineral content. **2.** in mechanics, an elastic body that will return to its original shape when stretched; common types are spiral spring, leaf spring, and coil spring. **3.** in the Northern Hemisphere, the period of the year from the vernal equinox (about March 21) to summer solstice (about June 22).

spurge family (SPURJ), see **Geraniales.**

sq. in., abbreviation for *square inch,* as in pounds per *sq. in.* pressure.

squall (SKWAWL), *n.* a sudden thunderstorm accompanied by violent winds, sudden changes in wind direction, and large drops in temperature; occurs where a large mass of cold air suddenly meets warm air.

squamous cell (SKWAY-muhs), any of a group of flat, thin cells linked like pavement stones; forms the outermost surface of tissue lining some body surfaces, internal body cavities, blood vessels, and gland ducts; see **epithelium.**

squid (SKWID), see **Cephalopoda.**

squirrel, see **Rodentia.**

Sr, symbol for **strontium.**

SSM, abbreviation for **surface-to-surface missile.**

stabilizer (STAY-buh-ly-zuhr), *n.* **1.** commonly, anything acting to maintain a motion or condition. **2.** in aircraft, any horizontal or vertical surface (usually on the tail) that provides smoothness and longitudinal balance in flight, but does not supply lift. **3.** in ships, a gyroscope-controlled device that operates fins to counteract rolling in heavy waves. **4.** in chemistry, a substance added to a colloidal suspension to prevent the suspended material from precipitating.

stable, *adj.* firm; unchanging; able to retain or quickly return to a particular position, condition, etc.: a *stable* isotope of an element is not radioactive. *n.* **stability.**

stage, *n.* **1.** in a microscope, a shallow platform mounted between the objective lens and the effective light source, through which light can pass; holds the specimen; can be moved by the operator. **2.** any of several rocket sections of a launch vehicle. **3.** an alternate term for *phase,* as in metamorphosis; see **phase.**

stagnant (STAG-nuhnt), *adj.* not moving; without current; a *stagnant* pool of water is often foul and odorous from lack of movement.

stain, *n.* any of several dyes used to emphasize various transparent parts of microorganisms to be studied under a microscope. *v.* **stain.**

stainless steel, a nonmagnetic, very hard alloy of iron, chromium, and nickel that does not rust in the presence of air and water; widely used in hospitals, restaurants, chemical laboratories, and kitchens.

stalactite (stuh-LAK-tyt), *n.* a mineral formation hanging from the roof of certain caves where evaporation of water has deposited calcium compounds on the roof; often shaped like a long cone.

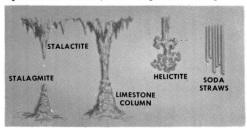

STALACTITE
STALAGMITE
HELICTITE
SODA STRAWS
LIMESTONE COLUMN

stalagmite (stuh-LAG-myte), *n.* a cone-shaped formation built up on the floor of certain caves when mineral water drips on the floor and evaporates, leaving calcium deposits; may build below a stalactite.

stalk (STAWK), *n.* a supporting structure in a plant, as the main stem or the petiole that supports the leaf blade; see also **peduncle.**

stall, *n.* any uncontrolled slowing down of an engine or vehicle; in aerospacecraft, such slowing is also accompanied by loss of altitude.

stamen (STAY-muhn), *n.* the male organ in a flower that produces pollen; usually includes anther and filament; see **flower.** *adj.* **stamenate.**

standard, *n.* an accepted measure of quantity, weight, value, etc., against which other measurements are compared; *standard temperature and pressure* is the pressure exerted by a column of mercury 760 mm high at the temperature of melting ice, 0°C.

standard time, mean solar time; the official time determined from Greenwich mean time by adding one hour for every 15 degrees east of the prime meridian or by subtracting one hour for every 15° west of the prime meridian.

standing wave, the still-appearing crests and troughs observed in a wave medium; commonly caused by 2 sets of vibrations of the same frequency but traveling in opposite directions.

stannite (STAN-eyt), *n.* the comparatively rare complex sulfide ore of tin, consisting of a sulfide of copper, tin, iron, and sometimes zinc; also called *tin pyrites.*

stapes (STAY-peez), *n.* one of the 3 small bones in the ear; passes sound vibrations to the oval window of the cochlea; has a stirrup shape; commonly called *stirrup;* see **ear.**

staphylococcus (staf-uh-luh-KAHK-uhs), *n.* any of numerous species of round bacteria which grow in grapelike clusters; often cause serious skin and mucous membrane infections in man.

star, *n.* a heavenly body that shines by its own light and remains relatively fixed in position among the other bodies in the universe; light and heat are generated in a star by the conversion of hydrogen into helium. Our sun is the closest star; Alpha Centauri, a triple star, is next, at 4½ light years away; see also **constellation, proton-proton reaction, spectral class.**

TWENTY BRIGHTEST STARS IN VISUAL MAGNITUDE				
Star	Visual Magnitude	Absolute Magnitude	Distance In Parsecs (&Light-Years)[1]	Spectral Class
Sirius (D)	−1.43	+1.4	2.7 (8.7)	A1
Canopus	−0.73	−4.5	30.7 (100)	F0
Alpha Centauri (T)	−0.27	+4.7	1.32 (4.3)	G2
Arcturus	−0.04	−0.2	11 (36)	K2
Vega	+0.04	+0.5	8.3 (27)	A0
Capella	+0.09	−0.6	14.4 (47)	G0
Rigel (D)	+0.16	−7.	167 (545)	B8
Procyon (D)	+0.37	+2.8	3.5 (11.3)	F5
Achernar	+0.53	−2.	19.9 (65)	B3
Agena	+0.66	−4.	61.3 (200)	B1
Betelgeuse	variable[2]		92 (300)	M2
Altair	+0.80	+2.2	4.8 (15.7)	A7
Aldebaran (D)	+0.85	−0.7	20 (68)	K5
Alpha Crucis (D)	+0.87	−4.	67.4 (220)	B1
Antares	+0.98	−4.	104 (340)	M1
Spica	+1.00	−3.	79 (260)	B1
Fomalhaut	+1.16	+1.9	7.1 (23)	A3
Pollux	+1.16	+1.0	10.7 (35)	K0
Deneb	+1.26	−7.	165.6 (540)	A2
Beta Crucis	+1.31	−4.	153.4 (500)	B1

D—double star; T—triple star
(1) Absolute magnitude—visual magnitude if all stars were the same distance (10 parsecs) from Earth.
(2) Magnitude varies over a 6-year period; frequently placed earlier in the list.

starch, *n.* a complex carbohydrate, the main food-storage substance in plants; derived chiefly from wheat, potatoes, corn, and rice; the presence of starch is determined with iodine which turns a deep blue; formula, $C_6H_{10}O_5$.

starfish, see **Echinodermata.**

static (STAT-ik), *n.* **1.** any electrical interference preventing clear radio or TV reception; may be from natural or man-made causes, such as fluorescent bulbs or auto ignition. **2.** noise in radio or TV receivers caused by such interference. **3.** *adj.* at rest; in equilibrium; pertaining to forces at rest rather than moving.

static electricity, an accumulation of positive or negative charges on a body; often caused by friction. Lightning is an electrical spark resulting from static electricity on a cloud.

stationary wave (STAY-shuhn-air-ee), an alternate term for **standing wave.**

statistics (stuh-TIS-tiks), *n.* the science of mathematically analyzing and interpreting natural phenomena that are subject to the laws of probability. *adj.* **statistical.**

stator (STAY-tuhr), *n.* a non-moving, soft-iron frame around which electric wires are wound to form one of 2 electromagnetic parts of a dynamo or generator; contrast with **rotor.**

statute mile (STATCH-oot), a measure of length equal to 5,280 feet; contrast with **nautical mile.**

steam, *n.* **1.** the mist that forms when water evaporated by boiling meets the cooler air and condenses, as above a steam kettle. **2.** commonly, water vapor, which is actually invisible.

steam engine, a reciprocating, piston-type engine operating on the pressure of expanding steam to drive the piston. James Watt developed the principles of the modern steam engine in 1769.

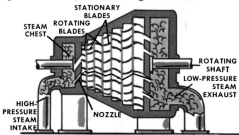

Reaction steam turbine: steam is directed against the revolving vanes by the stationary ones until, at the end of the series, the steam is greatly expanded and has no pressure and must be recompressed

steam turbine, a nonreciprocating engine in which jets of steam push against the movable blades on a fan-shaped wheel to produce continuous circular motion. Steam turbines run many electric generators and large ships.

stearic acid (STEER-ik), a colorless, odorless, waxy, organic fatty acid found in animal and vegetable fats; used for chemical synthesis, lubricants, and soaps; formula, $C_{18}H_{36}O_2$.

stearin (STEER-in), *n.* a colorless, odorless, tasteless, crystalline organic compound found in most fats; used for soaps, candles, candy, and adhesive pastes; the ester of glycerol and stearic acid.

steel, *n.* any of a group of iron alloys containing 0.5% to 1.5% carbon, with traces of other metals added to give special characteristics; steel is harder and tougher than iron and, with the exception of stainless steel, highly ferromagnetic.

steep-gradient aircraft, an aircraft requiring little or no runway for takeoff and landing, such as the helicopter and autogiro.

stegosaurus (steg-uh-SAW-ruhs), see **Ornithischia.**

stele (STEEL, STEE-lee), *n.* the central cylinder in a nonwoody plant stem or root; includes the vascular tissue and center pith, if present.

stellar (STEL-uhr), *adj.* **1.** having to do with stars, as *stellar* distances. **2.** like a star in shape, light, or other characteristic.

stellarator (STEL-uh-ray-tuhr), see **plasma.**

stem, *n.* that part of a plant that bears buds and leaves and carries water to the leaves and food from the leaves to other parts; also may carry on photosynthesis, if it is green, or store food.

step down, *v.* to decrease the electric current or voltage using a transformer; see **step up.**

steppe (STEP), *n.* a large, treeless plain covered with short grass and shrubs in spring but desert-like in summer, particularly the grazing plains of southeast Russia and Siberia.

step up, *v.* to increase either the electric current or voltage using a transformer; when current is stepped up, the voltage is stepped down, and vice versa; see also **transformer.**

sterculia family (stuhr-KYOO-lee-uh), see **Malvales.**

stereo- (STAIR-ee-oh), a word part meaning *3-dimensional* or giving the illusion of depth.

stereophonic (stair-ee-uh-FAHN-ik), *adj.* of recorded sound, being reproduced through 2 or more sound channels. The speakers of each channel are properly spaced to give the listener greater realism through his binaural hearing system.

stereoregulation, *n.* a method of making plastics using an organometallic catalyst to arrange the molecules in any specific pattern desired.

stereoscope (STAIR-ee-uh-skohp), *n.* an optical instrument through which 2 pictures printed side by side are viewed, one with each eye, giving the appearance of one 3-dimensional image.

sterile (STAIR-uhl), *adj.* **1.** uncontaminated by bacteria or other microorganisms. **2.** unable to reproduce or cause fertilization; as a *sterile* cow cannot produce a calf.

sterilize (STAIR-uh-lyz), *v.* **1.** to destroy bacteria or other microorganisms by means of heat or chemicals; a doctor *sterilizes* his instruments before using them. **2.** to make a living thing incapable of reproducing.

sterling (STUHR-ling), *adj.* referring to the silver alloy with the largest amount of silver in it; *sterling silver* has 925 parts silver to 75 parts copper; used extensively for jewelry and fine flatware.

sternum (STUHR-nuhm), *n.* the long plate of bone in the chest of vertebrates, except snakes and fish; the *breastbone;* see **skeletal system.**

steroid (STEER-oyd), *n.* any of a group of naturally occurring substances, chemically characterized by the presence of 3 linked benzene molecules (*phenanthrene*) with an additional pentane ring, as well as other side groups, attached. Most sex hormones, such as progesterone and testosterone, are steroids.

stethoscope (STETH-uh-skohp), *n.* a medical instrument used to transmit sounds of the heart, respiratory system, and other organs of a patient to the physician's ears.

stibnite (STIB-nyt), *n.* the ore of antimony and sulphur; dark gray or black in color; the principal commercial source of antimony; formula, SbS.

stigma (STIG-muh), *n.* in flowers, the somewhat enlarged apex of a pistil on which pollen grains adhere and germinate before ovule fertilization.

still, *n.* a device used to carry on the process of distillation; petroleum is distilled in a *cracking still;* see **distillation.**

stimulant (STIM-yuh-luhnt), *n.* a substance that temporarily increases the activity of an organ or of some bodily function; stimulants, such as adrenalin and caffein. *v.* **stimulate.**

stimulus (STIM-yuh-luhs), *n.* *pl.* **uli.** a change in environment detected by a sense organ; may change behavior or start a reflex action.

stoichiometry (stoi-ky-AHM-i-try), *n.* **1.** calculation of quantities of chemical elements or compounds in chemical reactions. **2.** branch of chemistry that deals with relationships of combining elements.

stipe (STYP), *n.* a supporting structure; the stalk of a mushroom and fern's "leaf-stalk."

stipule (STIP-yool), *n.* in certain plants, one of the 2 growths, often green and leaflike, at the base of the leaf petiole; see **leaf.**

stirrup (STUHR-uhp), common term for **stapes.**

stock, *n.* **1.** the main part of a plant onto which a part of another plant (the *cion*) is grafted. **2.** collectively, the animals of a farm; *livestock.*

STOL, abbreviation for **short-takeoff-and-landing.**

stolon (STOH-luhn), alternate term for **runner.**

stoma (STOH-muh), *n., pl.* **stomata.** a tiny opening in the surface of a leaf, used in transpiration and respiration; surrounded by guard cells that control opening size.

stomach (STUHM-uhk), *n.* the part of an animal that digests food; especially, in vertebrates, an enlarged section of the alimentary canal lined with mucous membranes that secrete hydrochloric acid, pepsin, and rennin; see **digestive system.**

stomata (STOH-mah-tuh), plural of **stoma.**

stone cell, see **sclerenchyma.**

stopcock, *n.* a faucetlike device for controlling, especially for stopping completely, the movement of liquid through some apparatus; may be important in accurate measurement of liquids in a laboratory.

storage battery, 2 or more electrochemical cells hooked together to give a larger voltage output; may be recharged to return the battery to its active state; most common type is the *lead-acid* battery used in automobiles; see **battery.**

stork, see **Ciconiiformes.**

storm, *n.* a disturbance in the air, frequently violent and accompanied by wind and precipitation, such as rain, snow, etc.

strabismus (struh-BIZ-muhs), *n.* an eye disorder in which one or both eyes do not line up on the normal axis of vision or do not point in the same direction; *cross-eye.*

straight-chain hydrocarbon, an organic molecule in which the carbon atoms are arranged in a straight chain, rather than branching or a ring, important in manufacture of detergents that can be destroyed during sewage disposal.

strain (STRAYN), *n.* **1.** a group of related plants or animals with a specific characteristic, desirable or undesirable; often bred to maintain or emphasize the characteristic; a *strain* of bacteria may develop immunity to an antibiotic. **2.** a stress, usually with force beyond what the object or organism can withstand.

strata (STRAY-tuh, STRAT-uh), plural of **stratum.**

stratification (strat-uh-fi-KAY-shuhn), *n.* **1.** in geology, a formation occurring in layers, or *strata.* **2.** the process of arranging or being arranged in strata. *v.* **stratify.**

stratigraphy (struh-TIG-ruh-fee), *n.* a branch of geology devoted to the study of layered or stratified rocks; chiefly concerned with sedimentary rocks but also with layered igneous rock, such as lava, and metamorphic rock formed from volcanic or sedimentary rock.

stratocumulus (stray-toh-KYOO-myoo-luhs), *n.* a low cloud formation, with an average elevation of about 6500 feet; often large, flat, dark rolls in winter skies.

stratopause (STRAT-uh-pawz), *n.* a region of the atmosphere above the stratosphere; 30-37 miles high; has the highest atmospheric temperatures.

stratosphere (STRAT-uh-sfeer), *n.* the layer of the earth's atmosphere above the tropopause and below the stratopause, generally about 6 to about 30 miles above the earth; characterized by low temperature and extremely thin, clear, dry air with no clouds.

stratospheric fallout, very tiny, radioactive particles, light enough to rise above the troposphere; may remain suspended in stratosphere for months or years before falling.

stratovision (STRAT-uh-vi-zhuhn), *n.* a means of television transmission that utilizes airborne aircraft to relay the signal to a broad area on the ground.

stratum (STRAY-tuhm, STRAT-uhm), *n., pl.* **strata. 1.** a layer of any substance arranged in layers. **2.** in geology, a layer of rock formed at a

A strata series in the earth may show past ages of great floods, volcanic activity, glacial erosion, abundant plant life, etc.

particular time and of a particular composition; used in determining geologic history and dating fossil formations.

stratus (STRAY-tuhs, STRAT-uhs), *n.* a low cloud never extending above about 6000 feet; frequently bringing rain or snow; usually covers a great horizontal area.

streak test, in geology, a quick test for general rock composition: a hard white surface, such as porcelain, is rubbed against a rock sample. The color of the powder streak obtained may be different from that of the rock, but will be characteristic for a specific kind of rock; a rock containing cinnabar, for example, will show a scarlet streak.

strychnine (STRIK-nyn), *n.* a white, crystalline, poisonous alkaloid obtained from the seeds of *Strychnos nux-vomica* of the logania family; at-

PORCELAIN TILE

PYRITE — BLACK
AZURITE — LIGHTER BLUE
BIOTITE — UNCOLORED
CINNABAR — SCARLET
HEMATITE — RED-BROWN
SPHALERITE — BROWN-YELLOW
REALGAR — YELLOW-ORANGE

stream, *n.* a steady flow, particularly of water, but also air, electrons, etc.

streamline, 1. *n.* the smooth path any freely flowing particle of fluid follows in moving without turbulence past a surface. **2.** *v.* to give a shape to a body so as to reduce the drag or resistance to motion of the fluid through which the body moves. *adj.* **streamlined.**

streptococcus (strep-tuh-KAHK-uhs), *n.* any of a group of spherical-shaped bacteria found either in chains or pairs; causes such illnesses as scarlet fever and *strep* throat.

streptomycin (strep-tuh-MY-sin), *n.* an antibiotic isolated by Waksman from cultures of *Streptomyces griseus;* has not yet been synthesized; used to arrest tuberculosis and leprosy.

stress, *n.* a force acting upon a body (organic or inorganic) that is outside the normal environment of the body; may affect equilibrium; see **homeostasis, shear, tension.**

striated muscle see **voluntary muscle.**

Strigiformes (strij-uh-FAWR-meez), *n.* an order of birds that are usually carnivorous and nocturnal; with large eyes and keen eyesight and hearing; includes the owls.

strip mining, mining after removal of earth and rock covering a mineral deposit.

stroboscope (STROH-buh-skohp), *n.* a device (usually a blinking light) for studying periodic motion, such as rotation. It gives the illusion that the motion has stopped.

stroke, *n.* **1.** any reciprocating motion in an engine, such as the stroke of the piston up and down; see **four-stroke cycle. 2.** a sudden attack of illness; see **apoplexy.**

strontianite (STRAHN-shuhn-eyt), *n.* the ore of strontium carbonate $SrCO_3$; originally *strontia.*

strontium (STRAHN-shee-uhm), *n.* a soft, silvery-white chemical element; an alkali earth metal; malleable, ductile, and very reactive; symbol Sr; *at. no.,* 38; *at. wt.,* 87.62; identified by Crawford in 1790. Radioactive Sr^{90} is found in fallout from hydrogen bomb tests.

strontium unit, unit used in determining the amount of radioactive strontium present in food; the micromicrocuries of strontium-90 radiation per gram of calcium; equal to .003 rem. *abbr.* **SU.**

structure (STRUHK-chuhr), *n.* the way the parts of something are organized: atomic *structure* takes in the relationships among neutrons, protons, electrons, and other particles. *adj.* **structural.**

strut (STRUHT), *n.* a supporting brace fitted so as to spread stress throughout its length.

Struthioniformes (stroo-thee-ahn-i-FAWR-meez), *n.* an order of flightless birds with 2-toed, padded feet; largest of living birds; rapid runners; includes the ostriches.

tacks the nervous system but is a safe stimulant in small doses; formula, $C_{21}H_{22}N_2O_2$.

sty, *n.* a pimple or boil-like infection of the follicles of eyelashes; also spelled **stye.**

style (STY-uhl), *n.* in flowers, the usually slender, elongated middle section of the pistil connecting the stigma and ovary.

styptic (STIP-tik), *adj.* **1.** astringent. **2.** causing contraction of the blood vessels. *n.* **styptic.**

styrene (STY-reen), *n.* an unsaturated (not fully hydrogenated) derivative of ethylbenzene; liquid with a boiling point of 146° C; the monomer of polystyrene; formula, $C_6H_5CH:CH_2$.

SU, abbreviation for **strontium unit.**

sub-, a word part meaning *under, below,* or *less than.*

subatomic particle, a particle having mass and occupying space that is smaller than the composite atom, as electrons, mesons, and neutrons.

subcutaneous (sub-kyoo-TAY-nee-uhs), *adj.* living under or having to do with the area under the skin; the sweat glands are *subcutaneous* glands.

suberic acid (soo-BER-ik), a colorless, crystalline organic acid; used as an organic intermediate; formula, $C_8H_{14}O_4$.

sublimation (sub-lih-MAY-shuhn), *n.* the act of going directly from the solid to the gas state without passing through the liquid state; occurs in carbon dioxide. *v.* **sublime.**

sublingual (sub-LIN-gwuhl), *adj.* describing either of a pair of saliva-producing glands on the side of the mouth.

submarine, 1. *n.* a warship able to travel underwater or on the surface. The submarine changes its buoyancy by taking in or pumping out water from its ballast tanks. **2.** *adj.* underwater.

submaxillary (sub-MAK-si-lair-ee), *adj.* referring to the lower jawbone or the nearby salivary glands.

CHANGE ATTITUDE
RETROROCKET FIRE
ORBIT INJECTION
STAGING
TRACKING AND COMMUNICATION
ENTER ATMOSPHERE
LAUNCH
RECOVER
DEPLOY PARACHUTE
ABOUT 300 MILES

Suborbital trajectory of a capsule and its attitude changes during a typical flight

suborbital flight, the launching of a rocket so that it is following a ballistic flight (parabolic curve) and does not establish an orbit around the earth; a technique frequently used to test new spacecraft before an orbital flight is attempted; the first

American astronauts made suborbital flights in the *Mercury* capsule before John Glenn's flight.

subsoil, *n.* the earth directly under the topsoil; it is above the bedrock but contains little organic matter and so cannot support crops.

subsonic (sub-SAHN-ik), *adj.* below the speed of Mach 1, or the speed of sound; slower than 760 miles per hour at sea level.

substance, *n.* a homogeneous species of matter, with a definite and unvarying composition; may be an element or a compound, but not a mixture.

substrate (SUB-strayt), *n.* a substance upon which an enzyme acts; also called *zymolyte.*

substratum, alternate term for **subsoil** or **substrate.**

succession (suhk-SESH-uhn), *n.* the occupation of an area by an orderly sequence of animal and plant communities.

succulent (SUHK-yuh-luhnt), *adj.* a general term describing any plant with fleshy or enlarged stems or leaves in which water is stored for future use, such as in most cacti.

sucker (SUHK-uhr), *n.* **1.** any structure in an animal that serves to hold on to something, as a tube foot in a starfish. **2.** in plants, a rapidly growing shoot from the roots or lower stem.

sucrose (SOO-krohs), *n.* an odorless, sweet, white crystalline disaccharide; sugar cane and sugar beets are main sources; used to sweeten foods, candies, and in making syrups for drugs; formula, $C_{12}H_{22}O_{11}$; also called *table sugar.*

suction (SUHK-shuhn), *n.* the creation of a partial vacuum or reduced pressure within a container or over a surface, causing the surrounding atmospheric pressure to increase relative to the vacuum. The increased atmospheric pressure forces the air or other fluid into the area of reduced pressure; occurs when using a soda straw.

Suctoria (suhk-TOH-ree-uh), *n.* a class of protozoans that are usually attached by a stalk in adult stage and feed by suckerlike "tentacles;" locomotion in young is by cilia; includes *Podophrya.*

sugar, *n.* **1.** any of a group of carbohydrates with some degree of sweetness; water soluble; see **saccharide.** **2.** table sugar; see **sucrose.**

sulcus (SUHL-kuhs), *n.* an indentation or wrinkle in an organ, such as on the cerebrum between convolutions.

sulfa drug, any of several synthetic coal-tar chemicals used to cure certain bacterial diseases; includes sulfanilamide and sulfapyrazine.

sulfanilamide (suhl-fuh-NIL-uh-myd), *n.* an odorless, white crystalline organic base; used in medicines; formula, $H_2NC_6H_4SO_2NH_2$.

sulfate (SUHL-fayt), *n.* the inorganic radical, SO_4, or any compound containing this radical.

sulfide (SUHL-fyd), *n.* any compound of sulfur with one or more metals, such as lead sulfide (galena), PbS.

sulfonic acid (suhl-FAHN-ik), any organic acid containing the sulfonic radical, SO_2OH, such as benzenesulfonic acid, $C_6H_5SO_2OH$; used primarily as catalysts; as strong as sulfuric acid.

sulfur (SUHL-fuhr), *n.* a yellowish, nonmetallic chemical element; exists in several different forms; used in making sulfur compounds, rubber, fertilizers, and gunpowder; symbol S; *at. no.,* 16; *at. wt.,* 32.064; known since early times; also spelled **sulphur.**

sulfur dioxide, a colorless gas that gives off extremely irritating fumes; used as an inorganic intermediate; formula, SO_2.

sulfuric acid (suhl-fyuhr-ik), a colorless, odorless, oily liquid; a strong and highly corrosive acid; used in fertilizers, dessicators, for chemical synthesis and refining, and as a general industrial acid; formula, H_2SO_4.

sulphur, alternate spelling of **sulfur.**

sumac family (SHOO-mahk, SOO-), see **Sapindales.**

summer (SUHM-uhr), *n.* in the Northern Hemisphere, the period of time between the summer solstice (about June 21) and the autumnal equinox (about September 22).

sun, *n.* **1.** the star around which the 9 planets in our solar system revolve. It is about 93,000,000 miles from Earth, has a temperature of about 6.000° C at the photosphere, a diameter of about

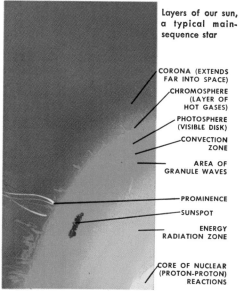

Layers of our sun, a typical main-sequence star

CORONA (EXTENDS FAR INTO SPACE)
CHROMOSPHERE (LAYER OF HOT GASES)
PHOTOSPHERE (VISIBLE DISK)
CONVECTION ZONE
AREA OF GRANULE WAVES
PROMINENCE
SUNSPOT
ENERGY RADIATION ZONE
CORE OF NUCLEAR (PROTON-PROTON) REACTIONS

864,000 miles, and a mass about 333,000 times that of Earth; a main-sequence star located in about the middle of the Milky Way. **2.** a unit of radiant energy equal to the amount that strikes the earth on a sunny, cloudless summer day at noon: 100 milliwatts per square centimeter.

sundew family, see **Sarraceniales.**

sunseeker, *n.* a device that uses the sun to lock a satellite in a particular angle relative to the sun; see also **attitude stabilization.**

sunspot, *n.* one of the dark areas on the photosphere of the sun; temporary and having a temperature lower than that of the surrounding photosphere. Sunspots occur in cycles and are related to changes in the sun's magnetic field.

sunstroke, *n.* a condition induced by prolonged exposure to the sun; characterized by coma, convulsions, and high temperature of the skin.

super-, a word part meaning *above, over.*

supercharger, *n.* a device to increase the power output of an internal-combustion engine; consisting of a compressor or blower to force more fuel and air into the cylinder than would normally be drawn in by the piston; especially needed in high-altitude flight.

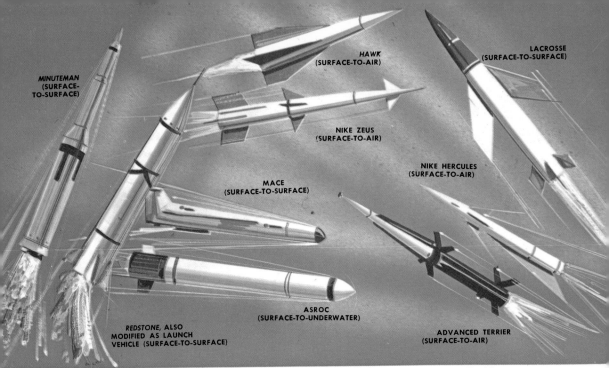

MINUTEMAN
(SURFACE-
TO-SURFACE)

HAWK
(SURFACE-TO-AIR)

LACROSSE
(SURFACE-TO-SURFACE)

NIKE ZEUS
(SURFACE-TO-AIR)

NIKE HERCULES
(SURFACE-TO-AIR)

MACE
(SURFACE-TO-SURFACE)

ASROC
(SURFACE-TO-UNDERWATER)

REDSTONE, ALSO
MODIFIED AS LAUNCH
VEHICLE (SURFACE-TO-SURFACE)

ADVANCED TERRIER
(SURFACE-TO-AIR)

superconductor, *n.* a metal that loses electrical resistance at extremely low temperatures and conducts much more readily than normally.

supercooled, *adj.* cooled below the normal freezing point of the liquid, yet remaining liquid; supercooled water is water below the normal freezing point, but is liquid not solid.

superfluid, *adj.* losing all cohesion and gravitational restraint at extremely low temperatures, as helium. *n.* **superfluidity.**

superheat, *v.* to heat a liquid to a temperature above its normal boiling point without the vapor pressure of the liquid becoming equal to the atmospheric pressure.

superheterodyne, *adj.* referring to a type of radio that mixes a signal of a lower frequency with the transmitted frequency by means of a local oscillator; resulting signal is more easily amplified in the intermediate frequency amplifier; see **radio.**

superior (soo-PEER-ee-uhr), *adj.* placed above certain other parts of the body, as the *superior vena cava* is above the *inferior vena cava.*

supernatural (soo-puhr-NATCH-uh-ruhl), *adj.* referring to happenings supposedly not explainable by the methods of the natural sciences.

supersaturate (soo-puhr-SATCH-uh-rayt), *v.* to create a *supersaturated solution,* one holding more solute at a given temperature than the solvent can normally hold; the solution is unstable.

supersonic (soo-puhr-SAHN-ik), *adj.* beyond the speed of sound, 760 miles per hour at sea level, but at lesser speeds in thinner, high-altitude air.

supinator (SOO-pi-nay-tuhr), *n.* any muscle that moves an appendage in a rotating action away from the median line of the body or of a limb, such as the muscle that turns the palm upward; contrast with **pronator.**

suppurate (SOOP-yuh-rayt), *v.* to form or to discharge pus, as from a wound.

suprarenal gland (soo-pruh-REE-nuhl), alternate term for **adrenal gland.**

surface (SUHR-fuhs), *n.* the outside plane or exterior of a body: the *surface* of a sphere is curved.

surface tension, a tendency of a liquid to contract to the smallest exposed surface possible, resulting from the cohesion of molecules in the liquid; causes liquid droplets to form spheres.

surface-to-air missile, a missile fired from the ground intended for a target in the air. *abbr.* **SAM.**

surface-to-surface missile, a missile fired from the ground intended to hit a target also on the ground. *abbr.* **SSM.**

surgery (SUHR-juh-ree), *n.* the medical science of healing or correcting abnormal physical conditions or diseases through operations. A *surgeon* may use instruments or manipulative procedures. *adj.* **surgical.**

survey (SUHR-vay), *v.* to determine boundaries, location, or other information through a systematic, detailed search using careful measurements; geologists *survey* land for oil. *n.* **survey.**

suspension (suhs-PEN-shuhn), *n.* a mixture of coarse, solid particles in a liquid; the particles settle out under gravity, are visible, and can easily be removed by filtration; contrast with **sol.**

suture (SOO-chuhr), *n.* **1.** the line where 2 immovable bones meet; the joints of skull bones form sutures. **2.** the seam made in closing an incision.

swallow, 1. *v.* to move food from the mouth through the esophagus into the stomach, a partly automatic reaction. **2.** *n.* any of several small passerine birds.

swamp, *n.* an area of low-lying wet land, too damp to be used for farming or grazing animals; does not have standing water on it and may be drained successfully.

swarm, *n.* a large, compact group of insects; especially honeybees, when they leave the hive and follow the queen bee to form a new colony.

sweat gland, a small, coiled tube located in the underlying dermal layer of the skin; secretes moisture and waste materials through pores on the surface of the skin; see **skin.**

sweet-gale family, see **Myricales.**

swelling, *n.* a protruding area such as the enlargement caused when excess lymph accumulates in a bruised part of the body. *adj.* **swollen.**

swift, see **Apodiformes.**

swimmeret, *n.* in many crustaceans, an abdominal appendage used in respiration, swimming, and, in females, egg carrying; may occur in many pairs.

switch, *n.* a device to open and close an electrical circuit.

sycamore family, see **Rosales.**

symbiosis (sim-bee-OH-sis), *n.* an association between unlike living plants and/or animals that is of mutual benefit to both, as in lichens; contrast with **parasitism.** *adj.* **symbiotic.**

symmetry (SIM-uh-tree), *n.* the regular arrangement of parts around a central axis (*radial* symmetry), or of parts placed in mirror image position (*bilateral* symmetry). *adj.* **symmetrical.**

sympathetic nervous system (sim-puh-THET-ik), a part of the autonomic nervous system consisting of 2 lengthwise chains of connected ganglia along the vertebrae and aorta: *preganglionic* fibers pass from the cord through the spinal nerves to these ganglia; *postganglionic* fibers pass from the ganglia to the organs; acts in opposition to the *parasympathetic* nervous system.

sympathetic vibration, a type of vibration induced in an object when the object's natural vibrating frequency has the same period as a vibrating object nearby.

symptom (SIMP-tuhm), *n.* a change in normal behavior or function that is taken as a sign of illness or disease; fever may be a symptom of infection. Many diseases are diagnosed by a specific set of symptoms. *adj.* **symptomatic.**

synapse (SIN-aps, suh-NAPS), *n.* the gap between the axon (or transmitting end) of a nerve cell and the dendrite (or receiving end) of an adjacent nerve cell; see **neuron.**

synapsis (suh-NAP-sis), *n.* the beginning of meiotic division; a male chromosome unites with a paired female chromosome and forms a chiasma; see **meiosis.**

synchrocyclotron (sin-kroh-SY-kloh-trahn), *n.* a particle accelerator using an oscillating voltage to increase the velocity of charged particles through a circular path.

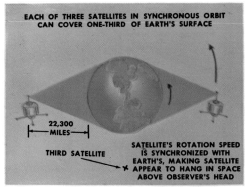

EACH OF THREE SATELLITES IN SYNCHRONOUS ORBIT CAN COVER ONE-THIRD OF EARTH'S SURFACE

22,300 MILES

THIRD SATELLITE

SATELLITE'S ROTATION SPEED IS SYNCHRONIZED WITH EARTH'S, MAKING SATELLITE APPEAR TO HANG IN SPACE ABOVE OBSERVER'S HEAD

synchronous (SIN-kruh-nuhs), *adj.* having some operation (usually the same) in 2 or more objects occurring simultaneously; of waves, having the same point on both waves occurring simultaneously. A *synchronous* motor is one in which the speed is proportional to the frequency of the applied current; a *synchronous* satellite, one whose speed in orbit just matches that of the point below it on earth.

synchrotron (SIN-kroh-trahn), *n.* a particle accelerator in which both the oscillating voltage and the magnetic field are variable and controllable. Energies of several billion electron volts have been achieved with the synchrotron.

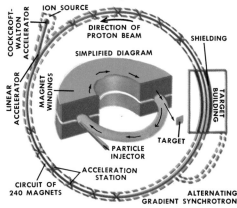

ION SOURCE
COCKCROFT-WALTON ACCELERATOR
DIRECTION OF PROTON BEAM
SHIELDING
SIMPLIFIED DIAGRAM
LINEAR ACCELERATOR
MAGNET WINDINGS
TARGET BUILDING
PARTICLE INJECTOR
TARGET
ACCELERATION STATION
CIRCUIT OF 240 MAGNETS
ALTERNATING GRADIENT SYNCHROTRON

synclinal (sin-KLY-nuhl), *adj.* forming a basin by folding slightly inward from opposite sides, especially a *synclinal* fold in sedimentary rock. *n.* **syncline.**

syndet, *n.* shortened term for *synthetic detergent,* made from long-chained alcohols with special additives.

syndrome (SIN-drohm), *n.* a number of symptoms occurring together; each disease has a characteristic *syndrome,* recognizable by a physician and used in diagnosis.

synovial (suh-NOH-vee-uhl), *adj.* **1.** referring to the clear viscous lubricating fluid secreted by the inner layer of a bursa at movable joints. **2.** referring to the inner layer itself.

synthesis (SIN-thuh-sis), *n.* **1.** the combination of parts into a whole. **2.** in chemistry, the formation of compounds from elements or simple compounds. *v.* **synthesize.**

synthetic (sin-THET-ik), *adj.* made by man, as opposed to occurring naturally; especially, *synthetic* organic compounds, as rayon, nylon, polystyrene, and many drugs and flavorings.

syphilis (SIF-uh-lis), *n.* an infectious venereal disease, caused by a spirochete. If not treated, it generally passes through 3 phases of severity, perhaps lasting years.

syringe (suh-RINJ), *n.* an instrument consisting of a suction tube and plunger, used with a needle to inject or withdraw fluids from the body.

system (SIS-tuhm), *n.* **1.** an arrangement of parts used for one purpose, as the *fuel system* of a rocket. **2.** a group of organs acting together to perform a main body function, such as the *circulatory system.*

systemic (sis-TEM-ik), *adj.* **1.** in physiology, referring to or affecting the entire body. **2.** in anatomy, referring to that part of a circulatory system not involving the pulmonary (lungs) vessels.

systole (SIS-tuh-lee), *n.* **1.** the period during which the heart contracts and pushes blood through the heart and into the arteries; contrast with **diastole;** see also **blood pressure. 2.** the muscular contraction itself, particularly contraction of the ventricles. *adj.* **systolic.**

Ta, symbol for **tantalum,**

table salt, common term for **sodium chloride.**

table sugar, common term for **sucrose.**

tachometer (tah-KAHM-uh-tuhr), *n.* an instrument that counts the number of revolutions or the velocity of a rotating shaft; measures boat and automobile engines in rpm.

tactile (TAK-tuhl, TAK-tyl), *adj.* referring to the sense of touch.

tadpole, *n.* a larval form of frogs, salamanders, and toads, between the egg stage and the adult. Tadpoles first breathe through gills, later develop lungs; lack appendages, later develop limbs; are characterized by a long tail that is slowly absorbed; commonly called *polliwog.*

tagged atom, a radioactive atom used to trace travel of an element through the body of a person during treatment, or through the body of an experimental animal in medical research.

taiga (TY-guh), *n.* a swampy, cold, arctic forest area of coniferous trees found near tundra areas.

takeoff, *n.* departure from the ground or water for flight; often considered to include the ground activities just prior to actual liftoff. *v.* **take off.**

talc (TALK), *n.* a very soft, white or greenish mineral, containing large amounts of magnesium; feels waxy or greasy; formula, $Mg_3Si_4O_{10}(OH)_2$.

tallow (TAL-oh), *n.* a mixture of fats obtained from the natural fat of sheep and cattle by melting the animal fats in water and skimming the tallow off the surface; used in soap and candle making.

talus (TAY-luhs), *n.* **1.** in geology, a pile of rocks and gravel fallen to the base of a cliff or slope; or a slope so formed; also called *scree.* **2.** astragalus; a bone in the ankle of certain animals and in man; see **skeletal system.**

tannin (TAN-in), *n.* tannic acid; an acid obtained from galls of oak or sumac; used in preparing leather and making dyes and inks.

tantalite (TAN-tuh-lyt), *n.* a hard mineral ore of tantalum; varies in color from black to reddish brown; formula, $Fe(TaO_3)_2$ or $Mn(TaO_3)_2$.

tantalum (TAN-tuh-luhm), *n.* a bluish-gray, hard, metallic chemical element; very unreactive; used in alloys for nuclear reactors and medical and dental equipment; symbol Ta; *at. no.,* 73; *at. wt.,* 180.948; isolated by Ekebert in 1802.

tapeworm, see **Platyhelminthes.**

tapir (TAY-puhr), see **Perissodactyla.**

taproot, *n.* a large primary root developing and growing downward from the radicle of the embryo and forming smaller secondary roots.

tar, *n.* **1.** a brown to black viscous fluid obtained by distilling organic matter such as wood, oil, coal, fats, or peat. Coal gives an alkaline tar; wood, an acid tar. **2.** the oily liquid obtained from incomplete burning of dried plants, especially tobacco; probably a carcinogen.

target, *n.* a piece of metal or other substance against which some form of radiation or a stream of electrons, alpha particles, or neutrons are directed; the end of a high-energy accelerator.

tarsal (TAHR-suhl), *adj.* referring to one of the 7 bones that make up part of the foot of many animals; see **skeletal system.** *n.* tarsus.

tarsier (TAHR-see-uhr, -see-ay), see **Primates.**

tartaric acid (tahr-TAHR-ik), a colorless to white, odorless, crystalline organic acid; used for organic synthesis; formula, $(CHOH)_2(COOH)_2$.

taste bud, a chemical receptor for taste consisting of several sensitive cells and a number of supporting cells; in man and higher animals, located

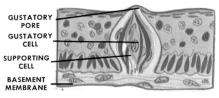

GUSTATORY PORE
GUSTATORY CELL
SUPPORTING CELL
BASEMENT MEMBRANE

Cross section of a taste bud in the tongue

mostly on the papillae of the tongue but some are on the palate or in the throat. Different cells in the different areas of the tongue and mouth react to give 4 basic tastes: *sweet, sour, salty,* and *bitter;* also called *gustatory bud.*

Taurus (TAWR-uhs), *n.* the *Bull,* a constellation appearing in the northern sky containing the Pleiades; thought to resemble a bull in shape.

taxidermy (TAK-si-duhr-mee), *n.* the applied science of treating the bodies and skins or pelts of various animals so that the "stuffed" animal may be displayed and studied.

taxis (TAK-sis), *n.* the fairly constant type of response by which an animal orients itself toward or away from a definite stimulus; see also **tropism.**

taxonomy (tak-SAHN-uh-mee) *n.* the science of the classification of living organisms; principal objectives are to discriminate among organisms and provide means for identification of similar groups (called *taxa*), to develop a suitable naming system for the taxa, and to perfect a meaningful order of classification in which the taxa can be arranged. *adj.* **taxonomic.**

Tb, symbol for **terbium.**

TB, abbreviation for **tuberculosis.**

Tc, symbol for **technetium.**

Te, symbol for **tellurium.**

tea family, see **Parietales.**

tear gland (TEER), any of several glands situated around the eye that secrete a clear, salty fluid to lubricate and cleanse the eye; also called *lachrimal gland.*

technetium (tek-NEE-shee-uhm), *n.* a radioactive, metallic chemical element; the first element made by man; used in nuclear research; symbol Tc; *at. no.,* 43; mass number of most stable isotope, 99; prepared by Perrier and Segrè in 1937; found in the spectrum of stars.

technician (tek-NISH-uhn), *n.* a person in science, engineering, or medicine who carries out technical tasks; usually with some professional training but not as much, or the same type, as that of a supervising engineer, scientist, or physician.

technology (tek-NAHL-uh-jee), *n.* the science of applying the discoveries and inventions of scientists to make them useful to man; engineering.

tectonic force (tek-TAHN-ik), see **deformation.**

teeth, plural of **tooth.**

tektite (TEK-tyt), *n.* a rounded object found in widely separated places such as Australia, Czechoslovakia, and Indonesia; probably originally from meteorites; glassy in appearance.

tele-, a word part meaning *far off* or operating *at a distance.*

telegraph (TEL-uh-graf), *n.* a device for sending coded messages over long distances. A key is used to open and close an electric circuit that activates a sounder for short (*dot*) and long (*dash*) periods of time. *Wireless* or *radiotelegraph* uses radio waves to transmit the signals; *line* telegraph transmits impulses directly through wires.

telemeter (tuh-LEM-uh-tuhr), *n.* a device for receiving and recording information taken and transmitted by a distant instrument. Information about space is transmitted from orbiting satellites to telemeters on the earth.

teleost (TEE-lee-ahst), *n.* any fish with a bony vertebral column; see **Osteichthyes.**

telophase (TEE-luh-fayz), see **mitosis.**

telephone (TEL-uh-fohn), *n.* a device for sending and receiving sound messages by changing

ceiver (picture or *kinescope* tube) converts the wave into electronic impulses, then back into video signals. *abbr.* **TV.** *v.* **televise.**

tellurium (tuh-LOO-ree-uhm), *n.* a semimetallic chemical element; exists in silvery-white crystalline or grayish solid form; used in certain alloys to increase strength, corrosion-resistance, and ductility; symbol Te; *at. no.,* 52; *at. wt.,* 127.60; isolated by Müller in 1782.

telson (TEL-suhn), *n.* **1.** the middle section of the broad, flaplike terminal appendage of a crustacean, such as the crayfish. **2.** the posterior tail-like spike of the horseshoe or king crab.

temper, *v.* to heat and then cool a metal to produce a desired degree of hardness; controls carbon content.

temperature (TEM-puhr-uh-chuhr), *n.* **1.** the average kinetic energy of the molecules of any substance containing heat energy (above absolute zero). **2.** commonly, the intensity of the heat in a body.

temperature inversion, a temporary air condition associated partly with smog, in which a layer of warmer air lies below cooler layers; holds down contaminants.

temperature scale, a scale on which the temperature of any body may be measured; the 4 most common (centigrade, Fahrenheit, Kelvin, and Rankine) are all based on the freezing point and boiling point of water.

temporal (TEM-puh-ruhl), *adj.* of or near the temples of the head, as the *temporal bones* of the skull; see **skull.**

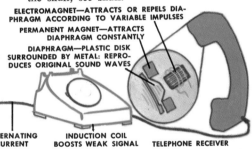

DIAPHRAGM—MOVEMENTS IN RESPONSE TO SOUND WAVES CHANGE ELECTRICAL RESISTANCE OF CARBON GRANULES

GRANULES MODULATE CURRENT IMPULSES: STRONG PULSE FROM AIR COMPRESSION, WEAK FROM AIR RAREFACTION

ELECTROMAGNET—ATTRACTS OR REPELS DIAPHRAGM ACCORDING TO VARIABLE IMPULSES

PERMANENT MAGNET—ATTRACTS DIAPHRAGM CONSTANTLY

DIAPHRAGM—PLASTIC DISK SURROUNDED BY METAL: REPRODUCES ORIGINAL SOUND WAVES

TELEPHONE TRANSMITTER — INDUCTION COIL CHANGES DC TO AC — ALTERNATING CURRENT — INDUCTION COIL BOOSTS WEAK SIGNAL — TELEPHONE RECEIVER

audio (voice) waves to electric pulses; after transmission over wires to a distance, pulses are changed to audio waves in the receiver.

telephotography (tel-uh-foh-TAHG-ruh-fee), *n.* a system for transmitting photographs over long distances by light-scanning by a photoelectric cell; changes in light and dark intensity are transmitted as electric impulses.

teleran (TEL-uh-ran), *n.* a system for transmitting information to aircraft via television to aid in aerial navigation; abbreviation for *tele*vision *radar air* navigation.

telescope (TEL-uh-skohp), *n.* an instrument used to observe distant objects; see **Gregorian telescope, refracting telescope, reflecting telescope.**

television (TEL-uh-vi-zhuhn), *n.* a system for electronically transmitting and receiving visual images; sound is often transmitted along with the *video* (picture). In the television camera, light rays are converted to electronic impulses in the *image orthicon tube;* the impulses are amplified and transmitted by means of a modulated, high-energy electromagnetic wave; the television re-

tendon (TEN-duhn), *n.* a tough, fibrous tissue band that connects muscle to bone; often called **sinew.**

tendril (TEN-dril), *n.* a slender, elongated modified leaf or stem of climbing plants; often spirals, by a touch response, to twine around any nearby object serving as a support.

tensile strength (TEN-suhl), the maximum stress a body can withstand before being pulled apart; expressed in pounds per square inch.

tension (TEN-shuhn), *n.* **1.** an abnormal stress or strain placed on an object, usually a pulling or elongating stress. **2.** in physics, electromotive force: a *high-tension* wire carries a high voltage.

tentacle (TEN-tuh-kuhl), *n.* **1.** a thin, whiplike process found around the head of some invertebrates, used for feeling, seizing food, or locomotion. **2.** a hairlike part of a flower that is sensitive to stimuli.

teratology (ter-uh-TAHL-uh-jee), *n.* that branch of science dealing with abnormal formations in plants and animals that may occur during embryonic development.

terbium (TUHR-bee-uhm), *n.* a very rare, silvery-white, metallic chemical element in the lanthanide series; symbol Tb; *at. no.,* 65; *at. wt.,* 158.824; identified by Mosander in 1843.

terminal (TUHR-mi-nuhl), **1.** *n.* an end point or connecting point, as a binding post in a dry cell. **2.** *adj.* located or occurring at the end.

terminal moraine (muh-RAYN), the mounds of rocks and boulders of all sizes and shapes left at a glacier's stopping point when it retreats.

termite (TUHR-myt), see **Isoptera.**

terramycin (tair-uh-MY-sin) *n.* an antibiotic produced by the soil microbe *Streptomyces rimosus* and used to cure amebic dysentery, diphtheria, rheumatic fever, and typhoid fever.

terrapin (TAIR-uh-pin), see **turtle.**

terrarium (tuh-RAIR-ee-uhm), *n.* a miniature living community containing a specific natural balance of plants and animals.

terrestrial (tuh-RES-tree-uhl), *adj.* referring to the earth or any of its characteristics; from the Latin for earth, *terra.*

Tertiary (TUHR-shee-air-ee), *n.* the first period of the Cenozoic era; also known as the *age of mammals;* lasted about 58 million years; modern plants and animals developed during this time; see **geologic time table.**

testa (TES-tuh), *n. pl.* **-tae.** a paper-thin covering around a seed; also called *seed coat.*

testes (TES-teez), plural of **testis.**

test flight, 1. a planned flight of an aircraft obtaining specific data or testing the overall performance of the craft, usually before extensive production of the craft. **2.** an experimental, unmanned flight of a spacecraft.

testicle (TES-ti-kuhl), *n.* the mammalian male sex gland often suspended in the scrotum within which spermatozoa and hormones regulating secondary sex characteristics are manufactured; also called *testis.*

testis (TES-tuhs), alternate term for **testicle.**

testosterone (tes-TAHS-tuh-rohn), *n.* the male hormone that induces and maintains the male secondary sex characteristics; a crystalline androgenic steroid originally isolated from bulls' testes, now prepared synthetically.

"Test tube baby" popular name for the first baby to be fertilized outside its mother's womb then put back into the womb to complete its development. Baby was born in 1978; see **genetic engineering.**

tetanus (TET-uh-nuhs), *n.* **1.** acute disease of the nervous system; caused by toxin made by the bacilli *Clostridium tetani* which enter through deep puncture wounds; also called *lockjaw.* **2.** continuous steady muscle contraction.

tetany (TET-uh-nee), *n.* disease causing severe muscle spasms, believed to result from an upset in inorganic salt metabolism, especially calcium.

tetra-, a word part meaning *four.*

tetracycline chemical term for **Achromycin.**

tetrad (TET-rad), *n.* **1.** a bundle of 4 chromatids produced during meiotic division; see **meiosis. 2.** any atom or radical having a valence of 4.

tetragonal (teh-TRAG-uh-nuhl), *adj.* **1.** 4-sided. **2.** referring to a crystal system with 3 perpendicular axes, 2 of equal length, the third longer or shorter; see **crystal system.**

tetrahedrite (tet-ruh-HEE-dryt), *n.* a gray or black, fairly hard, mineral ore of copper; formula, $4Cu_2S \cdot Sb_2S_3$; also known as *gray copper ore* or *fahlerz.*

tetrode (TET-rohd), *n.* an electronic vacuum tube containing 4 electrodes: usually a cathode, plate, grid, and screen grid.

Th, symbol for **thorium.**

thalamus (THAL-uh-muhs), *n.* the part of the brain that receives and transmits nerve impulses from the sensory tracts of the spinal cord to the cerebral cortex; see **brain.**

thallium (THAL-ee-uhm), *n.* a soft, blue-white, metallic element, resembling certain metals; its salts are poisonous and are used in rodent control; symbol Tl; *at no.,* 81; *at. wt.* 204.37; discovered by Crookes in 1861.

Thallophyta (thal-AHF-uh-tuh), *n.* a subkingdom of plants containing the algae, fungi, and lichens; *thallophytes* are characterized by a plant having a thallus but lacking true stems, roots, leaves, embryos, and vascular tissue.

(Left) Forked, seemingly specialized thallus of *Fucus,* a bladder kelp; (right) *Marchantia,* a liverwort, with flat thallus only a few cells deep

thallus (THAL-uhs), *n., pl.* **thalli.** a simple plant body consisting of similar cells, or a single cell, without any specialization into roots, stems, and leaves; structures that seem specialized are not homologous to organs of higher plants.

thaw, *v.* to change from the frozen to the unfrozen state by heating; commonly said of masses of ice or snow.

theine (THEE-uhn), *n.* caffeine appearing in, or isolated from, tea leaves.

theory (THEE-uh-ree), *n.* a set of assumptions, and the derivations from these, which are able to describe a particular body of physical facts and phenomena.

therapeutic (thair-uh-PYOO-tik), *adj.* helpful in healing, or referring to healing; drugs have *therapeutic* properties.

therapy (THAIR-uh-pee), *n.* the treatment of a disease or abnormal condition. *adj.* **therapeutic.**

therm (THUHRM), *n.* a unit of heat equal to 1000 Calories or 100,000 Btu's.

thermal (THUHR-muhl), **1.** *n.* a rising current of warm air always present in the atmosphere. **2.** *adj.* having to do with heat; also *thermic.*

thermal neutron, a neutron whose average kinetic energy is equal to the average kinetic energy of a molecule in air at room temperature; useful in nuclear power reactors; see **cold neutron.**

thermionic tube (thuhr-my-AHN-ik), an electron tube that uses the boiling off of electrons from a heated metal cathode as its electron source.

thermistor (THUHR-mis-tuhr), *n.* a device, usually made of semiconductor material, in which the resistance changes with a change of temperature; used to compensate for temperature-caused changes in other circuit elements or to measure temperature.

thermochemistry (thuhr-moh-KEM-is-tree), *n.* that branch of chemistry concerning the heat effects accompanying a chemical reaction and the nature and course of such a reaction.

thermocouple (THUHR-moh-kuhp-uhl), *n.* a device having 2 junctions that generates a voltage when the junctions are at different tempera-

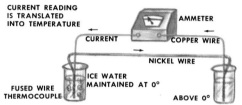

CURRENT READING IS TRANSLATED INTO TEMPERATURE

AMMETER

CURRENT

COPPER WIRE

NICKEL WIRE

ICE WATER MAINTAINED AT 0°

FUSED WIRE THERMOCOUPLE

ABOVE 0°

tures; junctions are of different metals, such as iron and copper.

thermodynamics (thuhr-moh-dy-NAM-iks), *n.* that branch of physics relating heat energy to other forms of energy, such as mechanical, electrical, or chemical, and their conversions.

thermoelectricity (thuhr-moh-ee-lek-TRIS-i-tee), *n.* **1.** electricity generated directly from heat. **2.** that branch of physics dealing with the conversion of heat to electricity or electrical energy to heat; a thermocouple is a *thermoelectric* device.

thermometer (thuhr-MAHM-uh-tuhr), *n.* any device for measuring temperature, as the common Fahrenheit fever thermometer.

thermonuclear (thuhr-moh-NOO-klee-uhr), *adj.* having to do with the heat energy released during the process of nuclear fission or fusion.

thermonuclear reaction, a high-temperature nuclear fusion, in which 2 lightweight nuclei combine and form a heavier nucleus plus a large amount of energy; occurs naturally in the sun; see also **proton-proton reaction.**

thermopile (THUHR-muh-pyl), *n.* a device for measuring changes of temperature, particularly of high temperatures; consists of several thermocouples and the appropriate connecting external electrical circuit.

thermoplastic (THUHR-moh-plas-tik), *adj.* of a plastic, reshapable; capable of being softened by heat. *n.* **thermoplastic.**

thermosetting (THUHR-moh-set-ing), *adj.* of a plastic, hard and unmoldable once it has been subjected to heat; contrast with **thermoplastic.** *n.* **thermoset.**

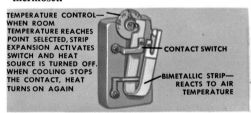

TEMPERATURE CONTROL— WHEN ROOM TEMPERATURE REACHES POINT SELECTED, STRIP EXPANSION ACTIVATES SWITCH AND HEAT SOURCE IS TURNED OFF. WHEN COOLING STOPS THE CONTACT, HEAT TURNS ON AGAIN

CONTACT SWITCH

BIMETALLIC STRIP— REACTS TO AIR TEMPERATURE

thermostat (THUHR-moh-stat), *n.* a device for automatically turning on or off a heating or cooling system, and thus controlling the temperature of a house, crystal oven, solution, etc.: usually depends on contraction or expansion of a bimetallic strip, liquid, or gas to make or break an electric circuit.

thermotropism (thuhr-MAHT-ruh-pizm), *n.* a growth movement of plants induced by response to heat.

thiamine (THY-uh-meen), *n.* vitamin B_1; a complex compound containing sulfur; deficiency usually leads to beriberi; functions in carbohydrate metabolism by being converted into important enzymes; now made synthetically and added to enriched flour and bread; formula, $(C_{12}H_{17}N_4OS)$-Cl; also called *aneurin.*

thigmotropism (thig-MAHT-ruh-pizm), *n.* a growth movement in plants induced by response to touch or contact.

thionine (THY-uh-neen), *n.* a dark green stain giving a dark purple color in solution and used as a stain in microscopy.

thistle tube, a 12 to 15-inch narrow glass tube expanded at one or both ends into a bulblike funnel; used in chemistry laboratories.

thorax (THOHR-aks), *n.* the middle part of an animal's body: **1.** in insects, the section between the head and abdomen where wings and 6 legs are attached. **2.** in vertebrates, the chest. *adj.* **thoracic.**

thorium (THOH-ree-uhm), *n.* a soft, silvery-white, radioactive, metallic chemical element in the actinide series; used in nuclear reactors to make uranium-233; symbol Th; *at. no.,* 90; *at. wt.,* 232.038; identified by Berzelius in 1828.

thorn (THAWRN), *n.* a sharp, pointed, woody outgrowth on a plant, as on the honey locust; produced from a modified stem and usually found in or just above the leaf axil.

thoroughbred (THUHR-uh-bred), *adj.* belonging to a homogeneous group of animals produced by man by means of controlled breeding of offspring derived from an original type form or stock; used especially of horses with controlled breeding.

thrombin (THRAHM-bin), *n.* the enzyme formed in the blood when shed (not circulating) that converts soluble fibrinogen to insoluble fibrin, thus forming a blood clot.

thrombocyte (THROM-buh-cyt), medical term for **platelet.**

thrombosis (thrahm-BOH-sis), *n.* a blood clot in a blood vessel or inside the heart, prevents normal circulation.

throttle (THRAHT-uhl), *n.* in an internal-combustion engine, the valve that regulates the flow of air-fuel mixture to the cylinders. *v.* **throttle.**

thrush, *n.* **1.** a fungus disease showing as white spots on the membranes of the mouth and upper digestive tract. **2.** in horses, a disease attacking the horny part in the center of the sole of the foot. **3.** any of several passerine birds.

thrust, *n.* the force exerted by moving gases that pushes an air or spacecraft forward; may be created by air movement by a propeller (as in conventional aircraft) or ejected burning fuel as in jet and rocket engines.

thulium (THOO-lee-uhm), *n.* a metallic chemical element in the lanthanide series; symbol Tm; *at. no.,* 69; *at. wt.,* 168.934; isolated by Cleve in 1879. Thulium-170, a radioactive isotope, is used in portable X-ray machines.

thunder, *n.* sound produced by violent expansion of air heated by lightning.

thymus gland (THY-muhs), an endocrine gland that is large in infancy and gradually decreases in size; appears to function in disease immunity until a natural immunity is built up in a growing child; see **endocrine gland.**

thyroid gland (THY-royd), an endocrine gland common to all mammals; in man, the hormone *thyroxine* regulates the general metabolism of the body; see **endocrine gland.**

thyroxine (thy-RAHK-sin) *n.* the active principal of the thyroid gland hormone; a crystalline compound containing iodine; formula, $C_{15}H_{11}I_4NO_4$; often made synthetically for use in thyroid malfunctions, such as simple goiter.

Ti, symbol for **titanium.**

tibia (TIB-ee-uh), *n.* **1.** the long, thick bone of the lower leg in vertebrates; the shinbone; see **skeletal system. 2.** the fourth segment of the jointed leg in insects.

tick, see **Arachnida.**

tidal wave, a common term for **tsunami.**

tide, *n.* the periodic rise and fall of the waters of the ocean, especially noticeable on shores and in bays; caused by the varying gravitational attraction of the moon and sun on different parts of Earth; occurs twice a day. *adj.* **tidal.**

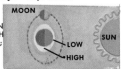

NEAP TIDE (AT FIRST AND THIRD QUARTER MOONS): GRAVITATIONAL PULLS OF SUN AND MOON COUNTERACT EACH OTHER; HIGH TIDE IS LOWEST; LOW TIDE IS LEAST LOW

MOON / SUN / LOW / HIGH

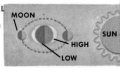

SPRING TIDE (AT NEW AND FULL MOONS): GRAVITATIONAL PULLS OF SUN AND MOON REINFORCE EACH OTHER; HIGH TIDE IS HIGHEST; LOW TIDE IS LOWEST

MOON / SUN / HIGH / LOW

OCEAN COAST

HIGH TIDE (TWICE A DAY)

RANGE OF TIDE

LOW TIDE (TWICE A DAY)

till, *n.* soil, gravel, clay, etc., that is carried or deposited by glaciers.

timber line, an imaginary line on mountainsides and in polar regions beyond which trees and most other common forms of vegetation do not grow.

timbre (TIM-buhr), *n.* the distinctive quality of sound of any given musical instrument or voice; determined by the overtones of the sound.

time zone, one of the 24 divisions of the earth's surface, about 15 degrees wide, centered around a longitude; each division has a standard time calculated from the solar time of Greenwich Observatory, England, at 0° longitude.

tin, *n.* a soft, grayish-white, metallic, chemical element; extremely malleable but not ductile; used in coatings to protect metals, to improve finish and corrosion-resistance of alloys, and in compounds; symbol Sn; *at. no.,* 50; *at. wt.,* 118.69; known since ancient times.

tincture (TINK-chuhr), *n.* an alcoholic solution of an animal or vegetable dye or other chemical, as *tincture of iodine.*

tissue (TISH-oo, TISH-yoo), *n.* a group of cells all having the same structure and performing the same function; different tissues may function together and form an organ.

tissue culture, the technique of keeping cells alive and growing outside the body in a sterile, nutrient medium; medium used is often synthetic; antibiotics may be used to control bacteria and fungi that attack the culture.

titanium (ty-TAY-nee-uhm), *n.* a grayish-white, metallic chemical element; very light in weight, strong, corrosion-resistant, and ductile; used in alloys, especially for parts in ships and airplanes; symbols Ti; *at. no.,* 22; *at. wt.,* 47.90; isolated by Gregor in 1791.

titmouse (TIT-mows), see **Passeriformes.**

titration (ty-TRAY-shuhn), *n.* a laboratory method of finding the chemical concentration of a solution by the addition of a measured amount of a solution of known composition, usually by use of a burette and indicator.

Tl, symbol for **thallium.**

Tm, symbol for **thulium.**

TNT, abbreviation for *trinitrotoluene,* a high explosive frequently used in blasting operations. Atomic and nuclear bombs are rated as equivalent to so many tons of TNT (in doing damage).

toad, *n.* a small amphibian resembling a frog with dry, warty skin, bulging eyes, webbed feet, and a long, sticky tongue for catching insects; see **Amphibia.**

toadstool, *n.* any poisonous mushroom; see **Basidiomycetes.**

tongue (TUNG), *n.* a muscular organ in the mouth of most vertebrates, useful in swallowing, tasting and, in man, speaking; see **digestive system.**

tonic (TAHN-ik), *n.* a stimulant to the muscles, especially a medicine to stimulate and invigorate.

tonsil (TAHN-sil), *n.* lymphatic tissue in the nasal passage and the throat that filters out and

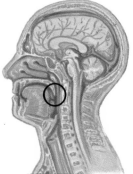

Location of the palatine tonsils (center of the circle) as seen in a longitudinal section of the head

destroys bacteria. The *palatine* tonsils (usually referred to just as the tonsils) sometimes become infected and must be surgically removed. The adenoids are *pharyngeal* tonsils; see **adenoid.**

tonsilitis (tahn-suh-LY-tis), *n.* an inflammation of the tonsils.

tonus (TOH-nuhs), *n.* the normal condition of a healthy muscle, especially its normal state of very slight tension independent of voluntary contraction.

tooth, *n., pl.* **teeth,** a bone-like projection in the mouth set in a jawbone socket; used for biting, tearing, or grinding, or, in man, to help produce certain speech sounds. A mammalian tooth is composed mostly of *dentine* (a hard calcium ma-

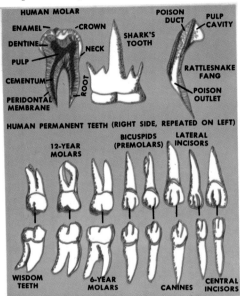

HUMAN MOLAR
ENAMEL — CROWN
POISON DUCT
PULP CAVITY
DENTINE
NECK
SHARK'S TOOTH
PULP
RATTLESNAKE FANG
CEMENTUM
ROOT
PERIDONTAL MEMBRANE
POISON OUTLET

HUMAN PERMANENT TEETH (RIGHT SIDE, REPEATED ON LEFT)
12-YEAR MOLARS
BICUSPIDS (PREMOLARS)
LATERAL INCISORS
WISDOM TEETH
6-YEAR MOLARS
CANINES
CENTRAL INCISORS

terial), covered with *enamel; pulp* chamber in center contains blood vessels and nerves; the *root canal,* also of pulp, is covered with a protective layer called *cementum;* root extends into the gum held by the *peridontal membrane; crown* extends into the mouth. There are 4 main types of teeth: sharp-edged *incisors* for cutting, *canines* (also called *eyeteeth* and *cuspids*) for tearing, double-pointed *bicuspids* for tearing and grinding, and broad, flattened *molars* for grinding.

tooth decay, an alternate term for **dental caries.**

topaz (TOH-paz) *n.* a hard, semiprecious mineral used in jewelry; color may be yellow (most precious), light blue, green, or pink; sometimes mistaken for quartz, but is harder (hardness 8); formula, $(AlF)_2SiO_4$.

topography (tah-PAH-gruh-fee), *n.* **1.** the study of the way in which the surface of the earth varies, as it is elevated by hills and mountains or depressed in valleys and ocean beds. **2.** the physical *features* of any area. *adj.* **topographical.**

topsoil, *n.* the fairly loose, porous soil often containing sand, silt, or clay, that lies over the subsoil; dark in color because it contains humus; can support plant life.

tornado (tawr-NAY-doh), *n.* a small, violent windstorm, characterized by a cloud shaped like a funnel in which winds may whirl at speeds of over 100 miles per hour over a small area; usually occurs during times of low pressure, high temperature, and high humidity; contrast with **hurricane.**

torque (TAWRK), *n.* a resulting force produced in a body by an outside force that tends to produce rotation in the body; torque has a value equal to the force times the perpendicular distance from the line of action of the force to the axis of rotation.

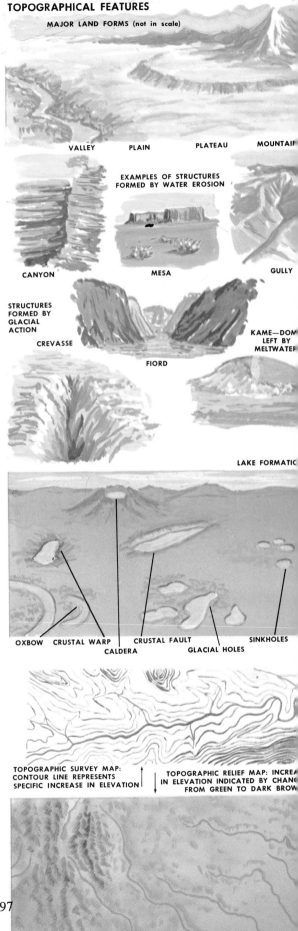

TOPOGRAPHICAL FEATURES
MAJOR LAND FORMS (not in scale)
VALLEY   PLAIN   PLATEAU   MOUNTAIN

EXAMPLES OF STRUCTURES FORMED BY WATER EROSION
CANYON   MESA   GULLY

STRUCTURES FORMED BY GLACIAL ACTION
CREVASSE
FIORD
KAME—DOME LEFT BY MELTWATER

LAKE FORMATION

OXBOW   CRUSTAL WARP   CRUSTAL FAULT   SINKHOLES
CALDERA   GLACIAL HOLES

TOPOGRAPHIC SURVEY MAP: CONTOUR LINE REPRESENTS SPECIFIC INCREASE IN ELEVATION

TOPOGRAPHIC RELIEF MAP: INCREASE IN ELEVATION INDICATED BY CHANGE FROM GREEN TO DARK BROWN

torsion (TAWR-shuhn), *n.* the stress or force required to twist a solid body.

tortoise (TAWR-tuhs), see **turtle.**

toucan (TOO-kan), see **Piciformes.**

tourmaline (TOOR-muh-leen), *n.* a complex silicate mineral, occurring in several crystalline forms; used as a gem when it is blue, green, red, pink, or black; extremely hard and somewhat brittle; see **gem.**

tourniquet (TUHR-ni-ket), *n.* a device for stopping the flow of blood from a wound by putting pressure on the blood vessel between the wound and the heart.

toxemia (tahk-SEE-mee-uh), *n.* a general poisoning of the body caused by absorption of bacterial products (*toxins*) formed at a local infection.

toxic (TAHKS-ik), *adj.* poisonous to man or other living things.

toxicology (tahk-si-KAHL-uh-jee), *n.* that branch of medical science dealing with poisons, their effects, antidotes, and identification.

toxin (TAHK-sin), *n.* a poison produced by a microscopic plant or animal causing such diseases as diphtheria and tetanus in man; contrast with **antitoxin.**

toxoid (TAHKS-oyd), *n.* a toxin treated to destroy its ability to cause disease, such as diphtheria, but to leave it able to produce immunity.

trace, 1. *n.* a very small amount of a foreign substance, usually too small to be measured by ordinary chemical means. **2.** *v.* to follow or track, as the passage of a radioactive isotope through organic tissue.

trace element, 1. one of a series of elements found in the soil in very small quantities; if missing, they must be supplied by fertilizers. **2.** an element that is needed by or occurs in an organism in very small quantities but is important for health, as cobalt or silicon in man.

tracer, *n.* a radioactive isotope that can be traced through chemical processes or biological activities by means of a radiation detector; may be used to measure absorption of an element by cells.

trachea (TRAY-kee-uh), *n., pl.* **-cheae. 1.** a tube used in vertebrate respiration and speech; commonly called *windpipe;* see **respiratory system, vocal cord. 2.** in insects and some other animals, an air tube leading from a spiracle. **3.** a long duct in plants carrying water and dissolved minerals.

tracheid (TRAY-kee-id), *n.* a long, thick-walled, pitted cell in the xylem of plants; nonliving at maturity; functions in conduction and strengthening in softwood.

Tracheophyta (tray-kee-AHF-uh-tuh), *n.* a large division containing the most familiar plants; *tracheophytes* are characterized by having a true vascular system consisting of xylem and phloem and with the dominant plant body belonging to the sporophyte generation; see **Psilopsida, Lycopsida, Sphenopsida, Pteropsida.**

tracheotomy (tray-kee-AHT-uh-mee), *n.* an incision into the trachea made during surgery to help respiration.

trachodon (TRAK-uh-dahn), see **Ornithischia.**

track, *n.* the path taken by subatomic particles as they appear in a cloud chamber, bubble chamber, or through photographic plates; useful in studying mass, speed, and life of the particle.

tracking station, a specially equipped installation for recording the course of satellites, receiving information from the spacecraft, and transmitting commands to the spacecraft.

traction (TRAK-shuhn), *n.* **1.** *friction:* the contact between wheels and pavement provides the *traction* to keep a car moving in place. **2.** a method of supporting and holding a broken bone in position with weights and pulleys.

trade wind, a steady, strong wind that blows across the Atlantic or Pacific Ocean in latitudes from 30°N to 30°S. In the Northern Hemisphere, it blows from northeast to southwest; in the Southern Hemisphere, from southeast to northwest.

trait (TRAYT), *n.* **1.** a characteristic of an organism the inheritance of which can be observed and tested by geneticists. **2.** commonly, any characteristic of an individual, whether it can be inherited or not.

trajectory (truh-JEK-tuh-ree), *n.* the path of any body moving in space; determined by the mass of the body, its initial direction and velocity, external forces applied to the body, and gravity.

tranquilizer (TRAN-kwi-ly-zuhr), *n.* **1.** a substance used to relieve nervous symptoms and to produce emotional calm in aggressive, overactive, disturbed patients; even in large doses should not produce coma or anesthesia and should not be habit-forming. **2.** any substance used to relieve anxiety and tension; can be habit-forming when used in large quantities, such as *azacyclonol* or *mephenoxalone.*

trans-, a word part meaning *over, across,* to the *other side, above,* or *beyond.*

transceiver (tran-SEE-vuhr), *n.* a device that can both transmit and receive radio signals. A walkie-talkie is a portable transceiver.

transducer (trans-DOOS-uhr), *n.* a device that converts one energy form to another, as a photoelectric cell changes light into electrical energy.

transfer orbit, a flight path of a space vehicle that connects the earth with the spatial target. The transfer orbit connects terminal points in the vehicle's flight path.

transformer (trans-FAWR-muhr), *n.* a device for increasing or decreasing the voltage in an AC

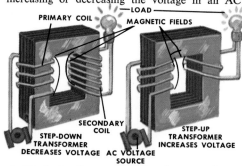

electrical circuit; consists of primary and secondary wire coils and an iron core; the change is induced by interacting magnetic fields.

transfusion (trans-FYOO-shuhn), *n.* a process for transferring blood from one person to another, usually through an intravenous needle. The blood of the donor must match or be compatible with the blood of the patient.

transistor (tran-ZIS-tuhr), *n.* a small device that serves as an amplifier of electrical power; often replacing a larger vacuum tube; contains a semiconductor, usually germanium.

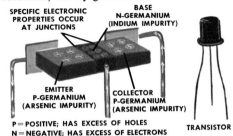

SPECIFIC ELECTRONIC PROPERTIES OCCUR AT JUNCTIONS

BASE N-GERMANIUM (INDIUM IMPURITY)

EMITTER P-GERMANIUM (ARSENIC IMPURITY)

COLLECTOR P-GERMANIUM (ARSENIC IMPURITY)

P = POSITIVE; HAS EXCESS OF HOLES
N = NEGATIVE; HAS EXCESS OF ELECTRONS

TRANSISTOR

transit (TRANS-uht), *n.* **1.** the passage of a heavenly body across the surface of a usually larger body, as Mercury across the face of the sun, as viewed from Earth. A body making such a passage is said to be *in transit.* **2.** the passage of a heavenly body across the viewing field of a telescope. **3.** a surveying instrument used to measure angles.

translucent (trans-LOO-suhnt), *adj.* having the property of allowing the passage of light rays only diffusely, so that an object behind such a material can be perceived only dimly or as a shadow; contrast with **opaque.**

transmission (trans-MISH-uhn), *n.* **1.** the part of an automobile that changes the high-speed, low-torque power from the engine to lower-speed, higher-torque power and transmits the power to the wheels. **2.** the sending of radio waves through the air. *v.* **transmit.**

transmitter (trans-MIT-uhr), *n.* any device that passes along a signal to a receiver; as the transmitter in a telephone changes audio impulses into electrical impulses and sends them along the line to the receiver.

transmutation (trans-myoo-TAY-shuhn), *n.* the process of changing one element into another; may occur spontaneously in radioactive elements, or may be caused artificially by bombarding an element with high-energy particles.

transparent (trans-PAIR-uhnt), *adj.* **1.** having the property of allowing the passage of light rays with little, if any, diffusion; contrast with **opaque. 2.** commonly, referring to any material that can be seen through easily; *clear.*

transpiration (trans-puh-RAY-shuhn), *n.* the evaporation and loss of water from aerial parts of plants, especially leaves, through the stomata.

transplant. 1. *v.* to remove a plant from one location and plant it in another, such as to a larger pot when the roots have grown too large. **2.** *n.* a young plant or seedling which has been planted in 2 or more places. **3.** a piece of tissue moved from one location and planted in another, such as *corneal transplants.*

transuranic (trans-yoo-RAN-ik), *adj.* referring to those elements beyond uranium in the periodic table; elements 93 to 103 in the actinide rare-earth series, all produced by bombarding atoms of other elements and all radioactive.

transverse, *adj.* **1.** located crosswise or diagonal to something, as a *transverse process* on a vertebra, the lateral projection off the main body of the bone. **2.** pertaining to transverse waves in

which wave movement is perpendicular to the vibrating object; see also **wave.**

trauma (TRAW-muh), *n.* **1.** a bodily injury produced by an outside agent, such as fire, chemicals, or violence. **2.** a shocking experience that has lasting psychological consequences.

tremor (TREM-uhr), *n.* a vibrating of the earth's crust; a slight earthquake.

trench mouth, a communicable disease of the mouth characterized by red, swollen, bleeding gums and sore cheeks and tongue; known medically as *Vincent's angina.*

tri-, a word part meaning *three.*

triad (TRY-ad), *n.* an element, atom, or radical with a valence of 3.

Triassic (try-AS-ik), *n.* the first period of the Mesozoic Era in geologic time; reptiles were the dominant animal form and cycad-type trees appeared; see **geologic time table.**

tributary (TRIB-yuh-tair-ee), *n.* a small stream or creek that runs into a larger stream or a river; a river and its *tributaries* make up a river system.

trichina (tri-KY-nuh), see **Nematoda, trichinosis.**

trichinosis (trik-uh-NOH-sis), *n.* a disease caused by trichinae, parasitic roundworms; caused by eating infected pork that has been improperly cooked; the larvae encyst in muscle tissue, causing pain, fever, and stiff, painful movement.

trichocyst (TRIK-uh-sist), *n.* a tiny capsule and hairlike organ used for stinging, found in some protozoans, as paramecia.

triclinic (try-KLIN-ik), *adj.* of a crystal, having 3 unequal, nonright-angle axes; the least symmetrical of crystal forms; see **crystal system.**

tricuspid (try-KUHS-pid), *adj.* **1.** having 3 points (called *cusps*), as some teeth. **2.** in medicine, referring to the valve on the right side of the human heart; see **heart.**

trilobite (TRY-luh-byt), *n.* any of a large class (*Trilobita*) of small, extinct crustaceans with 3 lengthwise body lobes, and many segments that

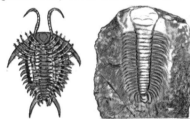

(Left) Reconstructed ventral surface of an Ordovician trilobite; (right) internal mold fossil of the dorsal surface of a Cambrian species

are easily seen in fossil remains. They were the dominant animal during Cambrian times (600 million years ago) and lasted until the end of the Paleozoic era.

trinitrotoluene, see **TNT.**

triode (TRY-ohd), *n.* an electron tube with 3 parts, used to amplify or detect radio waves; usually consists of a cathode, anode, and grid.

tritium (TRIT-ee-uhm, TRISH-), *n.* an unstable isotope of hydrogen, with one proton and 2 neutrons in the nucleus.

trochophore (TROHK-uh-fawr), *n.* the freely swimming larva of most mollusks and marine worms; see **larva.**

tropic (TRAHP-ik), *n.*   **1.** one of the 2 imaginary lines circling Earth, 23½ degrees north or south of the equator. Northern tropic (called the *Tropic of Cancer*) is the line at which the sun would appear directly overhead on the summer solstice; southern tropic (*Capricorn*), that at which the sun would appear directly overhead on the winter solstice.   **2.** *adj.* in endocrinology, describing a hormone that directs the action of a specific organ, such as ACTH.

tropical (TRAHP-i-kuhl), *adj.*   **1.** referring to that portion of the earth's surface between the 2 tropics.   **2.** referring to the hot, rainy climate typical of many areas between the 2 tropics.

tropism (TROH-pizm), *n.*   a growth movement in plants, resulting from any of a variety of external

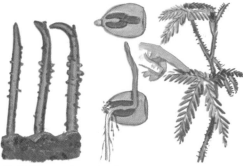

(Left) *Phototropism*, a positive reaction (movement toward) to sunlight; (center) *geotropism* in germinating corn—root reacts positively to gravity; stem shoot reacts negatively; (right) *thigmotropism*—leaf reacts to touch by closing along the midrib

stimuli, the direction of the movement being determined by the direction in which the original stimuli lay.   *adj.* **tropistic.**

tropopause (TROH-puh-paws), *n.*   that portion of the atmosphere between the troposphere and the stratosphere; height varies with season and with latitude.

troposphere (TROH-puh-sfeer), *n.*   the lower level of the earth's atmosphere, the upper limit varying between 30,000 and 60,000 feet, and characterized by weather and air turbulence.

tropospheric fallout, fallout of small particles that have been carried up to about 40,000 feet after an atomic or nuclear explosion; particles usually fall within a month after detonation.

trough (TRAWF), *n.*   the lowest point of a wave, between 2 crests; in general, the low point between any 2 higher points.

troy weight, a system of weights used for gold, silver, and some precious stones; see measurement tables on page 214.

truffle, see **Ascomycetes.**

trunk, *n.*   **1.** the main stem of a tree, not including branches.   **2.** the chief and usually largest section of a nerve or artery.   **3.** the long, nasal outgrowth (*proboscis*) of an elephant.   **4.** an animal body not including appendages; in man, the *torso.*

trypanosome (tri-PAN-uh-sohm), see **sleeping sickness, Protozoa.**

trypsin (TRIP-suhn), *n.*   an enzyme produced in the pancreas and secreted into the intestine; aids in breaking down proteins into peptides.

tsetse fly (TSET-see), see **sleeping sickness.**

tsunami (tsoo-NAH-mee), *n.*   a large wave crest of water in the ocean, caused by volcanic activity or crustal shifting; may be as high as 75 feet and travel hundreds of miles causing great damage to land in its path; commonly called *tidal wave.*

tube-nosed bird, any bird in order **Procellariiformes**.

tuber (TOO-buhr), *n.*   a much enlarged, fleshy, underground stem, not erect; characteristic of various plants and usually functioning as a food storage structure, such as the potato.

tubercle (TOO-buhr-kuhl), *n.*   **1.** a small, rounded swelling or nodule such as are found on the roots of various legume plants.   **2.** a lesion, or growth, of abnormal cells occurring in tuberculosis.

tuberculin (too-BUHR-kyuh-lin), *n.*   a growth product or an extract of the tubercle bacillus; when injected under the skin, a positive reaction shows exposure to tuberculosis.

tuberculosis (too-buhr-kyuh-LOH-sis), *n.*   a disease caused by a bacterium, *Mycobacterium tuberculosis;* characterized by growths called *tubercles,* usually found in the lungs but other body parts may be affected.   *adj.* **tubercular.**   *abbr.* **TB.**

Tubiflorales (too-bi-flawr-AY-leez), see **Polemoniales.**

tubular (TOO-byuh-luhr), *adj.*   resembling a tube; the earthworm has a *tubular* shape.

Tubulidentata (too-byoo-li-den-TAH-tuh), *n.*   an order of mammals with piglike bodies, donkey-like ears, tubular mouths with extensible tongues

African aardvark,
*Orycteropus
afer*

for collecting ants, and strong claws for digging; includes the aardvark.

tularemia (too-luh-REE-mee-uh), *n.*   a disease caused by *Pasteurella tulaensis,* a bacterium; carried by ticks, lice, deer flies; common in wild rodents and rabbits; may be caught by man; commonly called *rabbit fever.*

tumor (TOO-muhr), *n.*   an abnormal growth in a tissue or organ of the body, caused by a change in the normal growth pattern of the body cells. Tumors may be cancerous (*malignant*) or benign.

tundra (TUHN-druh), *n.*   a treeless, marshy plain, found between forest regions and areas of perpetual snow, as in Siberia and northern Canada.

tuner, *n.*   in electronics, a device or part of an electronic receiver that selects (by resonance) the signals to be amplified; the station selector in a radio; see also **capacitor.**

tungsten (TUHNG-stuhn), *n.*   a heavy, silvery-gray, metallic chemical element; extremely hard; used for electrical filaments and to increase tensile strength, hardness, and elasticity of iron and steel alloys; symbol W; *at. no.,* 74; *at. wt.,* 183.85; isolated by the Elhuyars in 1783.

tunicate (TOO-ni-kayt), see **Urochordata.**

tuning fork, an instrument with 2 prongs that vibrate at a precisely known sound pitch when struck; musical instruments can be tuned to its true pitch.

turbidity (tuhr-BID-uh-tee), *n.* the state of being opaque because of matter carried in suspension; in general usage, darkness, as in water, caused by suspension of opaque matter.

turbine (TUHR-buhn, -byn), *n.* a machine which changes the mechanical energy of a moving liquid or gas, into a rotary form of mechanical energy, such as a turning shaft or armature; see also **steam turbine.**

turbofan, *n.* a turbojet engine in which fans or blades force air of the same pressure as the hot

curved dorsal shell, called the *carapace,* and an almost flat, ventral shell, called the *plastron;* they live both on land and in water; are the longest-lived vertebrates. Instead of teeth, they have sharp plates and are both plant and flesh eaters; also called *terrapin;* if living on land, may be called a *tortoise.*

tusk, *n.* a very large tooth projecting beyond the lip; found on the elephant, walrus, narwhal, hippopotamus, and male wild boar; composed of ivory or dentine.

TV, abbreviation for **television.**

tweeter, *n.* a high-fidelity loudspeaker used to reproduce high sounds, usually of frequencies over 6000 cycles per second; contrast with **woofer.**

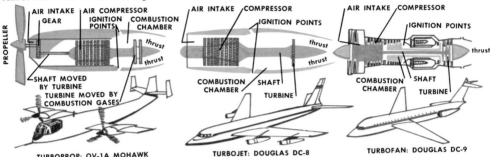

TURBOPROP: OV-1A MOHAWK   TURBOJET: DOUGLAS DC-8   TURBOFAN: DOUGLAS DC-9

exhaust gases into those gases; gives additional thrust without using more fuel.

turbojet, *n.* a kind of jet engine in which the escaping jet drives a turbine which in turn operates a compressor which forces additional thrust-giving air into the burner.

turbomachine, *n.* a small scale version of the turbojet, used in small planes and helicopters; power is provided by gears rather than a jet.

turboprop (TUR-boh-prahp), *n.* a jet engine to which a propeller has been added; the jet drives a turbine and the propeller is turned by the shaft connecting the turbine and compressor.

turbulence (TUHR-byuh-luhnts), *n.* a violently irregular state in a fluid, opposite of streamline motion; severe winds are caused by turbulence in the atmosphere; see **streamline.**

turgor (TUHR-guhr), *n.* the condition of being swollen and congested; may be abnormal or normal, as in plant cells made *turgid* with water.

turquoise (TUR-koyz), *n.* a noncrystalline mineral with a waxy luster when polished; blue-green in color; a hydrous phosphate of copper and aluminum; formula, $CuAl_6(PO_4)_4(OH)_8 \cdot 5H_2O$.

turtle (TUHR-tuhl), *n.* any of the order *Testudinata,* a large group of aquatic reptiles with a

24-hour orbit, orbit taken by a satellite whose orbital velocity is about 3 miles per second, close to that of a point below on the earth; also known as *synchronous orbit;* see **synchronous** picture.

twin, *n.* one of 2 offspring from the same pregnancy in the mother; results from 2 separate eggs (*fraternal* twins), or from a splitting apart of the blastomeres during early cleavage, forming 2 distinct individuals (*identical twins*).

two-stroke cycle, in an internal-combustion engine, a cycle that requires 2 strokes, or movements, of the piston to be completed; includes power-intake stroke and exhaust-compression stroke.

tympanum (TIM-puh-nuhm), *n.* a thin membrane stretched across the ear canal; vibrates in response to external vibrations, transferring them to inner ear organs; commonly called *eardrum;* see **ear.** *adj.* **tympanic.**

Tyndall effect (TIN-duhl), a change in color of a lighted object caused by the scattering effect of tiny particles suspended in the air. The atmosphere appears blue when viewed from Earth because of the Tyndall effect; discovered by John Tyndall, British physicist.

typhoid fever (TY-foyd), a communicable disease caused by the bacillus *Salmonella typhosa;* symptoms are high fever, severe intestinal inflammation, enlarged spleen; transmitted primarily through contaminated water, occasionally food.

typhus (TY-fuhs), *n.* a disease caused by *Rickettsiae,* characterized by headache, rash, high fever, nervousness, and total fatigue; transmitted by human body lice, chiggers, ticks, fleas, etc.

typhoon (ty-FOON), *n.* a violent tropical storm in the western Pacific Ocean and characterized by wind velocities of over 75 miles per hour; similar to hurricanes occurring in the Atlantic Ocean.

Tyrannosaurus (tuh-ran-uh-SAWR-uhs), see **Saurischia.**

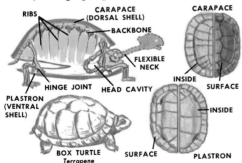

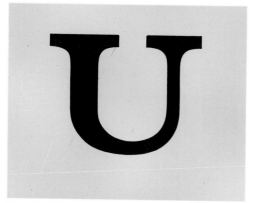

U, symbol for **uranium.**

udder (UD-uhr), *n.* the saclike mammary gland of cows, goats, and certain other mammals, usually having 2 or more nipples.

UFO, abbreviation for **unidentified flying object.**

UHF, abbreviation for **ultra-high frequency.**

ulcer (UL-suhr), *n.* an open sore occurring in soft tissue, either internally, as in the small intestine, or externally, as on the skin.

ulna (UL-nuh), *n.* **1.** in man, the large, inner bone of the forearm, opposite the radius; see **skeletal system. 2.** the long, thin bone in the forelimb of vertebrates and the wings of birds.

ultra-high frequency (UL-truh-), a portion of the electromagnetic spectrum commonly used for radio and television transmission with a frequency band of 300-3000 megacycles per second and a wavelength from 10-100 meters. *abbr.* **UHF.**

ultrasonic (uhl-truh-SAHN-ik), *adj.* above the threshold of human hearing, or above 2,000 cycles per second; *ultrasonic waves* are useful in detection of flaws in industrial materials.

ultraviolet (uhl-truh-VY-uh-luht), *adj.* referring to radiation beyond the violet light of the visible spectrum; thus, shorter in wavelength and higher in frequency than the visible spectrum.

Umbellales (um-buh-LAY-leez), *n.* an order of dicot herbs, shrubs, and trees having flowers clustered in *umbels* (groups in which the flower stalks all come from the same level like the spokes of an umbrella). The 3 families are: the ginseng family (*Araliaceae*); the carrot or parsley family (*Umbelliferae*)—celery, parsnip, coriander, dill; and the dogwood family (*Cornaceae*).

(left) Ginseng and its medicinal root, *Panax trifolins;* (center) flower and berry of dogwood, *Cornus canadensis;* (below) edible parsnip roots, *Pastinaca sativa*

umbilical cord (um-BIL-i-kuhl), a tubular structure containing blood vessels through which exchange of food, waste materials, and oxygen occurs between the embryo and the mother's body; clamped and cut after birth, becoming the *navel.*

umbra (UM-bruh), *n.* that part of a shadow that receives no light from the source; a total solar eclipse is observed at a point on the surface of the earth when the umbra of the moon's shadow covers that point; see also **eclipse.**

unconformity, *n.* a visible interruption in a sequence of rock strata of different ages; marks a time of erosion of the lower, older layer.

undertow, *n.* **1.** the water current at the bottom of a large body of water flowing in a direction opposite to that of the current at the surface. **2.** the underwater current at a beach, flows back toward the ocean.

undulant fever (UN-dyuh-luhnt, -juh-), a generalized infectious disease caused by bacteria; symptoms are cyclic fever, weakness, anemia, and neck pain; transmitted through unpasteurized milk products; called *brucellosis* in cattle.

undulation (un-dyuh-LAY-shuhn, -juh-), *n.* the pattern of motion of waves; see **wave.**

ungulate (UN-gyuh-luht), *adj.* belonging to the large group of mammals with hoofs such as horses, elephants, etc.; not a genuine taxonomic group; see **Artiodactyla, Perissodactyla.**

unicellular (yoo-ni-SEL-yuh-luhr), *adj.* composed of one cell, as the protozoans.

unidentified flying object, an object or pattern of light seen moving in the sky, for which there is no explanation; most commonly reported as having the shape of flying saucers, cigar-shaped saucers, or bell-shaped objects. *abbr.* **UFO.**

unipolar (yoo-ni-POH-luhr), *adj.* produced by or having only one magnetic pole.

univalve (YOO-ni-valv), see **Gastropoda.**

universal antidote (ANT-i-doht), an emergency treatment for most poisonings, given before a physician arrives: 2 parts powdered burned toast, one part milk of magnesia, one part strong tea.

universal donor, a person with type O blood. Type O blood may be given in a transfusion regardless of the receiver's blood type, providing Rh factor is compatible.

universal receiver, a person with blood type AB who can safely receive transfusions from persons of all blood types, providing the Rh factor is compatible; contrast with **universal donor.**

universe (YOO-ni-vuhrs), *n.* everything that exists anywhere in space; the solar system, all the galaxies, the space between them and possibly beyond them. *adj.* **universal.**

uranium (yoo-RAY-nee-uhm), *n.* a soft, silvery, radioactive, metallic chemical element in the actinide series; ductile and malleable; used as a source of nuclear energy and in alloys for nuclear research; symbol U; *at. no.,* 92; *at. wt.,* 238.03; identified by Klaproth in 1789.

Uranus (YOOR-uh-nuhs, yoo-RAY-nuhs), *n.* one of the 4 giant planets in the solar system; 7th in distance from the sun (about 1785 million miles); diameter, about 30,000 miles; period of revolution, 84 earth-years.

urea (yoo-REE-uh), *n.* a basic, nitrogenous derivative of carbonic acid, formed in the body during the metabolism of protein and excreted in human urine; starting material of some plastics, such as Bakelite; formula, $CO(NH_2)_2$.

ureter (yoo-REE-tuhr), *n.* a tube from the kidney that carries urine; see **excretory system.**

urethane (YOO-ruh-thayn), *n.* a white crystalline powder, freely soluble in water, alcohol, and chloroform; the ethyl ester of carbamic acid; formula, $C_2H_5O\cdot CO\cdot NH_2$.

urethra (yoo-REE-thruh), *n.* the canal that carries urine from the bladder to the point where it is excreted; in males also carries seminal fluid.

uric acid (YOO-rik), an acidic, white, crystalline solid, excreted in human urine in very small quantities, except when certain diseases are present, but the normal solid waste product excreted in many animals.

urine (YOO-rin), *n.* the yellowish fluid excreted by the kidneys and carrying liquid wastes.

Urochordata (yoor-uh-kawr-DAH-tuh), *n.* a subphylum of lower marine chordates with nerve cord reduced to a dorsal ganglion, cellulose-like body coating (the *test*) secreted by the mantle, and gill clefts; includes the tunicates.

urogenital (yoor-oh-JEN-i-tuhl), *adj.* referring to both the excretory and reproductive systems, a term used when the 2 systems share common tubes and ducts; also termed *genitourinary.*

urology (yoo-RAHL-uh-jee), *n.* the medical speciality that studies urine and urinary tract and treats urinary diseases; now includes the urogenital tract of both male and female.

Ursa Major (UHR-suh), *Great Bear,* a constellation of the northern sky containing the Big Dipper and the Pointers, pointing to Polaris.

Ursa Minor, *Little Bear,* a constellation in the northern sky containing the Little Dipper and Polaris.

Urticales (yoor-tuh-KAY-less), *n.* an order of dicot herbs, shrubs, and trees that often have nettles with stinging hairs, a one-celled ovary, indehiscent dry fruits, and leaves with stipules. The 4 families are: the elm family (*Ulmaceae*)

(1) Hackberry, *Celtis occidentalis;* (2) osage-orange, *Maclura pomifera;* (3) wild nettle, *Urtica doiica;* (4) marijuana, *Cannabis sativa*

—elm, hackberry; the mulberry family (*Moraceae*)—banyan, osage-orange, rubber plant; the nettle family (*Urticaceae*); and the hemp family (*Cannabinaceae*), source of hemp fiber and marijuana, a narcotic.

uterus (YOO-tuh-ruhs), *n.* a part of the female mammal's urogenital system that surrounds the embryo during pregnancy; contains the placenta; also called *womb. adj.* **uterine.**

uvula (YOO-vyuh-luh), *n.* the small, fleshy tissue that hangs from the back of the soft palate above the root of the tongue; used in production of certain speech sounds.

V, symbol for **vanadium.**

vaccine (vak-SEEN), *n.* a suspension of weakened or killed microorganisms, injected with hypodermic syringe, to prevent or treat infectious diseases; smallpox vaccine from coropox serum was the first used, and name is derived from *vacca,* Latin for *cows.*

vaccination (vak-suh-NAY-shuhn), *n.* an immunizing procedure in which vaccine is injected into the body to protect the body from a disease.

vacuole (VAK-yuh-wohl), *n.* any small cavity found in the protoplasm of a cell, often filled with fluid; in unicellular organisms, a vacuole discharges wastes and excess water; see **ameba.**

vacuum (VAK-yoo-uhm), *n.* a completely empty space; a *perfect* vacuum contains absolutely no matter and has not been attained; a *partial* vacuum contains only a very few molecules of gas.

vacuum tube, an electronic device that can detect, modulate, or amplify an electric current; classified by the number of electrodes inside as *diodes, triodes, tetrodes,* etc.

vagina (vuh-JY-nuh), *n.* **1.** any sheathlike structure in an organism, as plants. **2.** in female mammals, the canal leading to the uterus through which the sperm moves to fertilize the egg.

valence (VAY-luhns), *n.* a measure of the ability of an atom to combine with other atoms, the same or different; measured by the number of hydrogen atoms the atom will combine with, or will displace, depending on the number of electrons in the outer shell; a radical with a valence of 3 can combine with 3 hydrogen atoms.

valve, *n.* a device or structure that allows access to, or closes, an opening or passage. In living organisms this device is composed of tissue, as the valves that prevent the blood from flowing backward in the veins.

vanadinite (vuh-NAY-duh-nyt), *n.* one of the principal ores of vanadium; a fairly soft, crystalline mineral, yellow, brown or red; formula, $9PbO\cdot 3V_2O_5PbCl^2$.

vanadium (vuh-NAY-dee-uhm), *n.* a hard, light-gray, metallic element; difficult to obtain in pure state; used in steel to increase tensile strength and malleability; symbol V; *at. no.,* 23; *at. wt.,* 50.942; described by Del Rio in 1801, but called by him *erythronium.*

Van Allen belt, a region of charged atomic particles many miles above Earth held to it by its magnetic field; weakest at Earth's poles where the magnetic field is weakest. The belt is a danger to space travelers moving through such a region. Changes in the belt create radio interference and have an effect on auroras; discovered by James A. Van Allen, American physicist, in 1958, and originally thought to be 2 or more distinct belts; now known to be one with varying intensities.

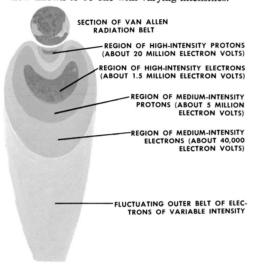

SECTION OF VAN ALLEN RADIATION BELT

REGION OF HIGH-INTENSITY PROTONS (ABOUT 20 MILLION ELECTRON VOLTS)

REGION OF HIGH-INTENSITY ELECTRONS (ABOUT 1.5 MILLION ELECTRON VOLTS)

REGION OF MEDIUM-INTENSITY PROTONS (ABOUT 5 MILLION ELECTRON VOLTS)

REGION OF MEDIUM-INTENSITY ELECTRONS (ABOUT 40,000 ELECTRON VOLTS)

FLUCTUATING OUTER BELT OF ELECTRONS OF VARIABLE INTENSITY

Van de Graaff generator (van dee GRAF), an accelerator for building up a high electrostatic potential between 2 electrodes by mechanically carrying charge to one of them. This potential is used to accelerate particles injected into the electric field between the 2 electrodes; named for Robert J. Van de Graaff, American physicist.

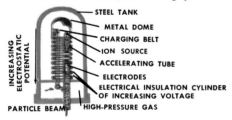

INCREASING ELECTROSTATIC POTENTIAL

STEEL TANK

METAL DOME

CHARGING BELT

ION SOURCE

ACCELERATING TUBE

ELECTRODES

ELECTRICAL INSULATION CYLINDER OF INCREASING VOLTAGE

PARTICLE BEAM

HIGH-PRESSURE GAS

vane (VAYN), *n.* **1.** a flat blade, usually metal, mounted in any fluid-flow device and responding to direction of flow, as in a turbine. **2.** a similar blade, often arrow-shaped, mounted on a pivot to show wind direction.

vapor (VAY-puhr), *n.* **1.** a gas. **2.** the gaseous state of a material normally either a liquid or solid at room temperature. Vapor is produced by evaporation of a liquid, as water, or by sublimation of a solid, as moth balls.

vaporization (vay-puh-ruh-ZAY-shuhn), *n.* evaporation, especially through the application of heat or change of pressure. *v.* **vaporize.**

variable star (VAIR-ee-uh-buhl), a star that varies in brightness periodically; must be distinguished from eclipsing binaries where the apparent change in brightness is due to the eclipse; see also **binary star, Cepheid.**

varicose veins (VAIR-uh-kohs), an abnormal condition in which veins become dilated due to back flowing blood; vein valves are no longer functioning properly.

variety (vuh-RY-i-tee), *n.* **1.** the taxonomic subdivision of a subspecies, indicated especially in plants as the third word in a scientific name, such as *Papaver somniferum album,* a particular variety of the opium poppy. **2.** a type of plant or animal produced by man by means of carefully controlled breeding.

varve (VARV), *n.* a set of alternately coarser and finer layers of sediments laid down in still water; useful in estimating geologic time much as time is measured by annual rings of trees.

vascular (VAS-kyuh-luhr), *adj.* referring to or composed of vessels or ducts formed by the walls of numerous connected cells or cellular tissue which convey fluids, such as sap in plants, and blood and lymph in animals.

vascular bundle, a strand of cells and tubes, consisting of xylem and phloem elements, that extends throughout a plant, conducting sap; also called *fibrovascular bundle;* see also **dicotyledon, monocotyledon.**

vascular plant, any Tracheophyta.

vas deferens, (VAS DEF-uh-ruhnz), in mammals, the duct leading from the gonads to the semen-ejecting mechanism in the male copulatory organ.

vasoconstrictor (vas-oh-kuhn-STRIK-tuhr), *n.* a chemical substance that acts to constrict blood vessels such as is secreted by the endings of sympathetic nerve fibers.

vector (VEK-tuhr), *n.* **1.** a quantity having both direction and magnitude; velocity, weight, and

If 2 boys push on opposite sides of a gate with the same push, there are 2 equal but opposite vector forces (magnitude shown by length of lines, direction by arrow); the resultant of the 2 forces is zero, so the gate does not move

displacement are vectors; contrast with **scalar.** **2.** a line representing such a quantity.

Vega (VEE-guh, VAY-), *n.* a first magnitude star in constellation Lyra; 5th brightest star in the sky in visual magnitude.

vegetation (vej-uh-TAY-shuhn), *n.* plants collectively or all plants in a given area.

vegetative reproduction (VEJ-uh-tay-tiv), **1.** asexual reproduction. **2.** plant reproduction by means other than seeds; some structures making natural vegetative reproduction possible are runners, rhizomes, tubers, and horizontal roots; see also **propagation.**

vein (VAYN), *n.* **1.** in animals, a blood vessel that carries carbon dioxide-filled blood to the heart and lungs; large veins contain valves to prevent the backward flow of blood; connected to the arteries by the capillary system; see **circulatory system.** **2.** a vascular bundle, especially in a leaf; see also **leaf** picture, **midrib, venation.** *adj.* **venous.**

velocity (vuh-LAHS-i-tee), *n.* the rate of motion (speed) of a body in a given direction; velocity = distance ÷ time. If the direction of a moving body changes but not the speed, the velocity of the body will have changed; a vector quantity.

velvet worm, see **Peripatus.**

vena cava (VEE-nuh KAY-vuh), *pl.* **venae cavae.** either of 2 large veins that carry blood from all parts of the body back to the right auricle of the heart. The *superior* vena cava carries blood from the arms and head; the *inferior* vena cava, from the lower limbs and trunk; see **circulatory system.**

venation (vuh-NAY-shuhn), *n.* **1.** in plants, the pattern of conducting tissue or vascular bundles in leaves, as *netted venation* in dicots and *parallel venation* in monocots; see **leaf** picture. **2.** in animals, the way veins are arranged, especially in the membranous wings of some insects.

venereal disease (vuh-NEER-ee-uhl), an infectious disease passed from one person to another by sexual contact. Syphilis and gonorrhea are 2 types of veneral diseases.

venom (VEN-uhm), *n.* the poisonous secretion of some insects, spiders, and snakes; injected through biting or stinging; usually attacks the blood corpuscles, lining of blood vessels, or the nerve centers of the prey. *adj.* **venomous.**

venous (VEE-nuhs), *adj.* pertaining to veins or the carbon dioxide-laden blood in the veins, as *venous* blood.

ventilate (VEN-tuh-layt), *v.* to circulate fresh air or oxygen and draw off stale air including carbon dioxide, in a room or other enclosed space.

ventral (VEN-truhl), *adj.* **1.** on or near the abdominal surface or underside of an animal. **2.** referring to the surface of a petal that faces the center of the flower.

as packaging and insulating material and, when expanded by heat into coarse grains, as a mulch.

vernal equinox (VUHR-nuhl), one of the 2 times of year when the sun appears directly over the equator; day and night are of equal length; about March 21st.

vernier (VUHRN-ee-uhr), *n.* **1.** a graduated scale adjoining the measuring scale of an instrument, and moving with it; graduated so that a number

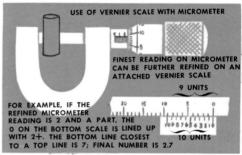

of units (usually 9) is equivalent to the interval between 2 markings on the main scale. **2.** anything that gives finer tuning, measurement, or control, than obtainable with a larger item.

vertebra (VUHR-tuh-bruh), *n., pl.* **-brae** (-bray), any of a number of segments in the spinal column (backbone) of vertebrate animals; made of bone or cartilage, to protect the spinal cord and support the back; joined by discs of fibrous tissue and spongy, gelatinlike material. In man, there are 7 in the neck (*cervical vertebrae*), 12 in the back of the chest (*thoracic*), 5 at the waist (*lumbar*), 5 in the small of the back (*sacral*), and 3-5 *caudal* vertebrae fused to form the coccyx; comparable groups occur in other vertebrates; see also **skeletal system.** *adj.* **vertebral.**

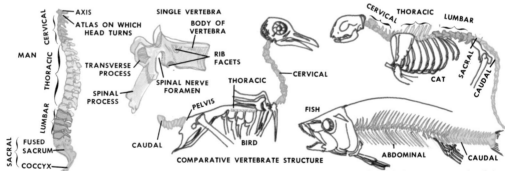

COMPARATIVE VERTEBRATE STRUCTURE

ventricle (VEN-tri-kuhl), *n.* **1.** a muscular chamber in the heart; in mammals, the 2 lower chambers that receive blood from the auricles and pump the blood into the aorta (left ventricle) and the pulmonary artery (right ventricle). **2.** a cavity in the brain of a vertebrate; see **brain.** *adj.* **ventricular.**

venule (VEEN-yool), *n.* a small branch of a larger vein; connects a capillary to a vein.

Venus (VEE-nuhs), *n.* a planet about the size of Earth in the solar system; second planet from the sun; diameter, 7700 miles; period of revolution, 225 earth-days.

Venus' flytrap, see **Sarraceniales.**

vermiculite (vuhr-MIK-yuh-lyt), *n.* a soft, light mineral; any one of the hydrous silicates; used

vertebrate (VUHR-tuh-bruht), *n.* any animal in subphylum *Vertebrata* of phylum *Chordata,* with an internal backbone and a cranium (bony covering of the brain); most can be grouped into 7 main classes; Cyclostomata, Chondrichthyes, Osteichthyes, Amphibia, Reptilia, Aves, and Mammalia; see also **Chordata.**

vertical-takeoff-and-landing (VUHR-ti-kuhl), *adj.* describing a research aircraft capable of taking off in a vertical line; may use jets, rotary wings, pivoting wings, or a combination of these to accomplish vertical takeoff. *abbr.* **VTOL.**

vertigo (VUHR-ti-goh), *n.* a symptom produced by anything that interferes with functioning of the semicircular canals; characterized by sensations of whirling and loss of equilibrium.

very-high frequency, a portion of the electromagnetic spectrum commonly used for radio and television transmission with a frequency band of 30-300 megacycles per second and a wavelength from 1-10 meters. *abbr.* **VHF.**

vesicle (VES-i-kuhl), *n.* any organ or structure in a plant or animal in the form of a sac or cavity with a thin wall, and often filled with a fluid, as a urinary bladder, a cyst, or an air sac in a plant. *adj.* **vesicular.**

vessel (VES-uhl), *n.* **1.** a tube, duct, or chamber used to circulate or store body fluids; veins, arteries, and capillaries are vessels. **2.** a tube in the xylem tissue of plant parts which conducts water and minerals. **3.** any chamber or utensil for holding something, especially fluids.

vestigial (ves-TIJ-ee-uhl), *adj.* without use, of reduced size, or remaining from an evolutionary change: the appendix is a *vestigial organ* in man. *n.* **vestige.**

veterinary medicine (VET-uh-rin-air-ee), that branch of medicine dealing with the treatment, and prevention, of disease in animals.

VHF, abbreviation for **very-high frequency.**

viable (VY-uh-buhl), *adj.* able to live; in medicine, often refers to a fetus that has developed enough to live outside the uterus; in genetics, refers to a nonlethal mutation.

vial (VY-uhl), *n.* a small glass container usually sealed with a cork, cap, or cotton plug and used for storage of substances, as in a laboratory.

vibration (vy-BRAY-shuhn), *n.* an oscillating, or back and forth, motion often producing waves. Sound waves are produced by a rapidly vibrating object; see **wave.** *v.* **vibrate.**

vibrissa (vy-BRIS-uh), *n., pl.* **-sae.** a long sensory hair growing around the eyes and mouth of some carnivores, rodents, and most other mammals, as the whiskers of a cat.

video (VID-ee-oh), **1.** *adj.* referring to or characteristic of that part of the television signal that carries information about the picture; also refers to the circuits, particularly in the receiver, that deal with this picture information; contrast with **audio.** **2.** *n.* television.

villus (VIL-uhs), *n., pl.* **villi.** a small, fingerlike projection, especially on a mucous surface, as the villi on the lining of the small intestine that increase the absorption area for digestion.

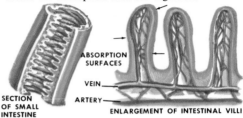

ABSORPTION SURFACES
VEIN
SECTION OF SMALL INTESTINE
ARTERY
ENLARGEMENT OF INTESTINAL VILLI

vine, *n.* **1.** any woody or herbaceous plant with a long stem that grows on the ground or climbs by aerial roots, tendrils, or winding around a support. **2.** any plant of the vine family.

vine family, see **Rhamnales.**

vinyl (VY-nuhl), *n.* the monovalent radical, CH_2CH, derived from ethylene which may be polymerized to form various plastics and resins.

violet family (VY-uh-luht), see **Parietales.**

virginium, former name for **francium.**

Virgo (VEER-goh), *n.* the *Maiden,* a constellation seen in the northern sky in spring and summer; has 39 stars with *Spica* being the brightest.

virtual image (VUHR-chuh-wuhl), an image that can be seen but not projected on a screen; it is always upright and appears to come from an image seen within the optical system, as in a microscope; behind the actual location of the virtual image; contrast with **real image.**

virulent (VIR-yuh-luhnt), *adj.* **1.** referring to the intensity of any process that can cause death. **2.** very deadly; certain snake venom is *virulent.*

virus (VY-ruhs), *n.* not a bacterium, any of many sub-living infectious nucleoproteins; usually submicroscopic; inactive when isolated; able to reproduce when in a living cell; often referred to as "naked genes;" cause such diseases as measles, poliomyelitis, colds, and others. *adj.* **viral.**

viscera (VIS-uh-ruh), *pl. n.* (*sing.* **viscus**). collectively, the soft organs found in body cavities, such as heart, lungs, spleen, etc. *adj.* **visceral.**

VITAMINS AND VITAMIN DEFICIENCIES		
VITAMIN	SOURCE	RESULT OF DEFICIENCY
A $C_{20}H_{30}O$	Carrots, tomatoes, green vegetables, fish-liver oil, liver, egg yolks, cheese, butter	Xerophthalmia, nightblindness, dry sore eyes, infection from breakdown of epithelial tissue, phrynoderma
B₁ (thiamin) $C_{12}H_{17}N_4OS$	Yeast, unpolished rice, peanuts, peas, lean pork, cereal grains	Beri-beri, nervous system affected, weakness, loss of appetite and weight, fatigue, nervousness, paralysis, swelling of limbs
B₂ (Riboflavin) $C_{17}H_{20}N_4O_6$	Liver, green leaves, milk, yeast, eggs, whole cereal grains, meats, legumes	Skin lesions around mouth and nostrils, photophobia, loss of energy, contributes to pellagra
B₆ (Pyridoxine) $C_8H_{12}NO_3$	Lean meat, yeast, liver, whole cereal grains, milk, lettuce, fish, eggs, lemon	Convulsions in infants, anemia & paralysis in some animals, weight loss in adults, impaired growth in children
B₁₂ (Cobalamin) $C_{63}H_{88}N_{14}O_{14}PCo$	Milk, eggs, liver, lean meat, fish	Pernicious anemia and weakness; gastric, intestinal & nervous disturbances, loss of sensory & motor power
M (Folic acid), $C_{19}H_{19}N_7O_6$	Synthesized in intestinal tract	Failure of nucleic acid metabolism, pernicious anemia
H (Biotin) $C_{10}H_{16}N_2O_3S$	Liver, egg yolk, milk, yeast	Severe dermatitis, paralytic symptoms, loss of hair, poor growth
Niacin (Nicotinic acid) $C_6H_5NO_2$	Lean beef, salmon, tuna, halibut, milk, eggs, yeast, chicken, liver, peanuts	Pellagra, dermatitis, & skin lesions, loss of appetite, soreness of mouth
Pantothenic acid, $C_9H_{17}NO_5$	Egg yolk, molasses, liver, yeast	Dermatitis, skin lesions, graying of hair, retarded growth
Choline, $C_5H_{15}NO_2$	Liver, egg yolk, lean meat, soybeans	Retarded growth, kidney hemorrhage, excessive fat in liver
Inositol, $C_6H_{12}O_6$	Liver, heart muscle, plant materials	Retarded growth in some yeasts and human tissue culture
C (Ascorbic acid) $C_6H_8O_6$	Adrenal cortex; fresh, frozen, or canned fruits and vegetables; citrus fruits	Scurvy, loss of weight, excessive weakness, swollen gums, loose teeth, sore joints, slow healing of wounds
D $C_{28}H_{44}O$	Formed in animals by action of the sun; body oils of fish	Rickets, failure of bones to mineralize normally; osteomalacia, soft bones, defective teeth, enlarging of wrists, knees, and ankles
E (Tocopherol) $C_{29}H_{50}O_2$	Wheat germ, vegetable oils, cottonseed oils, & soybean oils	Muscular dystrophy, reproductive failure, liver necrosis in rats
K $C_{31}H_{46}O_2$	Green leaves; in the intestine through fermentation	Failure of blood to clot—hemorrhaging

viscose (VIS-kohs), **1.** *adj.* referring to a process for producing filaments or sheets of certain cellulose-type plastics by forcing a basic, colloidal suspension of the cellulose chemical through small holes or slits into an acid solution which precipitates it. **2.** *n.* a material made by this process.

viscosity (vis-KAHS-uh-tee), *n.* the relative ease (or difficulty) with which a fluid flows; related to molecular motion; the lower the viscosity, the more quickly the fluid will flow. *adj.* **viscous.**

vision (VIZH-uhn), *n.* the total sensory experience of seeing, including the perception of an image with the eye and the registering of the image by the brain. *adj.* **visual.**

visual magnitude (VIZH-uh-wuhl), the classification of the brightness of stars as they appear to the naked eye; stars of magnitude 1 are brightest; stars of magnitude 6 are dimmest. This system was established by Ptolemy. Stars now known to be brighter than 1st magnitude are assigned minus numbers; the sun has a magnitude of −26.73; contrast with **absolute magnitude.**

visual purple, a purple-colored pigment found in the rods of the retina of the eye that changes composition when struck by light rays; believed to be a key part in transforming light rays into sensory signal; essential for night vision; also called *rhodopsin;* see **rod.**

vitamin (VY-tuh-muhn), *n.* an organic chemical necessary to life but not used as a source of energy; usually forms a part of some enzyme molecule. A deficiency of a vitamin in the diet may cause a disease.

vitelline (vy-TEL-uhn), *adj.* like or having to do with the yolk (food-storage portion) of an egg; the *vitelline membrane* surrounds the yolk.

vitreous humor (VIT-ree-uhs), a gelatinlike, transparent fluid filling the eye between the lens and the retina; see **eye.**

viviparous (vy-VIP-uh-ruhs), *adj.* bearing live young, as opposed to laying eggs; most mammals are viviparous.

vocal cord (VOH-kuhl), one of 2 white ligaments stretched across the opening of the larynx, vibrating when air passes over them to produce

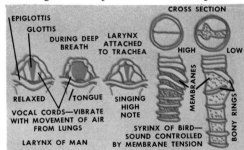

CROSS SECTION
EPIGLOTTIS
GLOTTIS
DURING DEEP BREATH
LARYNX ATTACHED TO TRACHEA
HIGH
LOW
RELAXED / TONGUE
VOCAL CORDS—VIBRATE WITH MOVEMENT OF AIR FROM LUNGS
SINGING HIGH NOTE
MEMBRANES
BONY RINGS
LARYNX OF MAN
SYRINX OF BIRD—SOUND CONTROLLED BY MEMBRANE TENSION

sound. Muscles attached to the vocal cords tighten and relax to regulate pitch and quality.

volatile (VAHL-uh-tuhl), *adj.* readily evaporating at ordinary temperatures and pressures: rubbing alcohol is *volatile* but water is not.

volcanism (VAHL-kuh-nizm), *n.* the characteristic activities of a volcano, such as spewing hot ash and lava, erupting with great force, etc. *adj.* **volcanic.**

volcano (vahl-KAY-noh), *n.* the cone-shaped mound built up on the surface of the earth when

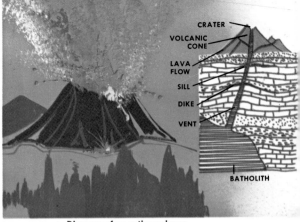

CRATER
VOLCANIC CONE
LAVA FLOW
SILL
DIKE
VENT
BATHOLITH

Diagram of an active volcano

molten rock (*magma*) is forced up through an opening in the surface when heat is built up; see also **intrusion.** *adj.* **volcanic.**

volt (VOHLT), *n.* a quantity of electrical potential difference: one volt is the potential difference across a conductor having a resistance of one ohm which makes a current of one ampere; named for Alessandro Volta.

voltaic cell (vohl-TAY-ik), a device for generating an electrical current, consisting of 2 dissimilar conducting materials in a conductive fluid.

voltmeter (VOHLT-mee-tuhr), *n.* an instrument for measuring the difference in potential between any 2 points in an electric circuit; always connected across a circuit element.

volume (VAHL-yuhm), *n.* **1.** the space bounded by a closed surface; *capacity.* **2.** the intensity (loudness) of a sound coming from a source, such as a loudspeaker.

voluntary muscle (VAHL-uhn-tair-ee), a muscle made of striated fibers (showing alternating light and dark bands) and connective tissue, attached

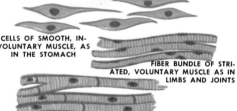

CELLS OF SMOOTH, IN-VOLUNTARY MUSCLE, AS IN THE STOMACH
FIBER BUNDLE OF STRI-ATED, VOLUNTARY MUSCLE AS IN LIMBS AND JOINTS
CARDIAC MUSCLE, STRIATED BUT VOLUNTARY

to the skeleton, and under willful control of the normal organism; also called *skeletal muscle* or *striated muscle;* contrast with **involuntary muscle.**

vomit (VAHM-uht), **1.** *v.* to expel, through the mouth, matter from the stomach by spasmic contraction of the abdominal muscles and walls of the stomach. **2.** *n.* matter expelled from the stomach through the mouth.

vortex (VAWR-teks), *n., pl.* **vortices.** a volume of whirling fluid that spirals in toward its center; an eddy. A *whirlpool* is a vortex.

VTOL, abbreviation for **vertical-takeoff-and-landing.**

vulcanize (VUHL-kuh-nyz), *v.* to harden raw rubber, either natural or synthetic, by mixing it with some form of sulfur and then heating it.

vulture (VUL-chuhr), see **Falconiformes.**

vulva (VUL-vuh), *n.* the exterior part of the genital organs in a female; includes the fleshy, liplike *mons veneris* and *labia majora,* and all structures, such as the clitoris (homologous to the penis), between.

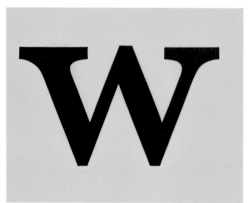

W, symbol for **tungsten** (formerly, *wolfram*).

wake, *n.* the trail of vortices or turbulence left after the passage of an elongated object through a liquid, as a boat through water, or a particle through a bubble chamber; caused by the liquid being set into rotation motion.

walnut family (WAHL-nut), see **Juglandales.**

walrus (WAHL-ruhs), see **Carnivora.**

wane (WAYN), *v.* to decrease in brightness at a steady rate; the moon *wanes* after it reaches the full-moon phase; contrast with **wax.**

Wankel engine (WAHN-kuhl, WAN-), a rotary, internal-combustion engine that uses a triangular-shaped power shaft with combustion chambers

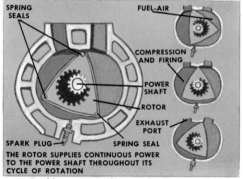

SPRING SEALS · FUEL-AIR · COMPRESSION AND FIRING · POWER SHAFT · ROTOR · EXHAUST PORT · SPARK PLUG · SPRING SEAL
THE ROTOR SUPPLIES CONTINUOUS POWER TO THE POWER SHAFT THROUGHOUT ITS CYCLE OF ROTATION

on 2 sides to transfer continuous power to a geared shaft.

warhead, *n.* the forward end of a missile containing the explosive; a missile equipped with a thermonuclear *warhead* is carrying either a hydrogen bomb or an atomic bomb.

warm-blooded, *adj.* having a body temperature nearly always constant regardless of environment; birds and mammals are warm-blooded; technically termed *homeothermal;* contrast with **cold-blooded.**

warm front, an occurrence in the atmosphere when a warm air mass advances, passes over, and displaces a cool air mass; may be accompanied by light rain.

wart (WAWRT), *n.* a small, tumorous growth on the skin, believed to be caused by a virus.

wasp (WAHSP), see **Hymenoptera.**

watch glass, a small, circular, shallow glass container; one type has thick sides and a grooved bottom to facilitate stocking; another is a thin concave glass resembling a watch crystal; used in laboratories for evaporation of liquids.

water, *n.* a compound of hydrogen and oxygen, H_2O; pure H_2O is a colorless, tasteless liquid with a freezing point of $0°C$ ($32°F$) and a boiling point of $100°C$ ($212°F$); the taste of water may be caused by various chemicals and minerals dissolved in it; see also **sea water.**

water cycle, the sequence of events and processes through which water leaves the ocean (evaporates) and is returned to the ocean in the form of rain, snow, glacier ice, rivers, streams, etc.

waterfall, *n.* a point in a river, stream, or other body of water where the bed, and the water in it, make a sudden drop from a high elevation to a lower one.

water flea, see **Crustacea.**

water-lily family, see **Ranales.**

water moccasin, any of a group of snakes, usually poisonous, that live in the swamps or along streams in southern United States; most common is the cottonmouth; see **snake.**

water-plantain family, see **Naiadales.**

water power, the energy of falling water that may be changed into mechanical or electrical energy through the use of a turbine or other machine; also called *hydroelectric power.*

watershed, *n.* the land on which rain falls and then drains into a river; a water drainage basin.

water-soluble, *adj.* capable of being dissolved in water.

waterspout, *n.* a tornado over water; reaches the surface of the water, creating clouds of spray.

water table, the level of ground below which the rock is saturated with water; the position of the water table determines the depth of wells.

water vapor (VAY-puhr), water in its invisible gas state. Water vapor is commonly present dissolved in air and evaporated from the liquid form; varies with rainfall.

water vascular system (VAS-kyuh-luhr), a system of canals, valves, and tube feet found in echino-

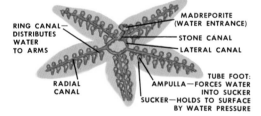

RING CANAL—DISTRIBUTES WATER TO ARMS · MADREPORITE (WATER ENTRANCE) · STONE CANAL · LATERAL CANAL · RADIAL CANAL · TUBE FOOT: AMPULLA—FORCES WATER INTO SUCKER · SUCKER—HOLDS TO SURFACE BY WATER PRESSURE

derms and used to move the animal from place to place; used for respiration in some species.

water wheel, a wheel, usually with fins on the rim, pushed around by the force of moving water.

watt (WAHT), *n.* a unit of electrical power; one watt equals the power consumed when a force of one newton acts through a distance of one meter in one second of time. One *kilowatt* = 1000 watts and is the commercial unit for electrical consumption; named for James Watt, American inventor.

watt-hour, *n.* a unit of electrical energy equal to one watt working for one hour.

watt-hour meter, an instrument that measures electric energy used in a circuit over a period of time; contrast with **wattmeter.**

wattmeter, *n.* an instrument that measures the amount of electric power (in watts) in a circuit at any instant; contrast with **watt-hour meter.**

wave, *n.* any disturbance in a medium by which energy can be transmitted; this energy can be mechanical, electrical, sound, etc.; occurs in 2 main forms: *longitudinal* (as sound) and *transverse* (as radiation).

wavelength, *n.* the distance between a point on a wave and the next point on the wave having the same direction and amplitude; equal to the velocity of the wave divided by the frequency.

acted upon by natural forces such as wind and water; see also **erosion.** *v.* weather.

weather satellite, any **meteorological satellite.**

weather station, a location maintained by the Weather Bureau for the recording and reporting of air pressure, direction and speed of wind, temperature, humidity, precipitation, visibility, etc.; may be a weather satellite.

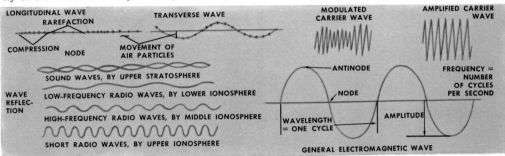

LONGITUDINAL WAVE — RAREFACTION — TRANSVERSE WAVE — COMPRESSION — NODE — MOVEMENT OF AIR PARTICLES — SOUND WAVES, BY UPPER STRATOSPHERE — WAVE REFLECTION — LOW-FREQUENCY RADIO WAVES, BY LOWER IONOSPHERE — HIGH-FREQUENCY RADIO WAVES, BY MIDDLE IONOSPHERE — SHORT RADIO WAVES, BY UPPER IONOSPHERE — MODULATED CARRIER WAVE — AMPLIFIED CARRIER WAVE — ANTINODE — NODE — WAVELENGTH = ONE CYCLE — AMPLITUDE — FREQUENCY = NUMBER OF CYCLES PER SECOND — GENERAL ELECTROMAGNETIC WAVE

wave mechanics, an alternate term for **quantum mechanics.**

wax, 1. *n.* any of the various semisolid, large-molecule hydrocarbons produced by plants or insects, or synthetically. Waxes are insoluble in water and their melting points vary with their composition. **2.** *v.* to increase in brightness at a steady rate; the moon waxes until it reaches the full-moon phase; contrast with **wane.**

weasel family (WEE-zuhl), see **Carnivora.**

weather, *n.* the conditions of pressure, temperature, humidity, cloud formations, etc., that characterize the atmosphere at any time and place.

Example of changing weather conditions: (top) rising barometer, temperature steady; (center) special air conditions bring falling barometer, rapidly rising temperature, and cumulonimbus rain clouds; (bottom) more extreme changes may produce tornado from the same cloud

weather forecast, the official report or prediction of what the weather is likely to be in a particular area for the next few hours, or sometimes, days. The U.S. Weather Bureau Analysis Center, Washington, D.C., is the official forecast center.

weathering, *n.* the physical and chemical changes of materials near the earth's surface after being

weather vane, any device that moves in response to changing wind direction, important in weather forecasting; also called *wind vane.*

web, *n.* **1.** a network of silk produced and expelled from the spinneret of the spider; used by the spider to capture insects. **2.** a membrane stretching between the toes of some animals, especially for use in swimming.

web-foot, a foot with 2 or more toes joined by a membrane, as on a duck.

wedge (WEJ), *n.* a simple machine shaped like 2 inclined planes placed back to back tapering to

HATCHET — WEDGE—2 JOINED INCLINED PLANES — PROW OF SHIP—A WEDGE THROUGH WATER

a point at one end; used for splitting and as a lift for heavy weights.

weed, *n.* generally, any plant growing where it is not wanted.

weevil (WEE-vuhl), *n.* any of a group of beetles with protruding snouts and larvae that destroy crops by boring and feeding on the inside of the plant, as the cotton boll weevil.

weight (WAYT), *n.* **1.** the gravitational force on an object pulling it toward the center of the earth; slightly greater at the poles than at the equator. **2.** an object of known weight used for comparison on a balance scale.

weight arm, that part of a lever extending from the fulcrum to the weight that transfers the force applied to the force arm; see **lever.**

weightlessness, *n.* the condition of zero-gravity theoretically possible in remote space; occurs during free fall of an object and experienced during the free fall of a vehicle in orbit around Earth.

well, *n.* an opening in the earth used to remove water or oil from beneath the surface; wells may be dug or drilled.

wen (WEHN), *n.* a cyst filled with fatty material, often occurring on the head.

wet bulb, see **psychrometer.**

wet cell, a chemical device capable of producing an electrical potential difference using a fluid as the electrolyte; the automobile storage battery is a group of wet cells.

wetting agent, any substance, such as a detergent, that reduces the surface tension where a liquid meets a solid surface, allowing the liquid to spread more easily and penetrate the surface.

whale (HWAYL), see **Cetacea.**

Wheel and axle: downward motion is converted to forward motion, as in a bicycle or winch (a windlass)

wheel and axle, a simple machine consisting of a wheel fixed to a rod; the rear driving wheels of an automobile, doorknobs, and water faucet handles are examples of the wheel and axle.

whey (HWAY), *n.* the liquid part of milk removed in making cheese.

whippoorwill (HWIP-uhr-wil), see **Caprimulgiformes.**

whirlpool, *n.* a vortex in oceans, lakes, or rivers; caused by the wind blowing against the current or 2 currents meeting, or by some formation of the land beneath the water.

white ant, common term for *termite;* see **Isoptera.**

white corpuscle, any one of 5 types of white or colorless blood corpuscles, some involved in the destruction of disease-producing organisms; this action is called *phagocytosis;* technically called *leucocyte;* see also **blood.**

white dwarf, one of the small, dense stars which has consumed all its energy and is dim. It may shine because of gravitational shrinking.

white gold, one of the alloys of gold with other metals, used chiefly for jewelry; composition may be either (in per cent): 75-85 Au, 8-10 Ni, 2-9 Zn, or 90 Au, 10 Pd.

white heat, the heat to which an object must be raised before it glows with a white light.

white light, light that is colorless in itself yet, when passed through a prism, will be dispersed into a spectrum of colored light.

white matter, a whitish, nervous tissue in the spinal cord and brain consisting chiefly of fibers covered with myelin; see also **gray matter.**

whooping cough (HUHP-ing), a childhood respiratory disease caused by the bacteria *Bordetella pertussis,* characterized by ordinary cold symptoms, then severe coughing spells.

whorled (HWAHRL-uhld), *adj.* **1.** with 3 or more leaves or branches at a node on a plant stem. **2.** forming a circle, as floral organs.

willow family (WIL-oh), see **Salicales.**

winch, an alternate term for **windlass.**

wind, *n.* a convection current of air moving along the surface of the earth; consists of sinking cool air and rising warm air; caused by unequal heating of Earth by the sun.

windlass (WEND-luhs), *n.* a device used to lift heavy loads, consisting of a wheel and axle and a chain or rope. The rope is wound around the axle and the force is applied to the large wheel; also called a *winch.*

windmill, *n.* a machine operated by the force of the wind turning a group of vanes or blades mounted on a shaft. The windmill has been widely used to pump water on farms.

windpipe, a common term for **trachea.**

windbreak, *n.* a line of shrubs or trees planted on a relatively treeless plain to break the force of the wind and prevent it from carrying away topsoil; any other material, such as a fence or long wall, used for the same purpose.

wind tunnel, a chamber used to test experimental aircraft and spacecraft. An airstream of known force is directed through the chamber and the temperature, stresses, and air flow around the model are observed.

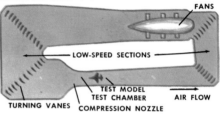

wing covert (KUHV-uhrt), the group of feathers covering the bases of the strong wing feathers on a bird; may have decorative coloring.

winter, *n.* in the Northern Hemisphere, the period of time between the winter solstice and the spring equinox (about December 21 to March 21).

wireless, *adj.* operating without wires, as a radio transmitter or radiotelegraph.

witch-hazel family, see **Rosales.**

wolfram, former name for **tungsten.**

wolframite (WUHL-fruh-myt), *n.* the chief source of commercial tungsten; a dark gray or brownish black mineral; formula, $(Fe \cdot Mn) WO_4$.

womb (WOOM), an alternate term for **uterus.**

wood, *n.* **1.** the hard material in the xylem, between the pith and vascular cambium of a tree. **2.** commonly, the hard material of a shrub or tree, whether growing or as lumber. **3.** a forest.

wood alcohol, alternate term for **methyl alcohol.**

woodpecker, see **Piciformes.**

wood-sorrel family, see **Geraniales.**

woofer (WUHF-uhr), *n.* a high-fidelity loudspeaker designed especially for reproducing low sounds; contrast with **tweeter.**

work, *n.* the result of a force acting in the same direction on a mass as the motion that produced it; both motion and force must be present for work to be done: Work = Force × Distance.

worker, *n.* any of the many unfertile bees, ants, etc., that do the work and feeding of a colony of social insects; see also **drone, queen.**

wound (WOOND), *n.* a break in the skin or internal tissue of the body either caused by accident or through surgery.

worm, *n.* any of the long, soft-bodied, adult animals without appendages (legs) or scales; sometimes incorrectly applied to the larvae of moths or butterflies; see **Nematoda, Platyhelminthes.**

XYZ

X, 1. a symbol used to indicate that something is experimental, as the X-15, an experimental aero-spacecraft. **2.** any unknown quantity.

xanthine (ZAN-theen), *n.* a white, amorphous base found in certain plant and animal tissues and which differs from uric acid only in the absence of oxygen at one position of the molecule; formula, $C_5H_4N_4O_2$.

xanthophyll (ZAN-thuh-fil), *n.* any of the yellow to orange pigments in the plastids of certain plant cells and associated wth carotenes.

X chromosome, a special chromosome that determines the sex of offspring in many species of animals; contained in half of the sperm cells and in all of the egg cells; in man, an X-Y chromosome combination produces a male; an X-X chromosome combination produces a female.

Xe, symbol for **xenon.**

xenon (ZEE-nahn), *n.* the rarest element in the noble gas family; colorless, odorless, and usually inert; used to fill flash lamps, arc lamps, X-ray counters, and ionization chambers; symbol Xe; *at. no.,* 54; *at. wt.,* 131.30; identified by Ramsay and Travers in 1898.

xenon tetrafluoride (ZEE-nahn tet-ruh-FLOO-uh-ryd), a compound of one atom of xenon and 4 of fluoride, existing in crystalline form that is stable at room temperature. The nature of the binding forces is not understood, since xenon is one of the inert gases and normally inert; obtained by heating a mixture of the 2 gases for one hour at 400° C and cooling to −78° C; one of the first compounds to be made from a rare gas.

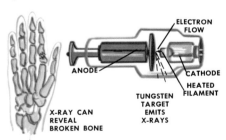

ELECTRON FLOW
ANODE
CATHODE
HEATED FILAMENT
TUNGSTEN TARGET EMITS X-RAYS
X-RAY CAN REVEAL BROKEN BONE

X-ray, *n.* an electromagnetic radiation of short wavelength (10^{-7} to 10^{-11} centimeters). X-rays are emitted whenever high-speed electrons strike a metal target; acts as light on photographic film; also called *Roentgen ray.*

xylem (ZY-luhm), *n.* a complex plant tissue consisting of various types of cells that conduct primarily water and dissolved mineral salts upward through stems, furnish support and, in woody plants, make up most of the woody tissue; see also **phloem, vascular bundle.**

LONGITUDINAL SECTION   MICROSCOPIC VIEW OF HARDWOOD

PIT

XYLEM VESSELS, OR TRACHEAL TUBES

MEMBRANE STOPPER

xylene (ZY-leen), *n.* a dimethyl benzene; a cleaning agent often used in histology; formula, $C_6H_4(CH_3)_2$; also called *xylol.*

Xyridales (zir-uh-DAY-leez), see **Farinales.**

Y, symbol for **yttrium.**

yam family, see **Liliales.**

yawn, *n.* an involuntary opening of the mouth with an accompanying inhalation and exhalation of breath; usually from fatigue.

yaws (YAWZ), *n.* a contagious tropical disease caused by spirochetes and characterized by raspberry-shaped skin lesions, pains in joints, and loss of weight and appetite.

Yb, symbol for **ytterbium.**

Y chromosome, a special chromosome that determines the sex of offspring in many animals; see **X chromosome.**

year, *n.* the period of time required for Earth to make one complete revolution around the sun; 365.25 days; see also **leap year.**

yeast, see **Ascomycetes.**

yellow fever, a tropical disease caused by a virus and characterized by jaundice, high fever, vomiting, and internal hemorrhage; the virus is transmitted by the bite of infected mosquitoes (genus *Aedes*); largely prevented by draining swampy areas where the mosquitoes breed.

yolk (YOHK), *n.* **1.** a part of the egg cell that provides food (minerals, proteins, fat, and water) for the developing embryo; varies in size and position depending on the animal. **2.** in bird eggs, the yellow substance as distinguished from the white (albumen).

ytterbium (ih-TUHR-bee-uhm), *n.* a soft, silvery-white, metallic chemical element in the lanthanide series; symbol Yb; *at. no.,* 70; *at. wt.,* 173.04; isolated by Urbain in 1907.

yttrium (IT-ree-uhm), *n.* a metallic chemical element with properties similar to lanthanide metals; used in alloys and to remove impurities from other metals; symbol Y; *at. no.,* 39; *at. wt.,* 88.905; identified by Gadolin in 1794.

zebra (ZEE-bruh), see **Perissodactyla.**

zenith (ZEE-nuhth), *n.* that point directly overhead at the end of an imaginary line going from the center of the earth through an observer; used in astronomical observations and celestial navigation; see **azimuth** picture.

zenith tube, an optical astronomical instrument pointed toward the observer's zenith, used to measure in precise terms time, position, and distance of stellar bodies.

zeolite (ZEE-uh-lyt), *n.* one of the hydrated double silicates of aluminum and a metal; sodium zeolite *(permutite)* is used in certain water softeners.

zeppelin (ZEP-uh-luhn), *n.* a rigid dirigible of the 1930's, designed by F. de Zeppelin.

zero gravity, a total lack of gravitational pull, producing the condition of weightlessness; see **gravity, weightlessness.**

zerophyte (ZEER-uh-fyt), *n.* a plant that grows in arid or dry areas such as a desert; adaptations for water storage or for protection against water loss are common.

zinc, *n.* a hard, gray-white, metallic chemical element; ductile, malleable, and corrosion-resistant; used to galvanize iron and steel, in alloys, and as a reducing agent; symbol Zn; *at. no.,* 30; *at. wt.,* 65.37; isolated by Marggraf in 1746.

zincite (ZIN-kyt), *n.* a red or yellow mineral ore of zinc; formula, ZnO; also called *red zinc ore.*

zinc ointment, a mild antiseptic ointment; astringent, protective, and sedative, it is used for inflammatory skin diseases and superficial wounds; may be either zinc oxide, zinc carbonate, or calomine, the native zinc carbonate.

zinc oxide, a powder which is yellow when hot but white when cold; almost insoluble in water; used as a nonpoisonous pigment in white paint, instead of white lead; formula, ZnO.

Zinjanthropus (zin-JAN-thruh-puhs), *n.* a fossil man discovered in Africa in 1959; lived about 600,000 years ago, and may be in the direct line of human ancestry; massive jaw gives him common name of *nutcracker man.*

zircon (ZUHR-kahn), *n.* a hard mineral silicate found in many colors and used as a semiprecious stone; hardness of 7½; formula, ZrSiO₄; also called *hyacinth* or *jargon.*

zirconium (zuhr-KOH-nee-uhm), *n.* a soft, strong, silvery-white, metallic chemical element; ductile and corrosion-resistant; used in constructing nuclear reactors and in surgical equipment; symbol Zr; *at., no.,* 40; *at. wt.,* 91.22; isolated by Klaproth in 1789.

Zn, symbol for **zinc.**

zodiac (ZOH-dee-ak), *n.* an imaginary circular belt in the heavens extending about 8° on either side of the sun along the ecliptic plane; includes 12 constellations that surround the solar system; see **constellation.**

zodiacal light (zoh-DY-uh-kuhl), a luminous streak in the sky seen at dusk or early morning; caused by reflection from meteoric matter traveling around the sun.

zoo, *n.* a place where living animals are displayed for people to observe and study; often in a setting matching the natural habitat; name is actually short for *zoological garden.*

zooid (ZOH-oyd), *n.* **1.** a cell of a protozoan or algal colony, such as volvox. **2.** an individual in a colonial coelenterate. **3.** an individual produced asexually, as a hydra that formed by budding. **4.** any cell that appears to be an individual but is not, as a motile mature sperm cell.

zoology (zoh-AHL-uh-jee), *n.* the study of animal life; *zoologists* are concerned with the following areas: **morphology,** the study of the structures of animals; **physiology,** the study of the way parts of animals work; **embryology,** the study of the development of an individual from the fertilized egg to the adult form; **genetics,** the study of heredity and variations; **taxonomy,** the study of the classification of animals; **ecology,** the study of animals in relation to their environment; **zoogeography,** the study of animal distribution on the earth at any period; **paleontology,** the study of animal distribution on the earth over the geological ages; and **organic evolution,** the study of development of the species, as distinct from the individual. *adj.* **zoological.**

zoonosis (zoo-AHN-uh-sis), *n.* an animal disease that can be caught by man from the animal; parrot fever and cowpox are examples.

zoophyte (ZOH-uh-phyte), *n.* any animal that resembles a plant in appearance, as coral.

zoospore (ZOH-uh-spawr), *n.* a motile asexual spore or reproductive cell produced by certain algae and fungi; germinates into new plants.

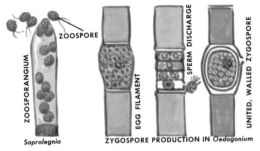

Saprolegnia   ZYGOSPORE PRODUCTION IN *Oedogonium*

Zr, symbol for **zirconium.**

zygospore (ZY-guh-spawr), *n.* a thick-walled, nonmotile spore or cell formed by the union of 2 similar reproductive cells produced by certain algae and fungi; a sexual type of reproduction.

zygote (ZY-goht, -gaht), *n.* a fertilized egg cell formed by the fusion of gametes, or male and female germ cells.

zymogen (ZY-muh-juhn), *n.* **1.** an inactive form of an enzyme, as pepsinogen and trypsinogen; activated by various agents but most often by co-enzymes which usually are vitamins. **2.** any of the bacteria that act as enzymes do.

HANDY REFERENCE TABLES

UNITS OF SIZE (Imperial or British System)

Linear (length or width)

12 inches (in.)	1 foot (ft.)
3 feet	1 yard (yd.)
6 feet	1 fathom
5½ yards	1 rod (rd.)
40 rods	1 furlong (fur.)
8 furlongs	1 statute mile (mi.)
1 nautical mile	1.1515 statute mile
3 miles	1 league (l.)

Square area (length and width)

144 square inches (sq. in.)	1 sq. ft.
9 sq. ft.	1 sq. yd.
30¼ sq. yd.	1 sq. rod
160 sq. rods	1 acre (A.)
640 acres	1 sq. mile
36 sq. miles	1 township

Cubic (length, width, height)

1728 cubic inches (cu. in.)	1 cu. ft.
27 cu. ft.	1 cu. yd.
128 cu. ft.	1 cord

UNITS OF WEIGHT

Avoirdupois (all products except precious stones, metals, drugs)

27¹¹/₃₂ grain (gr.)	1 dram (dr.)
16 drams	1 ounce (oz.)
16 ounces	1 pound (lb.)
100 pounds	1 hundredweight (cwt)
112 pounds	1 long hundredweight (l. cwt)
20 hundredweight	1 ton (tn.); 2000 pounds
20 long hundredweight	1 long ton (l. tn.); 2240 pounds

Troy (money, jewels, precious stones)

20 mites	1 grain
3.086 grains	1 carat
24 grains (gr.)	1 pennyweight (dwt)
20 pennyweights	1 ounce (oz.t.); 480 grains
12 troy ounces	1 pound (lb.t.); 240 pennyweights

Apothecaries' measure (dry drugs)

20 grains (gr.)	1 scruple
3 scruples	1 dram
8 drams	1 ounce; 24 scruples; 480 grains
12 ounces	1 pound

(fluid drugs)

60 minims	1 fluid dram
8 fluid drams	1 fluid ounce
16 fluid ounces	1 pint
8 pints	1 gallon

UNITS OF CAPACITY

Liquid measure

4 gills	1 pint
2 pints	1 quart
4 quarts	1 gallon
31½ gallons	1 barrel
2 barrels	1 hogshead

Dry measure

2 pints (pt.)	1 quart
8 quarts	1 peck
4 pecks	1 bushel
105 quarts	1 barrel

MECHANICAL UNITS

The basic units are those needed to set up a complete system of units; using these 3 basic units, any other unit can be defined. In scientific work, 2 such sets of basic units are used: the **mks**, or **meter-kilogram-second**, system and the older **cgs**, or **centimeter-gram-second**, system. The mks system is replacing the cgs system, although certain calculations are still done using cgs system units because the quantities are easier to handle.

mks system

meter = 1,650,763.73 wavelengths of the orange-red light from krypton-86.

kilogram = mass of the international kilogram, held at Paris, France.

second = 1/32,566,925.9747 of the tropical year 1900.

newton = the force which gives an acceleration of one meter per second per second to a mass of one kilogram.

joule = the work done (energy expended) in moving a mass of one kilogram with a constant force of one newton over a distance of one meter in the same direction that the force was applied; also called newton-meter.

cgs system

centimeter = one-hundredth of the standard meter, held at Paris, France.

gram = one-thousandth of the mass of the international kilogram.

second = 1/31,566,925.9747 of the tropical year 1900.

dyne = that force which gives an acceleration of one centimeter per second per second to a gram mass.

erg = the work done (energy expended) in moving a gram mass with a constant force of one dyne over a distance of one centimeter in the same distance that the force was applied. Also called gram-centimeter.

CONVERSION OF UNITS

Metric system into imperial system

centimeter	0.3937	inch
meter	39.37	inches (exactly)
square centimeter	.1549997	square inch
square meter	1.195985	square yards
hectare	2.47104	acres
cubic meter	1.3079428	cubic yards
liter	.264178	gallon
liter	1.05671	liquid quarts
liter	.908102	dry quart
hectoliter	2.83782	bushels
gram	15.432356	grains
kilogram	2.204622341	pounds, avoirdupois

Imperial system into metric system

inch	2.54005	centimeters
foot	30.4806	centimeters
yard	.9144018	meter
square inch	6.451626	sq. centimeters
square yard	.8361307	sq. meter
acre	.404687	hectare
cubic yard	.7645594	cubic meter
gallon	3.785332	liters
liquid quart	.946333	liter
dry quart	1.101198	liters
bushel	35.23833	liters
grain	.064798918	gram
pound, avoirdupois	.4535924277	kilogram

UNIT PREFIXES OF THE METRIC SYSTEM

Prefix	Symbol	Power of Ten	Multiple or submultiple
tera	T	10^{12}	1,000,000,000,000
giga	G	10^9	1,000,000,000
mega	M	10^6	1,000,000
kilo	k	10^3	1,000
hecto	h	10^2	100
deka	da	10	10
deci	d	10^{-1}	0.1
centi	c	10^{-2}	0.01
milli	m	10^{-3}	0.001
micro	μ	10^{-6}	0.000001
nano	n	10^{-9}	0.000000001
pico	p	10^{-12}	0.000000000001
femto	f	10^{-15}	0.000000000000001
atto	a	10^{-18}	0.000000000000000001

MKS MAGNETIC UNITS

Name	Unit	Equivalence	Explanation
energy	joule	(1 volt) x (1 coulomb)	Energy needed to move 1 coulomb of positive charge from a place where potential is $+V$ volts to a place where it is $+(V + 1)$ volts is 1 joule.
magnetic flux	weber	1 joule/ ampere turn	1 ampere flowing steadily through 1 loop of wire produces 1 weber when 1 joule of magnetic energy exists steadily due to this current.
magnetic induction	$\dfrac{weber}{meter^2}$		A magnetic flux of 1 weber passing through an area 1 square meter is 1 unit of magnetic induction.
magnetic field	$\dfrac{ampere\ turns}{meter}$		1 ampere flowing in 1 circular loop of wire of diameter 1 meter produces a magnetic field of 1 ampere turn/ meter at center of loop.
magnetomotive force	ampere turns		1 ampere flowing through 1 turn of wire produces 1 ampere turn of magnetomotive force.
reluctance	$\dfrac{ampere\ turns}{webers}$		1 ampere turn is required to produce a magnetic flux of 1 weber when a magnetic path has unit reluctance.
inductance	henry	$\dfrac{weber}{ampere}$	If 1 weber of magnetic flux caused by 1 ampere of current in 1 loop of wire links another loop, the inductance is 1 henry.

ELECTRICAL UNITS

coulomb: charge of 6.24×10^{24} electrons.

ampere: the current that transfers one coulomb of charge per second.

volt: the electrical pressure across a conductor carrying a current of one ampere and dissipating one watt a second.

ohm: the resistance of a conductor which carries a current of one ampere when a potential difference of one volt is impressed across it.

henry: the inductance of a conductor when one ampere flowing through the conductor induces an electromotive force of one volt in a direction that opposes the original current.

farad: the capacitance when a charge of one coulomb stored on the plates of a capacitor raise the potential difference across the plates by one volt.

watt: the power dissipated when one ampere of current flows through a device across which there is a potential difference of one volt.

NOTE: these are all the practical or absolute values.

UNITS OF LIGHT

Candle: A specified fraction of the average horizontal candle-power from a bank of 45 carbon filament lamps kept by the National Bureau of Standards.

Candle (new): 1/60 of the intensity of one square centimeter of a blackbody radiator at 2,046°K (the solidification temperature of platinum).

NOTE: With new interest in solar radiation and blackbody radiation, candle definition tends to be more and more the new candle, since this does not vary with time, age of lamps, etc.

lumen: the luminous flux emitted through a unit solid angle (steradian) from a uniform point source of one candle.

lux: one lumen per square meter.

phot: one lumen per square centimeter.

foot-candle: one lumen per square foot.

UNITS OF TIME

60 seconds	1 minute
60 minutes	1 hour
24 hours	1 day
7 days	1 week
14 days	1 fortnight
29½ days	1 lunar month
365 days, 5 hours, 48 minutes, 7 sec.	1 year
10 years	1 decade
100 years	1 century
1000 years	1 millenium

UNITS OF ARCS

60 seconds (″)	1 minute (′)
60 minutes	1 degree (°)
90 degrees	1 quadrant (quad)
4 quadrants	1 circle

UNITS OF ASTRONOMICAL DISTANCE

The astronomical unit—Distance from earth to sun
—149,501,201 kilometers
— 92,900,000 miles

The light second— 299,790 kilometers

The light-year—9.4614×10^{15} meters, which is approximately 6,000,000,000,000 miles

The parsec—the distance at which the annual parallax of a star would be 1 inch.
—3.258 light-years
—3.0838×10^{16} meters

RADIOLOGICAL UNITS

Quantity	Unit	Symbol
absorbed dose	rad	rad
absorbed dose rate	rad per second	rad/sec. or rad s^{-1}
activity	curie	c
dose equivalent	rem	rem
exposure	roentgen	R
exposure rate	roentgen per second	R/sec. or Rs^{-1}

ELEMENTS, THEIR PROPERTIES AND OCCURRENCE

Element	Symbol	Atomic Number	Atomic Weight	Specific Gravity (water 4°C=1)	Boiling Point (degrees C)	Principal Occurence in Earth
Actinium	Ac	89	227+			artificial; protactinium decay
Aluminum	Al	13	26.9815	2.702	2057	bauxite
Americium	Am	95	243+	11.7	1100	artificial; does not exist in nature
Antimony	Sb	51	121.75	6.684	1380	stibnite
Argon	Ar	18	39.948		−185.7	present in the atmosphere
Arsenic	As	33	74.9216	5.727	615	arsenopyrite, cobaltite, widespread traces
Astatine	At	85	210+			decay product
Barium	Ba	56	137.34	3.5	1140	barite
Berkelium	Bk	97	249			artificial
Beryllium	Be	4	9.0122	9.013	2970	beryl
Bismuth	Bi	83	208.980	9.80	1560	native ore, bismite (Bi_2O_3)
Boron	B	5	10.811	3.33	2550	borax, kermite ($Na_2B_4O_7 \cdot 4H_2O$)
Bromine	Br	35	79.909	2.928	58.78	seawater, numerous bromides
Cadmium	Cd	48	112.40	8.642	320.9	greenockite
Calcium	Ca	20	40.08	1.55	1240	calcite, fluorspar, apatite, etc.
Californium	Cf	98	251			artificial
Carbon	C	6	12.01115	2.25	4200	coal, atmosphere, petroleum, etc.
Cerium	Ce	58	140.12	6.90	1400	monazite sand
Cesium	Cs	55	132.905	1.873	670	carnallite, complex pollucite
Chlorine	Cl	17	35.453		−34.6	sodium chloride (salt)
Chromium	Cr	24	51.996	7.20	2200	chromite
Cobalt	Co	27	58.9332	8.9	2900	cobaltite, copper and sulfide ores
Copper	Cu	29	63.54	8.92	2336	chalcopyrite, bornite
Curium	Cm	96	247			artificial
Dysprosium	Dy	66	162.50	8.56	unknown	traces in rare-earth ores
Einsteinium	Es	99	254			artificial
Erbium	Er	68	167.26	9.16	unknown	gadolinite
Europium	Eu	63	151.96	5.24	unknown	monazite sand
Fermium	Fm	100	253			artificial
Fluorine	F	9	18.9984		−188	fluorspar, cryolite
Francium	Fr	87	223			decay product
Gadolinium	Gd	64	157.25	7.95	unknown	gadolinite
Gallium	Ga	31	69.72	5.904	1983	traces in bauxite
Germanium	Ge	32	72.59	5.35	2700	argyrodite
Gold	Au	79	196.967	19.3	2600	native metal, sylvanite ($AUAGTe_4$)
Hafnium	Hf	72	178.49	13.3	3200	traces in some rare-earth ores
Hahnium	Hn	105	260			artificial
Helium	He	2	4.0026		−268.9	natural gas; present in the atmosphere
Holmium	Ho	67	164.930	8.76	unknown	monazite sand, gadolinite
Hydrogen	H	1	1.00797		−252.8	everywhere, especially water
Indium	In	49	114.82	7.30	2000	traces in zinc blende
Iodine	I	53	126.9044			sea water, nitrate ores
Iridium	Ir	77	192.2			platinum ores
Iron	Fe	26	55.847	7.86	3000	hematite, siderite, magnetite, etc.
Krypton	Kr	36	83.80		−152.9	present in the atmosphere
Kurchatovium		104	260			artificial
Lanthanum	La	57	138.91	6.15	1800	monazite sand
Lawrencium	Lw	103	257			artificial
Lead	Pb	82	207.19	11.344	1620	galena; numerous ores
Lithium	Li	3	6.939	.534	1336	metoric rocks, tourmaline, lepidolite
Lutetium	Lu	71	174.97	9.74	unknown	traces in rare-earth ores
Magnesium	Mg	12	24.312	1.74	1107	magnesite, dolomite, serpentine, etc.

Element	Symbol	Atomic Number	Atomic Weight	Specific Gravity (water 4°C=1)	Boiling Point (degrees C)	Principal Occurrence in Earth
Manganese	Mn	25	54.9380	54.94	1900	manganese dioxide, manganese carbonate, numerous minerals
Mendelevium	Md	101	256			artificial
Mercury	Hg	80	200.59	13.55	356.58	mercuric sulfide (cinnabar)
Molybdenum	Mo	42	95.94	10.2	5560	molybdenite, wulfenite ($PbMoO_4$)
Neodymium	Nd	60	144.24	6.9	unknown	traces in rare-earth ores
Neon	Ne	10	20.183		−245.9	present in small quantities in the atmosphere
Neptunium	Np	93	237	19.5		artificial
Nickel	Ni	28	58.71	8.90	2900	iron ores, in recoverable amounts
Niobium	Nb	41	92.906	8.55	2900	columbite
Nitrogen	N	7	14.0067		182.96	everywhere, especially the atmosphere
Nobelium	No	102	254			artificial
Osmium	Os	76	190.2	22.48	75300	platinum and iridium ores
Oxygen	O	8	15.9994		182.96	everywhere, highly reactive, so occurs in most compounds
Palladium	Pd	46	106.4	11.40	2540	platinum and gold ores
Phosphorus	P	15	30.9738	1.82	280	apatite
Platinum	Pt	78	195.09	21.45	4300	native ores, sperrylite ($PtAs_2$)
Plutonium	Pu	94	242	19.82	3508	artificial
Polonium	Po	84	210			artificial
Potassium	K	19	39.102	.86	760	carnallite
Praseodymium	Pr	59	140.907	6.5	unknown	traces in rare-earth ores
Promethium	Pm	61	147			artificial, but may be detectable in uranium ores
Protactinium	Pa	91	231	15.37		usually artificial; occurs in some pitchblendes
Radium	Ra	88	226	5	1140	pitchblende, uraninite
Radon	Rn	86	222		−61.8	decay product of radium
Rhenium	Re	75	186.2	20.53	unknown	traces in molybdenum ores
Rhodium	Rh	45	102.905	12.4	72500	platinum ores
Rubidium	Rb	37	85.47	1.532	700	traces in rare-earth ores
Ruthenium	Ru	44	101.07	12.6	unknown	platinum ores
Samarium	Sm	62	150.35	6.93	unknown	traces in rare-earth ores
Scandium	Sc	21	44.956	2.5	2400	scandium-yttrium silicate
Selenium	Se	34	78.96	4.82	688	berzeliate (Cu_2Se), sulfur deposits
Silicon	Si	14	28.086	2.42	2600	about 28% of earth's crust, especially in quartz as silicon dioxide
Silver	Ag	47	107.870	10.5	1950	native ore, argentite, pyrargyrite
Sodium	Na	11	22.9898			sodium chloride (salt)
Strontium	Sr	38	87.62	2.6	1150	strontianite, celestite
Sulfur	S	16	32.064	2.07	444.6	native ore, purites, chalcopyrite, etc.
Tantalum	Ta	73	180.948	16.6	4100	tantalite
Technetium	Tc	43	99	11.49		some formed from neutron activity; usually artificial
Tellurium	Te	52	127.60			native metal, tellurides, tellurium ocher (TeO_2)
Terbium	Tb	65	158.924	8.33	unknown	small quantities in rare-earth ores
Thallium	Tl	81	204.37	302	1457	crookesite (CuTlAg)
Thorium	Th	90	232.038	11.2	73000	monazite sand; usually artificial
Thulium	Tm	69	168.934	9.35	unknown	traces in rare-earth ores
Tin	Sn	50	118.69	7.28	2270	cassiterite, stannite
Titanium	Ti	22	47.90	4.5	73000	ferrous titanate ($FeO \cdot TiO_2$)
Tungsten	W	74	183.85	19.3	5900	wolframite, scheelite
Uranium	U	92	238.03			pitchblende, carnotite
Vanadium	V	23	50.942			vanadinite, hematite, etc.
Xenon	Xe	54	131.30		−107	present in the atmosphere
Ytterbium	Yb	70	173.04	7.01	unknown	gadolinite, complex samarskite
Yttrium	Y	39	88.905	5.51	2500	gadolinite, fergusonite
Zinc	Zn	30	65.37	7.14	907	sphalerite, smithsonite, zinc oxide
Zirconium	Zr	40	91.22	6.4	72970	zircon, zirconia (ZrO_2)

217

ELEMENTARY ATOMIC PARTICLES

Particle and Charge	Mass	Symbol	Symbol of Anti-Particle	Duration (seconds)	Products of decay
Electron (negative)	1	e^-	e^+ (positron)	Infinite	—
Electron-neutrino (neutral)	0	ν_e	$\bar{\nu}_e$	Infinite	—
Gravitron (neutral)	0	—	—	Infinite	—
Meson					
Kaon (positive)	967.	K^+	$\bar{K}^+$	1.2×10^{-8}	π° and π^+
Kaon (neutral)	974.	K°	$\bar{K}^\circ$	1.0×10^{-10} & $6.\times10^{-8}$	π^+ and π^-
Muon	206.77	μ^-	μ^+	2.21×10^{-6}	electrons e-neutrinos & μ-anti-neutrinos
Muon neutrino (neutral)	Unknown	ν_μ	$\bar{\nu}_\mu$	Infinite	
Meson					
Pion (neutral)	264.	π°	π° (same)	1.9×10^{-16}	photons
Pion (positive)	273.2	π^+	π^-	2.5×10^{-8}	muon neutrino & anti-muon
Pion (negative)	273.2	π^-	π^+	2.5×10^{-8}	muon & anti-muon neutrino
Photon	0	γ (gamma ray)		Infinite	—
Heavy particles (baryons):					
Lambda baryon (neut.)	2182.8	Λ°	$\bar{\Lambda}^\circ$	2.52×10^{-10}	proton & neg. pion
Proton (nucleon) (positive)	1836.1	p	$\bar{p}$	Infinite	—
Neutron (nucleon) (neut.)		n	$\bar{n}$	1013.	electron, proton & anti-electron neutrino
Sigma baryons	2330.	Σ°	$\bar{\Sigma}^\circ$	?	photon & lambda particle
	2328.	Σ^+	$\bar{\Sigma}^+$	8×10^{-11}	neutron & π^+
	2340.	Σ^-	$\bar{\Sigma}^-$	1.5×10^{-10}	neutron & π^-
Xi baryons	2570.			$1.\times10^{-10}$	neutr. pion & lambda particle
	2580.			1.2×10^{-10}	neg. pion & lambda particle

Compiled from data of U.S. Atomic En. Comm., Argonne Nat'l Labs. and Univ. of California.

HOUSEHOLD AND WORKSHOP CHEMICALS

Name	Alternate or Chemical Names	Chemical Formula
Acetone	varnish solvent (flammable)	$CH_3CO\cdot CH_3$
Alum	potassium aluminum sulfate	$KAl(SO_4)_2\cdot 12H_2O$
Aqua regia	hydrochloric, nitric acids	$HCl + HNO_3$
Baking soda	sodium bicarbonate	$NaHCO_3$
Benzene	benzol	C_6H_6 (aromatic ring)
Benzine	hexane, pentane, heptane, etc.	C_nH_{2n+2}
Bitter almond oil	benzaldehyde	$C_6H_5\cdot CHO$
Bleaching powder	chloride of lime, calcium chloride-hypochlorite	$COCl_2$
Blue vitriol	copper sulfate, blue stone	$CuSO_4\cdot 5H_2O$
Boneblack	animal charcoal	C (carbon)
Calamine	zinc silicate	$(ZnO)_2\cdot SiO_2\cdot H_2O$
Calomel	mercury (-ous) chloride	HgCl
Camphor, synthetic	hydrochloride of pinene	$C_{10}H_{16}HCl$
Carbolic acid	phenol, hydroxy-benzene	C_6H_5OH
Caustic soda	lye, sodium hydroxide	NaOH
Chili saltpeter	Chili niter; sodium nitrate	$NaNO_3$
China clay	kaolin; aluminum silicate	$Al_2O_3\cdot 2(SiO_2\cdot H_2O)$
Chloride of lime	calcium hypochlorite	$CaOCl_2$
Cream of tartar	potassium acid tartrate	$KHC_4H_4O_6$
Dextrose	glucose, corn sugar, grape sugar	$C_6H_{12}O_6$
Epsom salts	magnesium sulfate	$MgSO_4\cdot 7 H_2O$
Formalin	40% solution of formaldehyde	H_2CO
French chalk	magnesium silicate	$Mg_3Si_4O_{11}+H_2O$
Gasoline	hexane, heptane, octane, etc.	C_6H_8, etc.
Glucose	see dextrose	
Glycerin	glycerol; trihydroxy-propanol	$C_3H_5(OH)_3$
Grain alcohol	ethyl alcohol, spirit of wine	C_2H_5OH
Hypo	sodium thiosulfate, fixing salt	$Na_2S_2O_3\cdot 5H_2O$
Iron oxide, red	ferric oxide; rouge	Fe_2O_3

Name	Alternate or Chemical Names	Chemical Formula
Lampblack	carbon; soot	C
Lime	calcium oxide (unslaked)	CaO
Lye	sodium hydroxide; caustic soda	NaOH
Methanol	wood alcohol	CH_3OH
Milk of magnesia	suspension of magnesium hydroxide	$Mg(OH)_2 + H_2O$
Milk sugar	lactose disaccharide	$C_{12}H_{22}O_{11}$
Muriatic acid	hydrochloric acid, spirit of salt	$HCl\cdot nH_2O$
Niter	potassium nitrate; Bengal saltpeter	KNO_3
Oil of vitriol	sulfuric acid, concentrated; oleum	H_2SO_4
Oil of winter-green, synth.	methyl salicylate	$CH_3CO_2C_6H_4OH$
Paris green	copper arsenite-acetate	$Cu(C_2H_3O_2)_2\cdot(CuAs_2O_4)_3$
Picric acid	trinitrophenol	$C_6H_2(NO_2)_3\cdot OH$
Plaster of Paris	calcium sulfate	$(CaSO_4)_2\cdot H_2O$
Potash	pearl ash, salt of tartar	K_2CO_3
Quicklime	anhydrous calcium oxide	CaO
Rectified spirit	approx. 95% ethyl alcohol	C_2H_5OH
Red lead	red lead oxide	Pb_3O_4
Rock salt	sodium chloride	NaCl
Rouge	ferric oxide, Indian red	Fe_2O_3
Saccharin	sulfimide of benzoic acid	$C_6H_4(CO)SO_2$—NH
Sal ammoniac	ammonium chloride	NH_4Cl
Slaked lime	calcium hydroxide	$Ca(OH)_2$
Soda	see baking & washing soda	
Sucaryl	sodium cyclohexane	$NaO\cdot C_6H_{11}$
T.S.P.	trisodium phosphate	$Na_5P_3O_{10}$
Tartar	potassium bi-tartrate	$KHC_4H_4O_6$
T.N.T.	trinitrotoluene	$(NO_2)_3C_6H_2CH_3$
Verdigris	copper acetate (basic)	$Cu(C_2H_3O_2)_2\cdot \frac{1}{2}CuO$
Washing soda	sodium carbonate; sal soda	$Na_2CO_3\cdot 10H_2O$
Water glass	10-30% sodium silicate solution	$Na_2O\cdot nSiO_2$ (n=2+)
White lead	lead carbonate (basic)	$PbCO_3\cdot \frac{1}{2}Pb(OH)_2$
Wood alcohol	wood spirit; methanol	CH_3OH

PLANETS OF OUR SOLAR SYSTEM

Planet	Symbol	Mean distance from sun (miles)	diameter (miles)	Period of revolution (Earth days)	Period of rotation*	Density (grams per cubic centimeter)	Surface gravity (Earth = 1)	Mass (Earth = 1)	Satellites—Diameter
MERCURY	☿	35,950,000	3,010	87.97	87.97d	5.3	.27	.053	none
VENUS	♀	67,180,000	7,600	224.70	14-30d?	4.95	.86	.815	none
EARTH	⊕	92,880,000	7,927	365.26	23h/56m/4.1s	5.52	1.00	1.000	moon—2,160
MARS	♂	141,520,000	4,200	686.98	24h/37m/22s	3.95	.39	.107	Phobos—10; Deimos—5
JUPITER	♃	483,320,000	88,700	4,332.59	9h/50m/30s	1.33	2.50	318.00	Io—2,020; Europa—1,790; Ganymede—3,120; Callisto—2,770; V—150; VI—100; VII—35; VIII—35; IX—17; X—15; XI—19; XII—14
SATURN	♄	889,880,000	75,100	10,759	10h/38m	0.69	1.12	95.22	Mimas—300; Enceladus—300; Tethys—700; Dione—700; Rhea—1,000; Titan—2,600; Hyperion—250; Iapetus—1,100; Phoebe—150
URANUS	♅	1,775,600,000	29,000	30,687	10h/49m	1.56	1.09?	14.55	Miranda—?; Ariel—300; Umbriel—250; Titania—600; Oberon—500
NEPTUNE	♆	2,797,200,000	28,000	60,184	15h/40m	2.27	1.12?	17.23	Nereid—180; Triton—2,240-3,000
PLUTO	♇	3,651,000,000	3,670	90,700	16h?	5?	.90?	.9	one

*d = days; h = hours; m = minutes; s = seconds

GREEK ALPHABET

Greek Letter	Pronunciation	Symbols Capital	Small	Equivalent	Example of Use
alpha	AL-fuh	A	α	a	Primary; first in position or importance
beta	BAY-tuh	B	β	b	Secondary; second in position
gamma	GAM-uh	Γ	γ	g	Third; unit of magnetic intensity
delta	DEL-tuh	Δ	δ	d	Shaped like a capital delta; increment (increase) in a variable
epsilon	EP-suh-lahn	E	ε	e	An arbitrary small amount
zeta	ZAY-tuh, ZEE-	Z	ζ	z	
eta	AY-tuh, EE-	H	η	e	
theta	THAY-tuh, THEE-	Θ	θ	th	
iota	ey-OH-tuh	I	ι	i	
kappa	KAP-uh	K	κ	k	
lambda	LAM-duh	Λ	λ	l	1/1000 of a cubic centimeter
mu	MYOO	M	μ	m	micro-; micron; amplification factor in an electron tube
nu	NYOO, NOO	N	ν	n	
xi	ZY, SY	Ξ	ξ	x	
omicron	OHM-uh-krahn	O	o	o	
pi	PY	Π	π	p	3.1416 (ratio of the circumference of a circle to its diameter)
rho	ROH	P	ρ	r	
sigma	SIG-muh	Σ	σ	s	millisecond; standard deviation
tau	TAW	T	τ	t	
upsilon	YOOP-suh-lahn	Υ	υ	u	
phi	FY, FEE	Φ	φ	ph	
chi	KY	X	χ	ch	
psi	SY	Ψ	ψ	ps	
omega	oh-MEE-guh, -MAY-	Ω	ω	oo	Last; in end position; angular velocity

REPRESENTATIVE MAMMALS OF THE WORLD

Common Name	Order	Native Habitat	Size (a) Weight (b)	Natural Food
Anteater—"Ant Bear"	Edentata	South America—swampy areas	a) 2 ft. high 8 ft. long b) 75 lbs.	termites, ants
Antelope (greater kudu)	Artiodactyla	Africa—brush or forest areas	a) male—5' high; female—smaller b) male—500-700 lbs., female—smaller	vegetation (cud-chewers)
Baboon	Primate	Africa, south of Sahara—open, rocky, hilly country. Ground-living.	a) size of large dog	insects, fish eggs, honey
Bat (Big Brown Bat)	Chiroptera	U.S. and Canada—open country, settlements, cities	a) 4½-5" long b) ½-¾ oz.	insects
Bear (Black Bear)	Carnivora	Canada, western U.S.—sea level to pine forest areas	a) 6' long 3' high b) about 300 lbs.	small mammals, fish, plants, berries
Beaver	Rodentia	most of U.S. and Canada—along waterways	a) 3-4½' long b) 70 or more lbs.	bark and outer layers of poplar and birch trees, willow bark, etc.
Bison (American buffalo)	Artiodactyla	western U.S. and Alaska on plain and prairie land	a) 10½-11' long 6' high b) male—1800 to 2000 lbs., female—800-1200 lbs.	grass and herbaceous plants
Camel	Artiodactyla	Egypt and Arabia—no longer found in wild state	a) 7' tall b) almost 3000 lbs.	grass, other vegetation
Chimpanzee	Primate	Equatorial Africa—tropical forests	a) up to 5' tall b) up to 150 lbs.	fruit and vegetation
Deer (White-tailed deer)	Artiodactyla	western U.S., coastal areas—forest areas near water	a) up to 4' high 6' long b) 50-300 lbs.	vegetation
Elephant (Indian)	Proboscidea	India—shady river valleys	a) up to 13' at shoulders b) over 6 tons	vegetation
Flying Lemur	Dermoptera	East India—forests	a) about 17" long	vegetation, fruit, insects
Fox (Red fox)	Carnivora	All of Canada and eastern U.S.—forest, prairie, and swampland	a) male 36" to 42" long b) 6-15 lbs.	small mammals, birds, carrion, fruit
Fur Seal	Pinnipedia	western U.S. and Canadian coastline—in ocean water	a) 4½' to 7' long b) male—400-700 lbs., female—75-125 lbs.	fish, squid, crustaceans
Giraffe	Artiodactyla	Africa south of Sahara—open brush country	a) 18' at top of head b) 1200-2000 lbs.	leaves and shoots of the Acacia tree
Gorilla	Primate	Africa—usually in forested plains areas	a) 5' tall, sometimes larger b) 400-600 lbs.	fruit and vegetation
Hippopotamus	Artiodactyla	Africa—lakes and rivers north of Zululand	a) 4½' high, up to 12' long b) up to 4 tons	aquatic reeds and grasses
Hyena	Carnivora	Africa—plains and edges of desert. Follows other animal herds.	a) male—5½' long, female larger b) up to 75 lbs.	carrion
Jack Rabbit	Lagomorpha	throughout U.S.	a) 19" to 26" long b) 4 to 12 lbs.	vegetation
Kangaroo	Marsupialia	Australia—plains land and desert edges	a) rabbit-size to 5' to 7' b) 10-200 lbs.	vegetation
Koala Bear	Marsupialia (subclass)	Australia—eucalyptus forests	a) less than 3' long b) up to 30 lbs.	eucalyptus and bluegum leaves
Lemur	Primate	Madagascar—in forest areas	a) some species 4' long, others 10"-17" b) variable	insects, fruit

Name of Group	Name of young (a) Name of male (b) Name of female (c)	Life Span	Gestation Period (a) Number of young (b)	Additional Information
adults solitary	a) b) No Names c)	over 14 years	a) unknown b) one	does not have constant body temperature; no teeth; mouth is a hole at end of long, tubular shaped head
herd or troop	a) calf, fawn b) bull, buck c) cow, doe	up to 11 years	a) 6-8 months b) one	horns vary in length from stubs to 60 inches; horns may be straight, coiled, lyre shaped, or grotesquely curved; swift, graceful runners
troup	a) batling b) no name c) no name	up to 9 years	a) about 6 months b) usually 1 or 2	active at night (nocturnal); hibernates in caves; reach adult size about 2 months after birth
colony	a) infant b) no name c) no name	up to 10 years	a) about 6 months b) one	troops are composed of male of overlord and 1-7 females; males fight for possession of females; any female attracted to another male is usually beaten to death by her overlord
sleuth	a) cub b) bear, he-bear c) sow, she-bear	12-15 years	a) 200-210 days b) usually 1 or 2	breed once every 2 years; hibernate in leaf-lined nests dug in ground or in caves
colony, lodge	a) kit, pup b) no name c) no name	up to 19 years in captivity	a) 3 months b) 1-6, usually 3 or 4	dam up streams to form small lakes; build nests (lodges) in middle of a lake; do not hibernate
herd	a) calf b) bull, ox c) cow	15 years, over 22 years in captivity	a) 9 months b) one	animal almost extinct, now heavily protected; once plentifully distributed in large herds all over U.S. plainsland
train, herd, drone, caravan	a) foal, calf, colt b) no name c) no name	about 40 years	a) 315-389 days b) one	can go up to 34 days without water; has 3-part stomach lined with water storage cells; dromedary has one hump, Bactrian Camel has 2 humps
often solitary troops of one male and several females	a) infant b) no name c) no name	up to 25 years	a) 9 months b) one	most intelligent of the apes; builds treehouses from vines and branches; moves from place to place as food becomes scarce
herd	a) fawn b) buck c) doe	up to 10 years, longer in captivity	a) 196 days b) one to 3	doe's first breeding season usually produces one offspring, following years 2 or 3 are born; females first breed when about 12 months old
herd	a) calf b) bull c) cow	50-67 years	a) 620-640 days b) one, 4-5 during lifetime	uses only 12 teeth at one time; if tooth is lost, one of the back teeth moves forward to replace it; carries food and water to mouth with trunk; eyesight is poor but has keen sense of smell
solitary	a) b) no names c)	unknown	a) unknown b) usually one, never more than 2	is not a lemur but an insectivore; active in the twilight hours; hangs by hind legs in trees during the day
skull	a) cub, kit, pup, whelp b) fox, stag, reynard c) vixen, bitch	up to 12 years in captivity	a) 49-55 days b) 1-10, usually 4 or 5	lives in long, underground burrows; breeds once a year; usually mates for life
trip, herd	a) pup, whelp b) bull c) cow	21-25 years	a) about one year b) one	bull controls herd of cows; first breed at about 4 years old; breeds only on the Pribilof Islands
herd	a) calf b) bull c) cow	up to 28 years in captivity	a) 14 to 15 months b) one	has very keen sight; herds of one male and 10-14 females common; can make sounds though vocal chords are underdeveloped
travel in groups of 2 or 3	a) infant b) none c) none	22-28 years in captivity	a) 9 months b) one	largest of the apes; usually walks on all fours; moves from place to place with food supply
herd, school	a) calf b) bull c) cow	up to 50 years	a) 8-9 months b) one	the hippo is related to the pig; skin pores secrete a pinkish oil to protect the skin, basis of legend that hippos sweat blood
solitary	a) puppies b) none c) none	25 years	a) three months b) 2-4 per litter	larger size of female an uncommon mammal characteristic; has a cry resembling the human laugh
solitary	a) kit, puss b) buck c) doe	probably no more than 3 years in the wild state	a) 41-47 days b) 1 to 6	is a hare rather than a rabbit; moves swiftly, sometimes leaps as high as 5 feet; young are born furred with eyes open
troop, herd, mob	a) Joey b) buck, boomer c) doe, flier	about 15 years	a) 30-40 days, in pouch 6 months b) usually one	small kangaroos are called wallabies; large kangaroos can travel 15-20 feet in one leap
solitary	a) cub, gum baby b) none c) none	up to 20 years	a) 35 days, in pouch 6 months b) one	look like small bears but are actually related to kangaroos and oppossums
troop	a) b) no names c)	unknown, though one specimen lived 25 years	a) black lemur—147 days, other lemurs —40 days b) one	some sleep through hot season (estivate); one group glides from tree to tree like "flying" squirrels

REPRESENTATIVE MAMMALS OF THE WORLD

Common Name	Order	Native Habitat	Size (a) Weight (b)	Natural Food
Lion	Carnivora	South Asia (rare), Africa south of Sahara in grassy plains	a) male—7′ plus 3′ tail, female smaller b) male—about 500 lbs., female—about 300 lbs.	antelope, zebra, small mammals
Mole	Insectivora	eastern ⅔ of U.S. in loose, well-drained field soil	a) 5½″ to 8″ long b) 1½ to 2 oz.	earthworms, insects, some plants
Mouse (House Mouse)	Rodentia	throughout U.S. and Canada in houses, building, and open fields	a) 6″ to 8″ long b) ½ to 1 oz.	paste, glue, soap, all foods —seeds and grain when outside
Oppossum	Marsupialia	eastern ⅔ of the U.S. on farmland near water	a) about size of housecat b) 4-14 lbs.	carrion, insects, snakes, frogs, vegetation, fruit, etc.
Orangutan	Primate	Borneo, Sumatra, in forest areas, tree-living	a) 4½′ tall, arm spread 7′ b) 150 to 200 lbs.	fruit
Polar Bear	Carnivora	Arctic seas	a) male—up to 9′ long, female smaller b) 1000 lbs. or more	seals, caribou, walrus cubs, fox, birds, shellfish
Porcupine	Rodentia	throughout Canada and western U.S. in pine and poplar woods	a) 25″ to 30″ long b) 8 to 15 lbs., occasionally larger	leaves, trees, flowers, and inner tree bark
Porpoise	Cetacea	warm ocean water, inshore waters, river mouths	a) 4′ to 6′ long b) 80-125 lbs.	fish, squid, some crustaceans
Rabbit (Cottontail)	Lagomorpha	western half of U.S. in field, brush, and swampland	a) 11″ to 17″ long b) 2 to 4 lbs.	bark, twigs, ground vegetation
Raccoon	Carnivora	throughout U.S. in swamps and woody areas near water	a) 25″ to 34″ long b) 12 to 16 lbs.	almost anything
Rat (Brown Rat)	Rodentia	throughout U.S. and western Canada in areas inhabited by man	a) 12½″ to 19″ b) 8 to 24 oz.	anything
Reindeer	Artiodactyla	northern Europe and Eurasia beyond the timberline	a) 5′ long, 3′ at shoulder b) male—300 lbs., female smaller	grasses, moss, and lichen
Rhinoceros	Perissodactyla	Africa south of the Sahara desert around lakes and swamps	a) 5′ at shoulder b) male—up to 3000 lbs., female smaller	vegetation, twigs, and bark
Skunk	Carnivora	throughout U.S. and Canada in open ground near forest-land	a) about size of housecat b) male—4 to 10 lbs., female is smaller	small mammals, beetles, other insects, vegetation
Squirrel (Red Squirrel)	Rodentia	eastern and western U.S. in pine forests, swamps, and hardwood areas	a) 19″ to 28″ long b) 1½ to 3 lbs.	nuts, berries, bark, fungi, young tree shoots
Tapir	Perissodactyla	Central and South America, Malayan area of Asia in swamps and near waterways	a) 6½′ long, 3″ tail b) up to 600 lbs.	water plants and forest foliage
Tiger	Carnivora	tropical Indian forests	a) 9′ long or more, ⅓ of length is tail b) 400 lbs.	deer, antelope, wild pigs, small mammals
Weasel	Carnivora	throughout U.S. almost anywhere except desert areas	a) 11½″-23″ long b) 12 to 16 lbs.	small mammals, birds, insects, earthworms
Whale (Blue Whale)	Cetacea	Pacific Coast of North America Nov. to May	a) 60′-90′ long b) 200,000 to 300,000 lbs.	microscopic plants and animals, small invertebrates
Whale (Sperm Whale)	Cetacea	Atlantic and Pacific coasts far offshore in open water	a) up to 80′ long b) over 80,000 lbs.	giant squid
Wolf (Gray Wolf)	Carnivora	throughout Canada and western U.S., southern U.S., on plains broken by canyons, ravines, woods	a) 26″-28″ high, 55″-66″ long b) 60-100 lbs.	deer, moose, caribou, small mammals
Yak	Artiodactyla	plateaus of Tibet	a) up to 6′ tall at shoulders b) up to 1200 lbs.	plateau grasses
Zebra	Perissodactyla	Africa in the eastern and southern open plains region	a) 4′2″ at shoulder b) 500 to 700 lbs.	grasses

Name of Group	Name of young (a) Name of male (b) Name of female (c)	Life Span	Gestation Period (a) Number of young (b)	Additional Information
pride	a) cub, whelp b) lion, tom c) lioness, she-lion	more than 25 years	a) 108 days b) 4 to 6 per litter	kill only for food, finishing one carcass before killing another animal; do not fight over food—group may share one carcass
solitary	a) b) no names c)	unknown, probably less than 4 years	a) unknown b) 2 to 5	has very poor eyesight but keen sense of smell; lives in deep tunnels lined with dry vegetation
solitary	a) b) no names c)	up to 6 years in captivity	a) 19 days b) 4-11, usually 5 to 7	extremely prolific—females breed when 40 days old and produce several litters each year
solitary	a) b) no names c)	less than 3 years	a) 12½ days b) 8 to 18, 7 usually surviving	young stay in pouch for 65 to 70 days; opossum frequently "plays dead" to avoid capture by its predators—a fright reaction
solitary	a) infant b) no name c) no name	25 years	a) 9 months b) one	can swing as far as 7 feet; second most intelligent ape; because of short body and long arms, leans on knuckles when erect
sleuth	a) cubs b) he-bear, boar c) she-bear, sow	up to 30 years in captivity	a) 9 months b) 1 to 4	have heavily haired feet for walking on ice; except for pregnant females, do not retreat to a den in the winter
solitary	a) porcupette b) boar c) sow	over 10 years in captivity	a) 7 months b) 1 to 4, usually 1 or 2	active at night (nocturnal); has long, barbed quills on back and sides, used for defense; can raise quills when frightened but cannot "shoot" them as is sometimes believed
school, shoal	a) cub b) no name c) no name	unknown	a) about one year b) one	young are born underwater; highly intelligent and as trainable as the primates
warren	a) kit, fawn b) buck c) doe	less than a year in wild state—up to 5 years in captivity	a) 28 days b) 4 to 5	very prolific—female breeds at 10 months, litters several times a year; makes fur-lined nests in burrows, earth cavities, and thickets
solitary	a) b) no names c)	around 7 years	a) 63 days b) 2 to 7, 4 common	wets food in water before eating it; is very fond of young corn, sometimes stripping whole fields of green ears
solitary	a) no name b) buck c) doe	around 3 years in captivity	a) 21 to 23 days b) 1 to 15, usually 7 to 9	prolific—female breeds at 4 months, produces several litters per year; destructive to man, consuming commercial grains and carrying numerous diseases
herd	a) calf, fawn b) bull, buck c) cow, doe	15 years	a) 230 to 246 days b) usually one	actually domestic caribou; only deer with antlers present on both males and females
crash	a) calf b) bull c) cow	up to 47 years in captivity	a) about 18 months b) usually one	has very poor eyesight; considered to be quite stupid
solitary	a) cub, kit, whelp b) boar c) sow	8 to 10 years in captivity	a) 63 days b) 4 to 7, usually 5	ejects an offensive spray for defense purposes
solitary	a) b) no names c)	6 years or longer in captivity	a) 45 days b) 1 to 6, usually 2 to 4	lives in tree hollows or nests lined with leaves; swift climbers
solitary	a) b) no names c)	up to 10 years	a) 390-395 days b) usually one	a hoofed mammal but is able to spread its toes
solitary or in family groups only	a) cub, kit, kittens b) tiger c) tigress	up to 25 years	a) 100 days b) 2 to 4 per litter	kills needlessly; tigers and lions have mated in captivity
solitary	a) b) no names c)	5 years in captivity	a) 220-327 days b) 4 to 9	active at night (nocturnal); kills needlessly; lives in the burrows of other animals
pod, herd, gam	a) calf, cub b) bull c) cow	about 20 years	a) about 1 year b) one	young born underwater; largest mammal ever known; baleen whale with small throat opening
pod, herd, gam	a) calf, cub b) bull c) cow	under 20 years	a) about one year b) one	young born underwater; toothed whale with large throat opening
pack	a) pups b) no name c) no name	10 to 18 years in captivity	a) 63 days b) 3 to 13, 6 to 7 average	lives in caves, holes, hollow logs; breeds once a year
herd, drone	a) calf b) bull, ox c) cow	about 30 years	a) 10 months b) one	used as beast of burden in Tibet; has very long hair covering eyes, feet, and ears
herd	a) colts, foals b) stallion, horse c) mare	up to 30 years	a) 11 to 13 months b) usually one	considered to be a white animal with black stripes

PLANTS AND THEIR USES

Lower Plants

Division	Plant	Part used	Use
Bryophyta	peat moss	whole	fuel, gardening, surgical dressing
Chlorophyta	marine algae	whole	puddings
Chrysophyta	diatoms	whole	scouring powder, explosives
Eumycophyta	mold	whole	cheese, plant & animal diseases
	mushroom	whole	food
	yeast	whole	leavening bread, alcoholic beverages
	truffles	whole	food
	morel	whole	food
	ergot	fruiting body	parasite on grasses
Phaeophyta	Irish moss	mucilage content	puddings
		colloidal content	baking, lotions, toothpaste
	kelp	whole	iodine, fertilizer, bleaching carbon
Rhodophyta	dulse	whole	food
	agar	mucilage content	used in making jellies, ice cream, medium for bacteria cultures, used in fish, siik & cosmetic industries
Schizomycophyta	helpful bacteria	whole	retting flax, curing tobacco, cheese products, nitrogen-fixing, etc.
	harmful bacteria	whole	scarlet fever, diphtheria, pneumonia, tuberculosis, spoilage of food, etc.
Tracheophyta	club moss	whole	house plants, used in tracer bullets & fireworks
	horsetails	whole	polishing agent
	fern	whole	house plant

Higher Plants/Cereal Grains

Plants	Parts	Use
barley	1 seeded fruit	cereal, flour, soups, stock feed
	whole	hay, nurse and smother crop
	sprouts	malt for alcoholic beverages
	stems & leaves	straw for bedding
buckwheat	whole	fertilizer or cover crop
	stems & leaves	straw for bedding
	whole grain	middlings for livestock
	endosperm	starchy flour
	flower	honey
corn	parts of seed	making artificial flowers, corn cake for stock food, cereal, paint, cooking, rubber substitute
	endosperm	starch, gluten, glucose syrup, grape sugar, artificial gums, mfg. of alcohol
	whole	silage, forage crop
	pith	explosives, packing material
	corn cob	tobacco pipes, charcoal
	stalks	coarse paper
	husks	stuffing for mattresses, cigarette paper
	embryo	corn oil
millets	seed	human and stock food, flour
	stems and leaves	hay
	whole	silage, forage
oats	1 seeded fruit	cereal, poultry food
	whole	pasture
	stems, leaves	hay, green forage
rice	1 seeded fruit	human food, "saké," flour
	hulls	stock feed
	stems & leaves	mfg. paper, & objects of straw
rye	1 seeded fruit	flour, cereal, stock food, source of alcohol
	stems & leaves	stable bedding, packing material, mfg. of paper & straw articles
sorghum	whole	stock feed, hay, pasturage
	grain	human food, oil, starch
	stems	mfg. brushes, building material, paper, syrup
	leaves	mats, fodder
	roots	fuel
sugar cane	stem	sugar, molasses, alcoholic beverages, stock feed, fertilizer, fuel, paper, wax
wheat	pericarp & seed coat	bran
	stems & leaves	silage, stuffing, straw hats, thatching, manure
	seed	flour, macaroni, spaghetti, cereal, alcoholic beverages
	endosperm	starch, sizing

PLANTS AND THEIR USES

Higher Plants/Medicinal Plants

Drug	Plant Part	Used For
aconite	herb root	for pain killer and fever reducer
agar	algae	to prevent constipation
aloe	herb leaves	glucosides used in purgatives, also treatment of burns
aureomycin	fungi	antibiotic
bay rum	tree leaves	used for skin irritation
belladonna	herb leaves and roots	used as pain killer, atropine for pupil dilation
camphor	tree leaves	colds, liniments
cascara	tree bark	laxative, tonic
chaulmoogra oil	seeds, tree	treatment of leprosy
chloromycetin	fungi	antibiotic
cocaine	shrub leaves	tonic, local anesthetic
colchicine	herb root	for treating rheumatism
croton oil	tree seeds	used as purgative
cubebs	vine fruit	treating catarrh, kidney stimulant
curare	tree bark, roots, stems	sedative, relaxes spastic conditions, used on shock victims
digitalis	herb leaves	digitoxin as a heart stimulant
dryopteris	fern	expel tapeworm
ephedrine	shrub, whole plant	treating various respiratory disorders
ergot	fungi	increase blood pressure
eucalyptus	tree leaves	oil used for fevers and throat inflammation
gentian	herb rhizome	glucoside used in tonics
goldenseal	herb rhizome	alkaloids for treating inflammation, tonic
henbane	herb leaves & flowers	sedative, used in hypnosis
hops	herb flower	poultices, tonic, sedative
ipecac	shrub roots & rhizome	drug used as cathartic
Jimson weed	herb leaves & flowers	alkaloids to treat asthma, belladonna substitute
licorice	herb root	flavoring for candy & tobacco, medicine
Lily of the Valley	herb root	cardiac stimulant
neomycin	fungi	antibiotics
nux vomica	tree seeds	tonic, stimulant
opium	herb fruit	contains morphine, pain killer
penicillin	fungi	antibiotic
psyllium	herb seed	laxative
quaiacum	tree stem	resin, laxative, stimulant
quassia	tree stem	insecticide, tonic, treating malaria
quinine	tree bark	treatment of malaria, antiseptic, tonic
stramonium	herb leaves & flowers	treating rheumatism and colds
streptomycin	fungi	antibiotics
strophanthus	woody climber seed	able to be changed into cortisone
strychnine	tree seeds	treating paralysis and nervous disorders
squills	sea plant bulb	human stimulant, also rat poison
terramycin	fungi	antibiotics
witch hazel	parts whole tree	tannin used to quell bleeding, astringent
wormseed	herb seed	used for infection by hookworm

PLANTS AND THEIR USES

Higher Plants/Vegetable Sources

Roots	Stems	Leaves	Flower	Fruit
beet	artichoke	cabbage	broccoli	beans
carrot	asparagus	celery	cauliflower	bread fruit
cassava	dasheen	chard		chayote
oyster	hops	collard		corn
plant	kohlrabi	endive		cucumber
parsnip	taros	kale		egg plant
radish	white pot.	lettuce		okra
rutabaga		onion		peas
sweet pot.		rhubarb		pepper
turnip		spinach		pumpkin
yam				squash
				tomato

Higher Plants/Spices and Flavorings

Name	Plant Part	Name	Plant Part
allspice	tree unripe fruit	mace	covering of nutmeg seeds
angelica	whole plant	marjoram	herb leaves
balm	herb leaves	mustard	herb seeds
basil	herb leaves	nutmeg	tree seed
bay	tree leaves	paprika	herb fruit
black pepper	vine unripe fruit	parsley	herb leaves
capers	shrub flower buds	peppermint	herb leaves
caraway	herb seed, part fruit	red pepper	herb fruit
cardamon	herb seeds	saffron	crocus flower
cassia	tree bark, unripe fruit	sage	herb leaves
celery	herb seed, part fruit	sarsaparilla	vine root
chilis	herb fruit	sassafras	tree root bark
cinnamon	tree bark	savory	herb leaves
cloves	tree flower buds	sesame	herb seed
coriander	perennial seed, part fruit	spearmint	herb leaves
dill	herb seeds, part fruit	star anise	tree fruit
fennel	perennial seeds, part fruit	tarragon	herb leaves
galangal	herb rhizome	thyme	herb leaves
garlic	herb bulbs	turmeric	perennial rhizome
ginger	herb root	vanilla	orchid vine fruit
horse radish	herb root	white pepper	vine almost ripe fruit
juniper	tree fruit	wintergreen	tree bark

AN ILLUSTRATED DICTIONARY OF SCIENTISTS
—— PAST AND PRESENT——

Abbé, Cleveland, 1838–1916, U.S. meteorologist; established daily telegraphic weather forecasting; founded U.S. Weather Bureau.

Abel, John Jacob, 1857–1938, U.S. pharmacologist and physician; isolated the insulin crystal; isolated adrenalin.

Adams, John Couch, 1819–1892, British astronomer; discovered Neptune (independent of Leverrier) through mathematical calculation of perturbation in the orbit of Uranus.

Adrian, Edgar D., 1889–1977, British physiologist; Nobel Prize in Phys. & Med.—1932, with Sherrington, for work on neuron function.

Aepinus, Franz M. U., 1724–1802, German physicist; discovered the electric properties of tourmaline; improved the optical microscope.

Agassiz, J. Louis R., 1807–1873, Swiss-American naturalist; did basic research in paleontology, classification, and natural history; established the Harvard collection of comparative zoology.

Agricola, Georgius, 1494–1555, German mineralogist; wrote De Re Metallica, first definitive book on mining and metallurgy, removing metal study from alchemy.

Aitken, Robert Grant, 1864–1951, U.S. astronomer; researched double-star phenomena, discovered over 3,000 double stars.

Alder, Kurt, 1902–1958, German chemist; Nobel Prize in Chemistry—1950, with O. Diels, for synthesis of organic dienes (double-bonded compounds).

Alvarez, Luis Walter, 1911– , U.S. physicist; researched radar; developed ground-control approach landing system.

Ampère, André Marie, 1775–1836, French scientist; formulated Ampère's law of electrodynamics; invented astatic needle; the ampere, unit of intensity, is named for him.

Amundsen, Roald, 1872–1928, Norwegian explorer; determined position of north magnetic pole; first to reach the South Pole.

Anaxagoras, 500?–428 B.C., Greek philosopher; formulated the first atomic theory and the idea of order in the universe.

Anderson, Carl David, 1905– , U.S. physicist; Nobel Prize in Physics—1936, for the discovery of the positron.

Andrews, Roy Chapman, 1884–1960, U.S. naturalist; discovered the Gobi fossil fields; found skeleton of Baluchitherium, the largest land mammal known, and the first dinosaur eggs.

Archimedes, 287–212 B.C., Greek mathematician; formulated Archimedes' Principle of fluid displacement; invented the Archimedean screw.

Aristotle, 384–322 B.C., Greek philosopher; delivered some of the earliest lectures and treatises on natural science.

Arrhenius, Svante August, 1859–1927, Swedish chemist and physicist; Nobel Prize in Chemistry—1903, for theory of ion dissociation of electrolytes.

Aston, Francis William, 1877–1945, British physicist; Nobel Prize in Chemistry—1922, for proving existence of isotopes; invented mass spectrograph.

Audubon, John James, 1785–1851, U.S. ornithologist; researched and illustrated Birds of America, the first complete work on the subject.

Baer, Karl Ernst von, 1792–1876, Estonian naturalist and embryologist; discovered the human ovum; developed theory of phylogeny.

Baird, John Logie, 1888–1946, Scottish inventor; invented the televisor; made first successful demonstrations of black and white, color, and transatlantic television.

Banting, Sir Frederick G., 1891–1941, Canadian physician; Nobel Prize in Phys. & Med. —1923, with Macleod, for discovery of insulin.

Bárány, Robert, 1876–1936, Austrian physician; Nobel Prize in Phys. & Med.—1914, for work on the equilibrium organs of the inner ear.

Bardeen, John, 1908– , U.S. physicist; Nobel Prize in Physics—1956, with Brattain and Shockley, for invention of the transistor.

Barkla, Charles G., 1877–1944, British physicist; Nobel Prize in Physics—1917, for studies on the diffusion of light and X radiation from elements.

Barnard, Edward E., 1857–1923, U.S. astronomer; discovered the 5th satellite of Jupiter; did basic research on nebulae and novae.

Bayliss, Sir William M., 1860–1924, British biochemist; isolated secretin, an intestinal hormone; coined the word hormone.

Beadle, George Wells, 1903– , U.S. geneticist; Nobel Prize in Phys. & Med.—1958, with Tatum, for discovery that gene function in the cell determines enzyme synthesis.

Beaumont, William, 1785–1853, U.S. surgeon; did early research on digestion through study of a man with a hole in the stomach wall.

Becquerel, Antoine H., 1852–1908, French physicist; Nobel Prize in Physics—1903, with the Curies, for discovery of radioactivity.

Beebe, Charles W., 1877–1962, U.S. naturalist; investigated the land and water animals of tropical countries; studied marine life by descending into the ocean in a bathysphere.

Békésy, Georg von, 1899–1972, Hungarian-American physiologist; Nobel Prize in Phys. & Med.—1961, for research on how the ear distinguishes sound; invented the audiometer.

Bell, Alexander Graham, 1847–1922, Scottish-American inventor; invented the telephone.

Bell, Sir Charles, 1774-1842, Scottish anatomist; discovered the difference between motor, sensory, and sensorimotor nerves.

Berliner, Emile, 1851–1929, German-American inventor; invented the telephone transmitter and the radio microphone.

Bernard, Claude

Bernard, Claude, 1813–1878, French physiologist; researched digestion and the function of the liver in storing glycogen.

Bernoulli, Daniel, 1700–1782, Swiss mathemativity of fluids; stated Bernoulli's Principle.

Berzelius, Jons Jakob, 1779–1848, Swedish chemist; discovered cerium, selenium, and thorium; isolated silicon and niobium; introduced present system of chemical symbols.

Best, Charles, 1899– , Canadian physiologist; with F. G. Banting, discovered insulin.

Black, Joseph, 1728–1799, Scottish chemist and physicist; defined latent and specific heat; discovered carbon dioxide; disproved phlogiston theory.

Blackett, Patrick M. S., 1897–1974, British

Brattain, Walter H., 1902– , U.S. physicist; Nobel Prize in Physics—1956, with Bardeen (see) and Shockley; discovered photo-effect of semiconductors, leading to transistors.

Braun, Karl Ferdinand, 1850–1918, German physicist; Nobel Prize in Physics—1909, with Marconi (see); invented the cathode-ray tube.

Braun, Wernher von, 1912–1973, German-American scientist; developed German rocketry; worked in U.S. attempts to establish interplanetary travel.

Bridgman, Percy Williams, 1882–1961, U.S. physicist; Nobel Prize in Physics—1946, for work on the physics of extremely high pressures.

Broglie, Louis V. de, 1892– , French physicist; Nobel Prize in Physics—1929, for discovery of the wave characteristics of electrons.

SIR FREDERICK BANTING   CHARLES BEEBE   LOUIS AGASSIZ   SIR CHARLES BELL   ALEXIS CARREL

physicist; Nobel Prize in Physics—1948, for the discovery of cosmic radiation phenomena.

Bloch, Felix, 1905– , U.S. physicist; Nobel Prize in Physics—1952, with E. M. Purcell, for work on magnetic resonance of atomic nuclei in solids, leading to measurements of nuclei.

Bode, Johann E., 1747–1826, German astronomer; discovered asteroids; catalogued over 17,000 stars.

Bohr, Niels H. D., 1885–1963, Danish physicist; Nobel Prize in Physics—1922, for study of atomic structure and radiations; adapted quantum theory to atomic structure; developed the Bohr Theory.

Bordet, Jules J. B. V., 1870–1961, Belgian bacteriologist; Nobel Prize in Phys. & Med.—1919, for work in immunology; discovered a reaction that is the basis of the Wassermann test for syphilis; found the whooping-cough bacillus.

Born, Max, 1882–1970, German physicist; Nobel Prize in Physics—1954, for work in cosmic radiation and quantum mechanics; conducted research on atomic structure.

Bothe, Walther W. G., 1891–1957, German physicist; Nobel Prize in Physics—1954, for work on cosmic rays and the *coincidence method* of counting minute time intervals in atomic phenomena; identifed the neutron.

Bovet, Daniel, 1907– , Swiss-Italian pharmacologist; Nobel Prize in Phys. & Med.—1957, for discovery of antihistamines; synthesized curare.

Boyle, Robert, 1627–1691, British chemist and physicist; invented the compressed-air pump; formulated Boyle's Law of gas volume and pressure.

Bragg, Sir William Henry, 1862–1942, and **Sir William Lawrence,** his son, 1890–1971, British physicists; shared Nobel Prize in Physics—1915, for study of crystal structures with X-rays.

Brahe, Tycho, 1546–1601, Danish astronomer; discovered the variations of the moon; located first new star seen in 1500 years; taught Kepler.

Bunsen, Robert W., 1811–1899, German chemist; with Kirchoff, discovered cesium and rubidium; invented the Bunsen laboratory burner.

Burbank, Luther, 1849–1926, U.S. horticulturist; developed and improved numerous varieties of potatoes, plums, tomatoes, corn, etc.

Burnet, Sir Frank MacFarlane, 1899– , Austrian virologist; Nobel Prize in Phys. & Med.—1960, with Medawar, for idea of successful tissue transplants by "acquired immunological tolerance"; proved by Medawar.

Calvin, Melvin, 1911– , U.S. chemist; Nobel Prize in Chemistry—1961, for studies in photosynthesis; traced chemical reactions of carbon-14 through a plant.

Cannizaro, Stanislao, 1826–1910, Italian chemist; discovered cyanamide; defined difference between atomic and molecular weights.

Carrel, Alexis, 1873–1944, French biologist; Nobel Prize in Phys. & Med.—1912, for work in surgery of blood vessels; demonstrated tissue survival outside an organ, important in new tissue transplants.

Carver, George Washington, 1864–1943, U.S. botanist; conducted research on industrial uses of the peanut.

Cavendish, Henry, 1731–1810, British chemist and physicist; determined the specific gravity of hydrogen and carbon dioxide; discovered the chemical makeup of water and nitric acid.

Celsius, Anders, 1701–1744, Swedish astronomer; first to describe a centigrade thermometer; published observations on the aurora borealis.

Cerenkov, Pavel A., 1904– , Russian physicist; Nobel Prize in Physics—1958, with Frank and Tamm, for discovery of *Cerenkov Effect:* light of charged particles moves faster than regular light moves through the same medium; devised detector to observe particle velocities.

Chadwick, Sir James, 1891–1974, British physicist; Nobel Prize in Physics—1935, for discovery of the neutron; British advisor on atomic bomb.

Chain, Ernst B., 1906–   , German-British biochemist; Nobel Prize in Phys. & Med.—1945, with Flory and Fleming (see).

Chamberlain, Owen, 1920–   , U.S. physicist; Nobel Prize in Physics—1959, with Segré, for discovery of the antiproton; researching neutron diffraction in liquids on alpha-particle decay.

Chamberlin, Thomas C., 1843–1928, U.S. geologist; formulated the planetesimal hypothesis to account for the origin of the earth; studied glacial deposits to determine past climates.

Charles, Jacques, 1746–1823, French physicist; studied the nature of gases; formulated Charles' Law of gas volume.

Cockcroft, Sir John D., 1897–1967, British physicist; Nobel Prize in Physics—1951, with Walton, for work on transmutation of elements by accelerating particles.

Cohn, Ferdinand J., 1828–1898, German botanist; proved that bacteria are plants founded the science of bacteriology.

Compton, Arthur H., 1892–1962, U.S. physicist; Nobel Prize in Physics—1927, for discovery of the Compton Effect on X-ray reflection from atoms; discovered the electrical nature of cosmic rays.

Coolidge, William D., 1873–1975, U.S. physical chemist; invented ductile tungsten filaments; developed the cathode-ray tube.

Copernicus, Nicolaus (Nicklas Koppernik), 1473–1543, Polish astronomer; regarded as the father of modern astronomy; established theory that Earth rotates daily on its axis and that the planets revolve around the sun.

Cori, Carl F., 1896–   , and his wife, **Gerty T.,** 1896–1957, Czech-American biochemists; shared Nobel Prize in Phys. & Med.—1947, for work on insulin; studied conversion of glycogen to lactic acid through enzyme reactions.

Coulomb, Charles A., 1736–1806, French physicist; demonstrated that the electrical charge is on the surface of the conductor; electrical unit, the *coulomb,* is named after him.

Cournand, André F., 1895–   , French-American physiologist; Nobel Prize in Phys. & Med.—1956, with Richards and Forssman, for catheterization of the heart; passed a flexible tube through a vein into the heart to study blood pressure and cardiac defects.

Crick, Francis H., 1916–   , British geneticist; Nobel Prize in Phys. & Med.—1962, with Watson (see) and Wilkins.

Cronstedt, Axel F., 1722–1765, Swedish chemist; discovered nickel; devised a mineral classification system based on chemical composition.

Crookes, Sir William, 1832–1919, British physicist; discovered thallium; invented the radiometer and the Crookes Tube, a type of vacuum tube; produced artificial diamonds.

Curie, Marie Sklodowska, 1867–1934, Polish physicist and chemist; Nobel Prize in Physics—1903, with Pierre Curie and Becquerel, for discovery of radioactivity; Nobel Prize in Chemistry—1911, for discovery of radium and polonium; studied compounds and properties of uranium.

Curie, Pierre, 1859–1906, French chemist; Nobel Prize in Physics—1903, with Marie Curie and Becquerel, for discovery of radioactivity.

Cuvier, Georges L.C.F.D., 1769–1832, French naturalist; began the natural system of animal classification; studied fossil mammals and reptiles.

Dale, Sir Henry H., 1875–1968, British physiologist; Nobel Prize in Phys. & Med.—1936, with Loewi, for discovery of chemical transmission of nerve impulses.

Dalton, John, 1766-1844, British chemist and physicist; arranged an atomic weight table; discovered the law of multiple proportions; formulated Dalton's Law of Partial Pressure; studied color blindness.

Darwin, Charles R., 1809–1882, British naturalist; wrote *The Origin of the Species,* the theory of natural selection; formulated theory of evolution.

da Vinci, Leonardo, 1452–1519, Italian artist-inventor-architect-scientist; studied rock formation and weather, designed a canal system still in use today, and drew plans for machinery that was perfected centuries later.

Davisson, Clinton J., 1881–1958, U.S. physicist; Nobel Prize in Physics—1937, with G. Thomson, for discovery of diffraction of electrons by crystals.

Davy, Sir Humphry, 1778–1829, British chemist; isolated potassium, sodium and calcium by electrolysis; demonstrated that chlorine is an element; discovered that diamond is carbon; theorized that hydrogen gives the acid character to acids.

Debierne, André L., 1874–1949, French chemist; discovered actinium; working with Marie Curie, isolated radium.

Debye, Peter J. W., 1884–1966, Dutch-American physio-chemist; Nobel Prize in Chemistry—1936, for study of molecular structure through study of dipole moments; researched X-ray diffraction.

De Forest, Lee, 1873–1961, U.S. inventor; designed over 300 devices for use in telegraphy, television, radio, and motion pictures.

Democritus, 470–370 B.C., Greek philosopher; formulated first atomic theory acknowledging atoms as indestructible and the basis of matter; defined *vacuum.*

de Vries, Hugo, 1848–1935, Dutch botanist; founded study of evolution by experiment; confirmed Mendel's Heredity Laws.

Diels, Otto P.H., 1876–1954, German organic chemist; Nobel Prize in Chemistry—1950, with K. Alder (see).

Dirac, Paul A. M., 1902–   , British physicist; Nobel Prize in Physics—1933, with Schrödinger, for revised atomic theory, stating the theory of the spinning electron.

Domagk, Gerhard, 1895–1964, German chemist; Nobel Prize in Phys. & Med.—1939, discovered prontosil, forerunner of sulphanilamide.

Dulong, Pierre L.

Dulong, Pierre L., 1785–1838, French chemist and physicist; formulated the Dulong-Petit Law: the specific heat of an element, multiplied by its atomic weight, is the same for all solid elements; discovered carbon trichloride.

Eccles, Sir John C., 1903– , Australian physiologist; Nobel Prize in Phys. & Med.—1963, for work on basic electrochemical transmission of nerve impulses.

Edison, Thomas Alva, 1847–1931, U.S. inventor; held over 1,000 patents, majority for telegraphic and electrical devices; invented the incandescent electric lamp, the phonograph, the talking motion picture, and the printing telegraph.

Ehricke, Krafft, 1917– , German-American aeronautical engineer; directed development of the Centaur rocket program.

Ehrlich, Paul, 1854–1915, German bacteriologist; Nobel Prize in Phys. & Med.—1908, with Metchnikoff, for work on germicidal dye compounds and a chemical explanation of immunity; discovered the first effective drug for syphilis; researched in immunology and chemotherapy.

Eijkman, Christiaan, 1858–1930, Dutch hygienist; Nobel Prize in Phys. & Med.—1929, for producing a deficiency disease in chickens leading to the discovery of the B vitamins.

Einstein, Albert, 1879–1955, German-Ameri-

Fermi, Enrico, 1901–1954, Italian physicist; Nobel Prize in Physics—1938, for discovery of transuranium elements; achieved the first controlled nuclear chain reaction; conducted research on atomic structure.

Fibiger, Johannes A.G., 1867–1928, Danish pathologist; Nobel Prize in Phys. & Med.—1926, for discovery of a cancer-causing parasite; first to produce cancer experimentally in rats.

Fischer, Emil, 1852–1919, German chemist; Nobel Prize in Chemistry—1902, for synthesis of purine derivatives, peptides, and sugars.

Fischer, Hans, 1881–1945, German chemist; Nobel Prize in Chemistry—1930, for studies of leaf and blood coloration; synthesized hemin, a crystalline form of the pigment portion of hemoglobin.

Fleming, Sir Alexander, 1881–1955, British bacteriologist; Nobel Prize in Phys. & Med.—1945, with Florey and Chain, for discovery and development of penicillin.

Fleming, Sir John A., 1849–1945, British electrical engineer; invented the electron tube; did work on telephony, telegraphy, and electronics.

Florey, Sir Howard W., 1898–1968, British pathologist; Nobel Prize in Phys. & Med.—1945, with Fleming (see) and Chain.

Flory, Paul, 1910– , U.S. chemist; Nobel Prize in Chemistry—1974, for his study of polymers and the temperatures that determine the length of their molecular chain.

MADAME CURIE   CHARLES DARWIN   PAUL EHRLICH   ALBERT EINSTEIN   ENRICO FERMI

can physicist; Nobel Prize in Physics—1921, for contributions to mathematical physics and statement of the law of the photoelectric effect; developed the theory of relativity and the unified field theory; formulated Brownian movement; described influence of gravity in light propagation and originated the law of photoelectric effect and the electromagnetic laws.

Enders, John F., 1897– , U.S. microbiologist; Nobel Prize in Phys. & Med.—1954, with Weller and Robbins, for development of a process to grow polio virus in tissue culture; research on measles vaccine.

Erlanger, Joseph, 1874–1965, U.S. physiologist; Nobel Prize in Phys. & Med.—1944, with Gasser, for work on nerve fibers and fiber reaction to stimuli.

Fabre, Jean H., 1823–1915, French entomologist; studied insects by direct observation; studied Coleoptera, Hymenoptera, and Orthoptera.

Faraday, Michael, 1791–1867, British chemist and physicist; discovered how to generate electricity by means of magnetism; invented the transformer; discovered benzene.

Forbes, Edward, 1815–1854, British naturalist; founded the science of marine biology; started systemization of studies in natural history.

Forssman, Werner, 1904– , German physician; Nobel Prize in Phys. & Med.—1956, with Cournand (see) and Richards; catheterized own heart.

Foucault, Jean B. L., 1819–1868, French physicist; invented the Foucault prism, gyroscope, and Foucault pendulum; measured velocity of light in air.

Franck, A. James, 1882–1964, German-American physicist; Nobel Prize in Physics—1925, with Hertz (see).

Frank, Ilya, 1908– , Russian physicist; Nobel Prize in Physics—1958, with Cerenkov (see) and Tamm; working on electrons and gamma-ray conversion into electron-positron pairs.

Franklin, Benjamin, 1706–1790, American statesman-philosopher-scientist; in science, known for his experiments with electricity.

Fraunhofer, Joseph von, 1787–1826, German physicist; invented the achromatic microscope; devised a diffraction grating for studying the sun's spectra; perfected technique for manufacturing large lenses, vital for accurate telescopes.

Freud, Sigmund, 1856–1939, Austrian physician; developed the method of treating mental illness called psychoanalysis.

Frisch, Karl von, 1886– , Austrian zoologist; Nobel Prize in Phys. & Med.—1973, with Lorenz and Tinbergen; studied insect behavior and sensory physiology.

Funk, Casimir, 1884–1967, Polish-American bio-chemist; discovered vitamins.

Gabor, Dennis, 1900– , Hungarian-born industrial scientist; Nobel Prize in Physics—1971, for developing the hologram.

Gajdusek, Daniel C., 1923– , U.S. physician; Nobel Prize in Medicine—1976, with Blumberg, for studies on the origin and spread of infectious diseases.

Galen, 2nd century A.D., Greek physician; wrote down all medical knowledge of his time; considered, for centuries, the most authoritative medical writer.

Galileo (Galileo Galilei), 1564–1642, Italian astronomer and physicist; improved the early telescope; advanced the Copernican theory of heavenly bodies based on observation; discovered that the acceleration of falling bodies increases proportionally to the time that they fall.

Galle, Johann G., 1812–1910, German astronomer; located Neptune after studying Leverrier's calculations predicting the location of the planet; discovered 3 comets.

Galton, Sir Francis, 1822–1911, British scientist; studied heredity; founded science of eugenics.

Galvani, Luigi, 1737–1798, Italian physiologist; originated research on the effect of electric shock on frog muscles later called *galvanism*.

Garwin, Richard L., 1928– , U.S. physicist; research in particle physics, liquefaction of helium, and superconductors.

Gasser, Herbert S., 1888–1963, U.S. physiologist; Nobel Prize in Phys. and Med.—1944, with Erlanger (see).

Gauss, Karl F., 1777–1855, German physicist; formulated the mathematical theory of electricity; the *gauss*, an electromagnetic unit, is named for him.

Giauque, William F., 1895– , U.S. chemist; Nobel Prize in Chemistry—1949, for study of reactions to extreme cold; discovered oxygen isotopes and developed the demagnetization method of temperature reduction.

Giffard, Henri, 1825–1882, French engineer; invented the steam boiler injector; built a steam propulsion engine for lighter-than- air craft.

Glaser, Donald A., 1926– , U.S. physicist; Nobel Prize in Physics—1960, for the invention of the bubble chamber.

Goddard, Robert H., 1882–1945, U.S. scientist; conducted basic rocketry experiments; developed rocket-propulsion foundation of modern rocketry.

Goldschmidt, Victor M., 1888–1947, Norwegian geochemist; helped establish the field of geochemistry; studied the crystal structures of many elements with spectroscopy.

Golgi, Camillo, 1844–1926, Italian physician; Nobel Prize in Phys. & Med.—1906, with Ramon y Cajal, for nerve tissue studies; proved theory of nerve mixing; discovered 3 types of malarial parasites.

Gray, Asa, 1810–1888, American botanist; investigated botanical structure and did basic classification of North American fauna.

Gullstrand, Allvar, 1862–1930, Swedish opthalmologist; Nobel Prize in Phys. & Med.—1911, for work on light refraction by the eye and other lenses; formulated theory of optical images.

Haber, Fritz, 1868–1934, German chemist; Nobel Prize in Chemistry—1918, for invention of a process to produce ammonia from atmospheric nitrogen.

Haeckel, Ernst H., 1834–1919, German biologist; developed biogenetic law that the individual animal passes through the phases of the species' evolution during its development, often stated: "ontogeny recapitulates phylogeny."

Hahn, Otto, 1879–1968, German physicist and chemist; Nobel Prize in Chemistry—1944, for work on atomic fission; discovered mesothorium and protactinium; demonstrated, with Meitner, that the uranium-neutron reaction produced barium and krypton.

Haldane, John S., 1860–1936, British physiologist; discovered that carbon dioxide tension in the brain determines breathing mechanism.

Hale, George E., 1868–1938, U.S. astronomer and astrophysicist; discovered magnetic fields in sun spots; helped design and build large telescopes for use in astronomical observatories.

Halley, Edmund, 1656–1742, British astronomer; accurately cataloged the stars in the Southern Hemisphere; a comet named after him appears every 72 years.

Hallwachs, Wilhelm, 1859–1922, German physicist; discovered principle of the photoelectric cell.

Harvey, William, 1578–1657, British physician; studied circulation of the blood; formulated first accurate theory of blood circulation.

Haworth, Sir Walter N., 1883–1950, British chemist; Nobel Prize in Chemistry—1937, for research on carbohydrates and vitamin C; synthesized ascorbic acid.

Heisenberg, Werner, 1901–1976, German physicist; Nobel Prize in Physics—1932, for investigation of quantum mechanics; developed the principle of indeterminacy in quantum mechanics.

Helmholtz, Hermann F. von, 1821–1894, German physicist; developed principle of the conservation of energy; invented the ophthalmoscope; determined the velocity of nerve impulses.

Helmont, Jan B. van, 1577–1644, Flemish physician and chemist; coined the word *gas*; discovered gases were separate from air; studied digestion; did classic experiment in plant metabolism.

Hench, Phillip S., 1896–1965, U.S. physician; Nobel Prize in Phys. & Med.—1950, with Kendall (see) and Reichstein.

Henle, Friedrich G. J.

Henle, Friedrich G. J., 1809–1885, German pathologist and anatomist; investigated structure of the kidneys, lacteal vessels, and central nervous system; recognized pathology as a science; *loop of Henle* in the nephron is named for him.

Henry, Joseph, 1797–1878, U.S. physicist; invented low and high resistance galvanometers; developed the electromagnet; discovered the principle of the electromagnetic telegraph; developed method of producing induced current; the *henry* unit is named for him.

Herschel, William, 1738–1822, and his sister, **Caroline,** 1750–1848, German-British astronomers; discovered Uranus, 2 moons of Uranus, the sixth moon of Saturn, and the seventh moon of Saturn; determined Saturn's period of rotation; discovered the motion of binary stars; founded sidereal astronomy.

Hertz, Gustav, 1887–1975, German; Nobel Prize in Physics—1925, with Franck, for formulation of the laws of collision between electrons and atoms, verifying Planck's quantum theory.

Hertz, Heinrich, 1857–1894, German physicist; demonstrated the existence of electromagnetic waves predicted by Maxwell; proved that electromagnetic waves move as rapidly as light waves.

Hess, Victor F., 1883–1964, Austrian physicist; Nobel Prize in Physics—1936, with C. Anderson, for the discovery of cosmic rays.

Hevesy, Georg von, 1885–1966, Hungarian chemist; Nobel Prize in Chemistry—1943, for work with isotopes as indicators in chemical reactions, replacing the stable elements; discovered the element hafnium, with Coster.

Heymans, Corneille, 1892– , Belgian physiologist; Nobel Prize in Phys. & Med.—1938, for work on respiration regulation by the aortic and carotid sinuses.

Hill, Archibald V., 1886– , British physiologist; Nobel Prize in Phys. & Med.—1922, with Meyerhof, for research on heat production in muscles.

Hinshelwood, Sir Cyril N., 1897–1968, British chemist; Nobel Prize in Chemistry—1956, with Semenov, for work on chemical chain reactions; theorized that bacteria acquire resistance to drugs through change in the bacterial cell's enzyme patterns.

Hipparchus, 160?-125? B.C., Greek astronomer; developed trigonometry; predicted the equinoxes and devised method of locating geographical position through use of longitude and latitude.

Hippocrates, 460?–337? B.C., Greek physician; originated code of medical ethics now known as the *Hippocratic Oath.*

Hodgkin, Alan L., 1914– , British physiologist; Nobel Prize in Phys. & Med.—1963, with A. Huxley (see).

Hoff, Jacobus H. van't, 1852–1911, Dutch physical chemist; Nobel Prize in Chemistry—1901, for formulating the laws of chemical dynamics and osmotic pressure.

Hofstadter, Robert, 1915– , U.S. physicist; Nobel Prize in Physics—1961, for work on the principles of elasticity, and the kinetic hypoth-e-sis of gases.

Hooke, Robert, 1635–1703, British chemical philosopher; explained the true nature of combustion; located Earth's and the moon's centers of gravity; developed first Gregorian telescope; worked on theories concerning Jupiter's rotation, the principles of elasticity, and the kinetic hypothesis of gases.

Hopkins, Sir Frederick G., 1861–1947, British biochemist; Nobel Prize in Phys. & Med.—1929, for discovery of the growth vitamins; isolated an essential amino acid and discovered the connection between muscular contraction and lactic acid.

Houssay, Bernardo A., 1887–1971, Argentine physiologist; Nobel Prize in Phys. & Med.—1947, for study of the pancreas and pituitary glands and their hormones.

Hubble, Edwin P., 1889–1953, U.S. astronomer; discovered the expanding universe by proving the existence of galaxies beyond the sun's.

Huxley, Andrew F., 1917– , British neurologist; Nobel Prize in Phys. & Med.—1963, with Hodgkin, for research on the nature of nerve impulses; studied the chemical and physical reactions of nerve fiber.

Huxley, Thomas H., 1825–1895, British biologist; early advocate of Darwin's theory of evolution; wrote extensively on zoology and animal anatomy.

Huygens, Christian, 1629–1695, Dutch physicist and astronomer; developed the Huygens theory of light: particles can transmit a wave of motion without themselves being moved; discovered one of the moons of Saturn and one of Saturns' rings.

Jenner, Edward, 1749–1823, British physician; discovered the immunization vaccination, first used to control smallpox.

Joliot-Curie, Frederic, 1900–1958, and his wife **Irène,** 1897–1956, French physicists; shared Nobel Prize in Chemistry—1935, for synthesis of several radioactive elements.

Joule, James P., 1818–1889, British physicist; devised Joule's Law relating heat and electric current in a conductor; discovered several methods of determing the mechanical equivalence of heat.

Karrer, Paul, 1889–1971, Swiss chemist; Nobel Prize in Chemistry—1937, for study of vitamins A and B_2.

Kelvin, Lord (William Thomson), 1824–1907, British scientist; devised an absolute temperature scale; originated the 1st and 2nd laws of thermodynamics; conducted research for laying the Atlantic cable.

Kendell, Edward C., 1886–1972, U.S. biochemist; Nobel Prize in Phys. & Med.—1950, with Hench and Reichstein, for isolation of cortisone and ACTH; isolated thyroxin.

Kendrew, John C., 1917– , British physician; Nobel Prize in Chemistry—1962, with Perrutz (see).

Kepler, Johannes, 1571–1630, German astronomer; discovered the 3 laws of planetary motion; anticipated the law of refraction; performed mathematical investigations contributing to the development of calculus; completed Brahe's astronomical tables.

Kirchhoff, Gustav R., 1824–1887, German physicist; with Bunsen, devised the method of spectrum analysis which he used to discover cesium and rubidium.

Klaproth, Martin H., 1743–1817, German chemist; discovered cerium (independent of Berzelius), chromium (independent of Vauquelin), zirconium, and uranium.

Koch, Robert, 1843–1910, German bacteriologist; Nobel Prize in Phys. & Med.—1905, for discovery of the tubercle bacillus and tuberculin; isolated the anthrax bacillus.

Kornberg, Arthur, 1918–   , U.S. biochemist; Nobel Prize in Phys. & Med.—1959, with Ochoa, for making artificial nucleic acids.

Kossel, Albrecht, 1853–1927, German physiological chemist; Nobel Prize in Phys. & Med.—1910, for study of the cell's nuclear elements; investigated cell chemistry; discovered adenine and thymine.

Krebs, Sir Hans Adolf, 1900–   , British biochemist; Nobel Prize in Phys. & Med.—1953, with

Langley, Samuel, 1834–1906, U.S. aeronautical engineer; invented the bolometer; constructed the first heavier-than-air machines that flew, though his first manned craft failed.

Langmuir, Irving, 1881–1957, U.S. chemist; Nobel Prize in Chemistry—1932, for work on surface absorption of molecular film; discovered a method of cloud-seeding to produce artificial rainfall.

Laveran, Charles L. A., 1845–1922, French bacteriologist; Nobel Prize in Phys. & Med.—1907, for study of protozoan diseases; discovered the blood parasite causing malaria.

Lavoisier, Antoine L., 1743–1794, French chemist; named oxygen, developed theory of combustion; contributed to system of chemical nomenclature from which present system is derived.

Lawrence, Ernest O., 1901–1958, U.S. physicist; Nobel Prize in Physics—1939, for the invention of the cyclotron; produced artificial radioactivity; obtained transmutation of some elements; 103rd element, *lawrencium*, is named for him.

Le Châtelier, Henry L., 1850–1936, French chemist; formulated the law of chemical equilibrium.

Lederberg, Joshua, 1925–   , U.S. geneti-

ARCHIBALD HILL

ANDREW HUXLEY

ROBERT KOCH

ANTON VAN LEEUWENHOEK

CAROLUS LINNAEUS

Lipmann, for work on metabolism; discovered the citric-acid cycle of carbohydrate metabolism and metabolic catalysts.

Krogh, August, 1874–1949, Danish physiologist; Nobel Prize in Phys. & Med.—1920, for discovery of capillary functions.

Kusch, Polycarp, 1911–   , U.S. physicist; Nobel Prize in Physics—1955, for determining the magnetic moment of the electron and behavior of the hydrogen atom.

Laënnec, René T., 1781–1826, French physician; invented the stethoscope.

Lamarck, Jean B. P. A. M., 1744–1829, French naturalist; classified animals into vertebrates and invertebrates; proposed theory that animals adapt to their environment by changes in structure.

Lamb, Willis E., 1913–   , U.S. physicist; Nobel Prize in Physics—1955, worked on fine structure of the hydrogen spectrum.

Landau, Lev D., 1908–1968, Russian physicist; Nobel Prize in Physics—1962, for work in cryogenics, especially the superfluid behavior of helium.

Landsteiner, Karl, 1868–1943, Austrian-American pathologist; Nobel Prize in Phys. & Med.—1930, for discovery of the 4 blood types; identified the polio virus and transmitted it to monkeys.

cist; Nobel Prize in Phys. & Med.—1958, for work on gene recombination and the structure of genetic material in bacteria.

Lee, Tsung-Dao, 1926–   , Chinese-American physicist; Nobel Prize in Physics—1957, with Yang, for discovery of the violations of the law of parity, previously accepted as a basic law of nuclear behavior.

Leeuwenhoek, Anton van, 1632–1723, Dutch naturalist; built the first accurate microscopes; described the blood corpuscles, spermatozoa, plant stems, muscle fibers, and capillary action.

Levene, Phoebus A. T., 1869–1940, U.S. biochemist; purified vitamin B_2; discovered the structure of nucleic acids.

Leverrier, Urbain J., 1811–1877, French astronomer; predicted the discovery of Neptune by mathematical calculation based on the motion of Uranus, independent of J. C. Adams.

Lewis, Gilbert N., 1875–1946, U.S. chemist; investigated molecular electron pairs, revising theory of valence; isolated heavy hydrogen.

Libby, Willard F., 1908–   , U.S. chemist; Nobel Prize in Chemistry—1960, for discovery and use of carbon-14 in dating plant and animal remains.

Lilienthal, Otto, 1848–1896, German aeronautical engineer; built gliders using wing curvature similar to a bird's wing.

Linnaeus, Carolus

Linnaeus, Carolus (Carl von Linné), 1707-1778, Swedish naturalist; devised specific binomial names for plants (previously known only by common name), systematizing botanical science.

Lipmann, Fritz A., 1899– , U.S. biochemist; Nobel Prize in Phys. & Med.—1953, with Krebs (see).

Lipscomb, William N., Jr., 1919– , U.S. chemist; Nobel Prize in Chemistry—1976, for research on the three dimensional and electronic structures of boron hydrides.

Lister, Joseph, 1827–1912, British physician; founded aseptic surgery after studying Pasteur's work on fermentation; first physician to advocate cleanliness and disinfecting of instruments, greatly reducing surgical mortality.

Lockyer, Sir Joseph Norman, 1836-1920, British astronomer; explained sunspots by spectroscopic analysis; applied spectroscope to the stars; devised a theory of solar energy.

Loeb, Jacques, 1859–1924, German-American biologist; explained tropisms by demonstrating that plant tropisms and animal instincts are identical phenomena; experimented with artificial parthenogenesis, using solutions for sperm.

Loewi, Otto, 1873–1961, German-American pharmacologist; Nobel Prize in Phys. & Med.—1936, with Dale (see).

Lorenz, Konrad, 1909– , Austrian ethologist and zoologist; Nobel Prize in Phys. & Med.—

trace the course of blood through the human body; studied insect anatomy.

Marconi, Guglielmo, 1874–1937, Italian electrical engineer; Nobel Prize in Physics—1909, with Braun, for inventing the wireless telegraph.

Marignac, Jean C. G., 1817–1894, Swiss chemist; discovered ytterbium and gadolinium; determined the atomic weights of many elements.

Maury, Matthew F., 1806–1873, U.S. oceanographer; studied ocean currents and winds; charted the Atlantic floor to illustrate the practicability of a transatlantic cable.

Maxwell, James Clerk, 1831–1879, Scottish physicist; worked on theory of electromagnetism, explaining magnetic phenomena as the result of local strains and motions in a material medium; researched kinetic theory of gases and color perception.

Mayer, Maria Goeppert, 1906–1972, German-American physicist; Nobel Prize in Physics—1963, with J. H. D. Jensen of Germany, for theory of shell arrangement of neutrons, somewhat similar to electron shells; second woman to win physics prize.

Medawar, Peter B., 1915– , British zoologist; Nobel Prize in Phys. & Med.—1960, with M. Burnet (see); proved Burnet's theory.

Meitner, Lise, 1878–1968, Austrian-American physicist; researched radium and thorium disin-

GUGLIELMO MARCONI   MARIA GOEPPERT MAYER   ELIE METCHNIKOFF   JOHANNES PURKINJE   JOHN RAY

1973, with Frisch and Tinbergen, for research on animal and human behaviors as adaptive evolution.

Lowell, Percival, 1855–1916, U.S. astronomer; predicted the discovery of Pluto by mathematical calculation; photographed Mars.

McCollum, Elmer V., 1879–1967, U.S. biochemist; identified vitamin A; discovered vitamin B in lactose; discovered D vitamins.

MacLeod, Colin M., 1909– , U.S. microbiologist; researched genetic transformation in bacteria.

MacLeod, John J. R., 1876–1935, Scottish physiologist; Nobel Prize in Phys. & Med.—1923, with Banting (see); researched metabolic control of carbohydrates.

McMillin, Edwin M., 1907– , U.S. physicist; Nobel Prize in Chemistry—1951, with Seaborg (see).

Mach, Ernst, 1838–1916, Austrian physicist; studied bodies moving at high speed through gases; this laid the foundation for Einstein's theory of relativity.

Malpighi, Marcello, 1628–1694, Italian physiologist; founded microscopic anatomy; first to

tegration; with Hahn, discovered protactinium; with Frisch, demonstrated nuclear fission in the uranium atom.

Mendel, Gregor, 1822–1884, Austrian monk and botanist; laid the foundations for the study of heredity with his work on dominant and recessive inheritance traits.

Mendeleev, Dmitri I., 1834–1907, Russian chemist; formulated the Periodic Law and devised periodic table to classify chemical elements; predicted discovery of 6 elements to account for gaps in the table.

Metchnikoff, Élie, 1845–1916, Russian bacteriologist; Nobel Prize in Phys. & Med.—1908, with Ehrlich, for work on immunity; formulated theory of phagocytosis; studied intracellular digestion.

Meyerhof, Otto, 1884–1951, German physiologist; Nobel Prize in Phys. & Med.—1922, with A. Hill (see).

Michelson, Albert Abraham, 1852–1931, German-American physicist; Nobel Prize in Physics—1907, for invention of the interferometer and measurement of the speed of light; demonstrated, with Morley, that the speed of light is constant in inertial systems, disproving the existence of ether and serving as a basis for Einstein's theory of relativity.

Millikan, Robert Andrew, 1868–1953, U.S. physicist; Nobel Prize in Physics—1923, for isolating the electron and measuring its charge; conducted research on cosmic rays, Brownian movement in gases, and the ultraviolet spectrum.

Moissan, Henri, 1852–1907, French chemist; Nobel Prize in Chemistry—1906, for isolating fluorine and developing the electric arc furnace.

Morgan, Thomas Hunt, 1866–1945, U.S. zoologist; Nobel Prize in Phys. & Med.—1933, for study of chromosomes; formulated the chromosomal theory of heredity.

Morley, Edward W., 1838–1923, U.S. physicist; with Michelson (see), disproved existence of ether.

Morrison, Phillip, 1919– , U.S. physicist; studying elementary particles and the theory of nuclei.

Morse, Samuel F. B., 1791–1872, U.S. inventor; devised the Morse Code and a telegraphic device for transmitting it.

Mosander, Carl G., 1797–1858, Swedish chemist; discovered didymium, erbium, terbium, and lanthanum.

Moseley, Henry G., 1887–1915, British physicist; studied X-ray spectra of elements; originated the atomic number system of atoms, further developing Mendeleev's Periodic Law.

Mössbauer, Rudolf L., 1929– , German physicist; Nobel Prize in Physics—1961, for discovering the Mössbauer Effect, the production of gamma rays with predictable wave motion, leading to the use of gamma rays in making precise measurements.

Mueller, Paul H., 1899–1965, Swiss chemist; Nobel Prize in Phys. & Med.—1948, for discovery of DDT as an insecticide and for synthesizing it.

Muller, Hermann Joseph, 1890–1967, U.S. geneticist; Nobel Prize in Phys. & Med.—1946, for discovery of genetic mutations by X-rays.

Neel, Louis, 1904– , French physicist; Nobel Prize in Physics—1970, with Alfven, for work on magnetic effects of ferrites.

Nernst, Walther H., 1846–1941, German physicist and chemist; Nobel Prize in Chemistry—1920, for work on heat changes during chemical reactions; researched chemical equilibrium, ionic theory, and solutions.

Newton, Issac, 1642-1727, British scientist; invented differential and integral calculus; originated the idea of universal gravitation; worked in optics, developing an improved telescope; formulated the 3 laws of motion.

Nicolle Charles J. H., 1866–1936, French bacteriologist; Nobel Prize in Phys. & Med.—1928, for discovering that the body louse carries the typhoid bacillus.

Nobel, Alfred B., 1833–1896, Swedish inventor and philanthropist; invented smokeless gunpowder; bequeathed $9,000,000 to establish the Nobel Prizes; first awarded in 1901.

Northrop, John H., 1891– , U.S. biochemist; Nobel Prize in Chemistry—1946, with Stanley (see).

Ochoa, Severo, 1905– , U.S. biochemist; Nobel Prize in Phys. & Med.—1959, with Kornberg (see).

Oersted, Hans Christian, 1777–1851, Danish physicist; founded science of electromagnetism; discovered that a magnetic needle is deflected by electric current; the oersted unit is named for him.

Ohm, Georg Simon, 1789–1854, German physicist; discovered relationship between electric current intensity, electromotive force, and a circuit's resistance; the ohm unit is named for him.

Onnes, Heike K., 1853–1926, Dutch physicist; Nobel Prize in Physics—1913, for experiments with low temperatures and liquefied helium; discovered electrical superconductors.

Oppenheimer, J. Robert, 1904–1967, U.S. physicist; chief of atomic-bomb project; research in elementary particles and cosmic rays.

Osler, Sir William, 1849–1919, Canadian physician; improved the methods of teaching and practicing medicine.

Ostwald, Wilhelm, 1853–1932, German chemist; Nobel Prize in Chemistry—1909, for work on chemical catalysts, equilibrium, and reaction rates.

Paracelsus (Theophrastus Bombastus von Hohenheim), 1493?–1541, Swiss alchemist-physician; taught that diseases are specific entities, responding to specific remedies; recognized the value of observation in the practice of medicine.

Paré, Ambroise, 1517–1590, French surgeon; invented the surgical ligature for stitching wounds together, and other surgical instruments.

Parsons, Charles Algernon, 1854–1931, British inventor; invented the steam turbine.

Pascal, Blaise, 1623-1662, French scientist; developed the mathematical theory of probability; worked on barometric pressure and on the equilibrium of liquids; formulated Pascal's law.

Pasteur, Louis, 1822–1895, French chemist; discovered the existence of bacteria; developed inoculations against rabies, anthrax, and cholera.

Pauli, Wolfgang, 1900–1958, Austrian physicist; Nobel Prize in Physics—1945, for discovery of Pauli's Principle of electrons, stating that no 2 electrons in an atom may be in the same quantum state; discovered the neutrino.

Pauling, Linus, 1901– , U.S. chemist; Nobel Prize in Chemistry—1954, for work on the binding forces of matter; won the Nobel Peace Prize —1963, for efforts in banning atmospheric nuclear testing; working on quantum mechanics in chemistry, and the molecular chemical bond.

Pavlov, Ivan P., 1849–1936, Russian physiologist; Nobel Prize in Phys. & Med.—1904, for work on the physiology of digestion; conducted classic conditioning experiments with dogs.

Pease, Francis G., 1881–1938, U.S. astronomer; designed the telescopes at Mt. Palomar and Mt. Wilson; noted for photographs of the moon.

Peltier, Jean C. A., 1785–1845, French physicist; discovered the Peltier Effect, the apparent absorption of heat at the intersection of 2 metal rods, occuring when current flows through both rods in the same direction as the current heating them.

Perrin, Jean Baptiste

Perrin, Jean Baptiste, 1870–1942, French physicist; Nobel Prize in Physics—1926, for study of the discontinuous structure of matter and and measurement of the size of atoms; his experiments on Brownian movement confirmed Einstein's theories of suspended particles.

Perutz, Max F., 1914–   , British physicist; Nobel Prize in Chemistry—1962, with Kendrew, for study of hemoglobin and myoglobin structure with X-rays.

Petit, Alexis T., 1791–1820, French physicist; with Dulong (see), developed the Dulong-Petit Law.

Pfeffer, Wilhelm, 1845–1920, German botanist; did early research in plant physiology; discovered the process of osmotic pressure in plant cells.

Piccard, Greenleaf W., 1877–1956, U.S. electrical engineer and inventor; invented the crystal set, radio compass, and static eliminator.

Piccard, Jacques, 1922–   , Swiss oceanographer; reached the lowest known level of the ocean floor in a bathyscaphe he designed.

Planck, Max K. E. L., 1858–1947, German physicist; Nobel Prize in Physics—1918, for his statement of the quantum theory of light; originated quantum theory based on research of black-body radiation; did work in thermodynamics

Poincaré, Jules Henri, 1854–1912, French mathematician; worked on the electromagnetic theory of light; leading to a specialized theory of relativity.

Porter, Rodney, 1917–   , British biochemist; Nobel Prize in Phys. & Med.—1972, with Edelman, for research into structure and mechanisms of antibodies.

Powell, Cecil F., 1903–1969, British physicist; Nobel Prize in Physics—1950, for study of nuclei and mesons with photography; developed photographic method of tracing elementary particles.

Pregl, Fritz, 1869–1930, Austrian chemist; Nobel Prize in Chemistry—1923, for development of a method of quantative microanalysis of organic substances.

Prelog, Vladimir, 1906–   , Yugoslavian-born organic chemist; Nobel Prize in Chemistry—1975, with Cornforth, for work in stereochemistry; studied the spatial arrangement of atoms in organic compounds.

Priestley, Joseph, 1733–1804, British chemist; discovered oxygen; isolated nitrous oxide, ammonia, sulfur dioxide, etc.; discovered method of decomposing ammonia electrically.

Ptolemy, Claudius, 2nd Century A.D., Alexandrian astronomer; described a system of the universe based on his theory that the sun, planets, and stars revolved around Earth; Ptolemy's universe was accepted until the 16th century.

Purcell, Edward Mills, 1912–   , U.S. physicist; Nobel Prize in Physics—1952, with F. Bloch (see).

Purkinje, Johannes E., 1787–1869, Czech physiologist; discovered ciliary movements in vertebrates and ganglionic bodies in the brain; the *Purkinje cell,* in brain cortex is named for him.

Rabi, Isidor I., 1898–1953, U.S. physicist; Nobel Prize in Physics—1944, for recording the magnetic properties of nuclei; conducted research on the radio-frequency spectra of atoms and molecules.

Raman, Sir Chandrasekhara V., 1888–1971, Indian physicist; Nobel Prize in Physics—1930, for discovery of frequency changes in light scattered by a fluid medium.

Ramon y Cajal, Santiago, 1852–1934, Spanish neuroanatomist; Nobel Prize in Phys. & Med.—1906, with Golgi (see); developed method of staining nerve tissue for microscopic study.

Ramsay, Sir William, 1852–1916, Scottish chemist; Nobel Prize in Chemistry—1904, for discovering and isolating helium, xenon, neon, and krypton; investigated the molecular density of pure liquids; proved that disintegrating radium produces helium.

Ray, John, 1627–1705, British naturalist; devised system of plant classification; distinguished monocotyledons and dicotyledons.

Rayleigh, Baron John W. S., 1842–1919, British mathematician and physicist; Nobel Prize in Physics—1904, for the discovery of argon and the study of gas densities.

Redi, Francisco, 1626?–1698?, Italian physicist; disproved the theory of spontaneous generation by experiment.

Reed, Walter, 1851–1902, U.S. surgeon; discovered that yellow fever is carried by the *Aedes* mosquito.

Reichstein, Tadeus, 1897–   , Swiss chemist; Nobel Prize in Phys. & Med.—1950, with Hench and Kendall (see); isolated 26 adrenal hormones.

Richards, Dickinson Woodruff, 1895–1973, U.S. physician; Nobel Prize in Phys. & Med.—1956, with Cournant (see) and Forssman.

Richards, Theodore William, 1868–1928, U.S. chemist; Nobel Prize in Chemistry—1914, for determining many atomic weights.

Richardson, Sir Owen W., 1879–1959, British physicist; Nobel Prize in Physics—1928, for study of thermionic effect and electrons sent off by hot metals.

Richet, Charles Robert, 1850–1935, French physiologist; Nobel Prize in Phys. & Med.—1913, for discovery of the *anaphylaxis* phenomena, the often fatal reaction to foreign serum proteins, caused by natural antibodies developed after a previous serum injection.

Robbins, Frederick Chapman, 1916–   U.S. pediatrician; Nobel Prize in Phys. & Med.—1954, with Enders (see) and Weller.

Robinson, Sir Robert, 1886–1975, British chemist; Nobel Prize in Chemistry—1947, for work on plant substances; discovered the detailed structure of alkaloids.

Roemer, Olaus, 1644–1710, Danish astronomer; disproved theory of instantaneous light transmission; estimated the speed of light.

Roentgen, Wilhelm K., 1845–1923, German physicist; Nobel Prize in Physics—1901, for the discovery of X-rays, often called *Roentgen* rays.

Ross, Sir Ronald, 1857–1932, British physician; Nobel Prize in Phys. & Med.—1902, for discovery of the cause and transmission of malaria.

Rutherford, Ernest, 1871–1937, British physicist; Nobel Prize in Chemistry—1908, for discovery of atom disintegration through alpha rays; theorized that atoms were not indestructible; described the atom as a nucleus surrounded by revolving electrons; discovered the 3 main types of radioactive emanations.

Sanger, Frederick, 1918–   , British biochemist; Nobel Prize in Chemistry—1958, for determining the structure of the insulin molecule.

Scheele, Carl W., 1742–1786, Swedish chemist; discovered manganese, barium, chlorine, and oxygen (independent of Priestley); discovered several of the vegetable acids and explained the nature of graphite; estimated the proportion of oxygen in air; discovered glycerine.

Schleiden, Matthias J., 1804–1881, German botanist; theorized on the nature of cell construction; discovered the importance of the cell nucleus.

Schrieffer, John R., 1931–   , U.S. physicist; Nobel Prize in Physics—1972, with Bardeen and Cooper, for explanation of superconductivity in metals cooled to near-absolute zero temperatures.

Schrödinger, Erwin, 1887–1961, Austrian physicist; Nobel Prize in Physics—1933, with Dirac (see).

Schultze, Max J. S., 1825–1874, German anatomist; studied the living cell; discovered the importance of protoplasm in cellular function.

Milky Way; showed the clustering tendency of galaxies; pinpointed center of the universe.

Sherrington, Sir Charles S., 1861–1952, British physiologist; Nobel Prize in Phys. & Med.—1932, with Adrian (see).

Shockley, William, 1910–   , U.S. physicist; Nobel Prize in Physics—1956, with Bardeen and Brattain, for work on semiconductor properties leading to the invention of the transistor.

Siegbahn, Karl M. G., 1886–   , Swedish physicist; Nobel Prize in Physics—1924, for work on X-ray spectroscopy of atoms, revealing internal structure.

Smith, William, 1769–1839, British geologist; devised use of index fossils to date and identify rock formations.

Soddy, Frederick, 1877–1956, British chemist; Nobel Prize in Chemistry—1921, for study of radioactivity; worked with Rutherford on the theory of radioactive disintegration; researched isotope formation.

Spallanzani, Lazzaro, 1729–1799, Italian naturalist; studied digestion and blood circulation; disproved spontaneous generation.

Spemann, Hans, 1869–1941, German biologist; Nobel Prize in Phys. & Med.—1935, for discovery of the directive function of some tissues (called *organizer* tissues) during the development of the embryo.

Sperry, Elmer Ambrose, 1860–1930, U.S. electrical engineer; invented the gyroscope; developed the high-intensity arc light.

CARL SCHEELE   THEODOR SCHWANN   FREDERICK SODDY   ORVILLE WRIGHT   AUGUST WEISMANN

Schwann, Theodor, 1810–1882, German physiologist; originated the cell theory; worked on digestion; discovered pepsin.

Seaborg, Glenn T., 1912–   , U.S. chemist; Nobel Prize in Chemistry—1951, with McMillin, for discovery of neptunium and plutonium; also discovered elements 95, 96, 97, 98, and 101, and many useful radioisotopes; Chairman of the U.S. Atomic Energy Commission.

Seebeck, Thomas J., 1770–1831, German physicist; discovered thermoelectricity; developed the thermocouple to measure temperature.

Segrè, Emilio, 1905–   , U.S. physicist; Nobel Prize in Physics—1959, with O. Chamberlain (see).

Semenov, Nikolai N., 1893–   , Russian chemist; Nobel Prize in Chemistry—1956, with Hinshelwood (see).

Semmelweis, Ignac, 1818–1865, Hungarian physician; discovered that puerperal (childbed) fever is contagious; proved that maternal mortality could be radically reduced in an antiseptic environment.

Shapley, Harlow, 1885–1972, U.S. astronomer; researched use of Cepheids as astronomical measuring sticks; studied structure of the

Stanley, Wendell M., 1904–1971, U.S. biologist; Nobel Prize in Chemistry—1946, with Northrop, for isolating and crystallizing enzymes and viruses, proving they obey chemical laws.

Stark, Johannes, 1874–1957, German; Nobel Prize in Physics—1919, for discovery of the Stark Effect, the splitting of spectrum sections when subjected to a strong electric field.

Staudinger, Hermann, 1881–1965, German; Nobel Prize for Chemistry—1953, for study of polymers, leading to development of plastics and synthetic fibers.

Stein, William H., 1911–   , U.S. biochemist; developed methods for analyzing proteins; studied amino acids and enzymes.

Steinmetz, Charles Proteus, 1865–1923, German-American electrical engineer; formulated the law of hysteresis; discovered many practical applications for alternating current; improved the electric generator.

Stern, Otto, 1888–1969, German-American; Nobel Prize in Physics—1943, for the molecular-beam method of atomic study.

Stokes, Sir George Gabriel, 1819–1903, British physicist; formulated the undulatory light theory, and the theory of wave motion.

Sumner, James Batcheller, 1887–1955, U.S. biochemist; Nobel Prize in Chemistry—1946, for the crystallization of enzymes; isolated urease.

Sutherland, Earl, 1913–1974, U.S. biochemist; Nobel Prize in Phys. & Med.—1971, for discovering cyclic AMP, the intermediate agent between hormones and the cells they affect.

Swammerdam, Jan, 1637–1680, Dutch naturalist and biologist; first to describe red blood corpuscles; intensively studied plant and animal structure with a microscope.

Szent-Györgyi, Albert, 1893–   , Hungarian-American biochemist; Nobel Prize in Phys. & Med.—1937, for research on catalytic action in cellular oxidation, the role of vitamins in metabolism, and the chemistry and structure of muscle tissue; discovered actin.

Szilard, Leo, 1898–1964, Hungarian-American biophysicist; worked with Fermi on first controlled nuclear chain reaction; devised the graphite controls for the reaction.

Tamm, Igor, 1895–1971, Russian physicist; Nobel Prize in Physics—1958, with Cerenkov (see) and Frank.

Tatum, Edward Lawrie, 1909–1976, U.S. biochemist; Nobel Prize in Phys. & Med.—1958, with Beadle (see).

Tesla, Nikola, 1856–1943, Croatian-American inventor; discovered the rotating magnetic field; devised method of utilizing alternating current by invention of the induction motor.

Theiler, Max, 1899–1972, South African microbiologist; Nobel Prize in Phys. & Med.—1951, for the development of yellow fever vaccine.

Theorell, A. H. T., 1903–   , Swedish biochemist; Nobel Prize in Phys. & Med.—1955, for work on enzyme oxidation; produced a pure form of the enzyme responsible for cellular oxidation.

Thompson, Benjamin, 1753–1814, British physicist; developed the theory that heat is a form of motion rather than a material substance.

Thomson, Sir George P., 1892–1975, British physicist; Nobel Prize in Physics—1937, with Davisson (see).

Thomson, Sir Joseph John, 1856–1940, British physicist; Nobel Prize in Physics—1906, for discovery of the electron and electron discharge through gases.

Tinbergen, Nikolaas, 1907–   , British biologist and ethologist; Nobel Prize in Phys. & Med.—1973, with Lorenz and Frisch (see).

Tiselius, Arne W. K., 1902–1971, Swedish chemist; Nobel Prize in Chemistry—1948, for the development of electrophoresis to separate serum proteins.

Todd, Sir Alexander R., 1907–   , British chemist; Nobel Prize in Chemistry—1957, for research on cellular nuclear proteins.

Tombaugh, Clyde W., 1906–   , U.S. astronomer; discovered the planet Pluto in the position predicted by Percival Lowell.

Torricelli, Evangelista, 1608–1647, Italian physicist; discovered principles of, and constructed, mercurial barometer.

Tyndall, John, 1820-1893, British physicist; discovered that atmospheric density affects sound transmission; discovered the particle reflection principle (Tyndall Effect) that makes the sky appear blue.

Urey, Harold Clayton, 1893–   , U.S. chemist; Nobel Prize in Chemistry—1934, for the discovery of deuterium and other radioactive isotopes.

Vesalius, Andreas, 1514–1564, Belgian physician; published the first systematic description of the human body, laying the foundation for the field of anatomy.

Vigneaud, Vincent du, 1901–   , U.S. biochemist; Nobel Prize in Chemistry—1955, for the synthesis of pituitary hormones; discovered structure of biotin.

Virchow, Rudolf, 1821–1902, German pathologist; founded the science of cell pathology.

Volta, Alessandro, 1745–1827, Italian physicist; conducted research on atmospheric pressure; invented the electrical condensor and electroscope; the *volt* unit is named for him.

Waksman, Selman Abraham, 1888–1973, U.S. microbiologist; Nobel Prize in Phys. & Med.—1952, for discovery of streptomycin and neomycin.

Wallace, Alfred Russel, 1823–1913, British naturalist; developed, in correlation with Darwin's theory of species origin, the idea of survival of the fittest.

Walton, Ernest T. S., 1903–   , Irish physicist; Nobel Prize in Physics—1951, with Crockcroft (see).

Warburg, Otto H., 1883–1970, German physiologist; Nobel Prize in Physics & Med.—1931, for discovery of respiratory enzymes.

Watson, James Dewey, 1928–   , U.S. geneticist; Nobel Prize in Phys. & Med.—1962, with Crick and Wilkins (see), for devising a model of the double-helix DNA molecule.

Watt, James, 1736–1819, Scottish inventor; improved the steam engine; invented the double-acting engine, the condensing engine, and the centrifugal governor; the *watt* unit of electric power is named for him.

Weismann, August, 1834–1914, German biologist; developed theory of continuity of cellular germ-plasm, stating that death of an organism never occurs because of that continuity.

Weller, Thomas H., 1915–   , U.S. physician; Nobel Prize in Phys. & Med.—1954, with Enders (see) and Robbins.

Werner, Alfred, 1866–1919, Swiss chemist; Nobel Prize in Chemistry—1913, for coordination theory of atomic arrangement.

Wieland, Henrich O., 1877–1957, German chemist; Nobel Prize in Chemistry—1927, for study of gall acids; defined the structure of the bile acids.

Wien, Wilhelm, 1864–1928, German physicist; Nobel Prize in Physics—1911, for discovery of heat radiated by black objects.

Wilkins, Maurice H., 1916–   , British biophysicist; Nobel Prize in Phys. & Med.–1962, with Crick and Watson (see), for the basic X-ray studies of DNA molecular structure.

Willstätter, Richard, 1872–1942, German chemist; Nobel Prize in Chemistry–1915, for work on chlorophyll pigmentation in plants; determined the structure of plant alkaloids and synthesized them.

Wilson, Charles T. R., 1869–1959, Scottish physicist; Nobel Prize in physics–1927, for invention of the cloud chamber to trace ionized particles.

Windaus, Adolf, 1876–1959, German chemist; Nobel Prize in Chemistry–1928, for discovery that ultraviolet light activates ergosterol; determined the structure of cholesterol; discovered histamine.

Wöhler, Friedrich, 1800–1882, German chemist; synthesized urea, now used in plastics; isolated beryllium and aluminum.

Wright, Orville, 1871–1948, and his brother, **Wilbur,** 1867–1912, U.S. inventors; built the first successful engine-powered airplane; corrected tables of aerodynamic pressures.

Yang, Chen Ning, 1922–   , U.S. physicist; Nobel Prize in Physics–1957, with Lee (see).

Yukawa, Hideki, 1907–   , Japanese physicist; Nobel Prize in Physics–1949, for predicting discovery of the meson.

Zernicke, Frits, 1888–1966, Dutch physicist; Nobel Prize in Physics–1953, for inventing the phase-contrast microscope, used to show differences in depth by differences in phase of light.

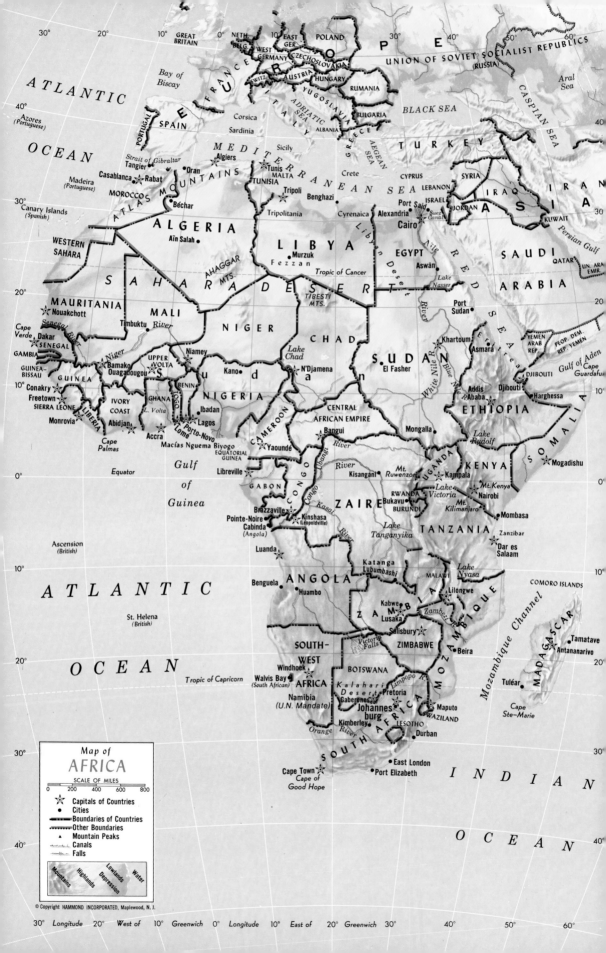

Map of ANTARCTICA

STEREOGRAPHIC PROJECTION

Scale of Miles

0   300   600

© Copyright HAMMOND INCORPORATED, Maplewood, N.J.

INDIAN OCEAN

ATLANTIC OCEAN

PACIFIC OCEAN

INDIAN OCEAN

PACIFIC OCEAN

ANTARCTICA

ANTARCTIC CIRCLE

Antarctic Circle

C. Batterbee

MAWSON (Austr.)

ENDERBY LAND

C. Norvegia

Riiser-Larsen Peninsula

Lützow-Holm Bay

MOLODEZHNAYA (U.S.S.R.)

Amery Ice Shelf

American Highland

West Ice Shelf

Davis Sea

Shackleton Ice Shelf

Vincennes Bay

C. Poinsett

C. Goodenough

DUMONT d'URVILLE (Fr.)

SOUTH MAGNETIC POLAR AREA

WILKES LAND

QUEEN MAUD LAND

NEW SCHWABENLAND

NOVOLAZAREVSKAYA (U.S.S.R.)

VOSTOK (U.S.S.R.)

PLATEAU STA. (U.S.)

South Polar Plateau

AMUNDSEN-SCOTT STA.(U.S.)—SOUTH POLE

Queen Maud Ra.

Mt. Markham 14,272

VICTORIA LAND

C. Adare

Ross Ice Shelf

Roosevelt I.

MC MURDO (U.S.)

SCOTT(N.Z.)

Ross I. St.

McMurdo Sd.

ROSS SEA

COATS LAND

Filchner Ice Shelf

Berkner I.

Ronne Ice Shelf

Ellsworth Mts.

Vinson Massif 16,864

BYRD STA. (U.S.)

Mt. Sidley 13,317

MARIE BYRD LAND

Getz Ice Shelf

C. Dart

Thurston I.

Amundsen Sea

WEDDELL SEA

Larsen Ice Shelf

ANTARCTIC PENINSULA

GRAHAM LAND

PALMER LAND

ELLSWORTH LAND

Alexander I.

Bellingshausen Sea

Antarctic Circle

PALMER STA. (U.S.)

S. Shetland Is. (Br.)

Drake Passage

(Br.)

Sea Below Sea Level

300 ft.

600 ft.

1,600 ft.

3,200 ft.

6,500 ft.

16,000 ft.

Map of
ASIA
SCALE OF MILES
0 200 400 600 800 1000

✶ Capitals of Countries
● Cities
▬▬▬ Boundaries of Countries
▬▬▬ Other Boundaries
▲ Mountain Peaks
∼∼∼ Canals

Mountains Highlands Lowlands Depression Water

© Copyright HAMMOND INCORPORATED, Maplewood, N.J.

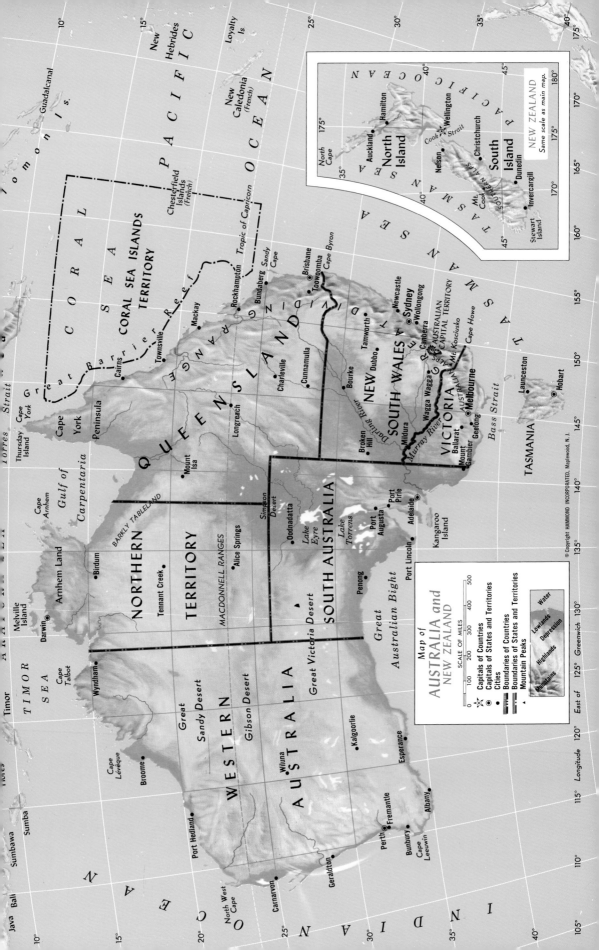

Map of
NORTH AMERICA
SCALE OF MILES

0 200 400 600 800

⭐ Capitals of Countries
● Cities
▬ ▬ ▬ Boundaries of Countries
▲ Mountain Peaks
Canals

Mountains Highlands Lowlands Depression Water

© Copyright HAMMOND INCORPORATED, Maplewood, N.J.

ASIA

ARCTIC OCEAN

70° 80° 120°100°80° 60° 20°
140°
160°
180°   North Pole   20°
160°   40°
140°120° 100° 80° 60°

80° 70° 60°

GREENLAND
(Danish)

ICELAND

Bering Strait

Point Barrow

North Magnetic Pole

Thule

Ellesmere Island

Baffin Bay

UNITED STATES
Yukon River
Alaska
Anchorage
Mt. McKinley

Whitehorse

Juneau

Queen Charlotte Islands

Victoria Island

Great Bear Lake

Arctic Circle

Baffin Island

Davis Strait

Mackenzie River

Great Slave Lake

Hudson Bay

Labrador

Goose Bay

Newfoundland

St. Pierre & Miquelon (French)

CANADA

ROCKY MOUNTAINS

Vancouver Island

Seattle

Portland

Cascade Range

Columbia R.

Edmonton

Calgary

Lake Winnipeg

Winnipeg

Great Plains

Missouri River

Churchill

Great Lakes

St. Lawrence River

Montréal
Ottawa ⭐
Toronto

Halifax
Nova Scotia

Minneapolis

Detroit

Cleveland

Boston

New York

Vancouver

40°

SIERRA NEVADA

San Francisco

Great Salt Lake
Salt Lake City

Denver

Kansas City

St. Louis

Chicago

Philadelphia

Washington ⭐

APPALACHIAN MOUNTAINS

Cape Hatteras

Bermuda (British)

30°

Los Angeles

San Diego

Phoenix

Mt. Whitney

Colorado R.

UNITED STATES

Memphis

Mt. Mitchell

Atlanta

Jacksonville

El Paso

Rio Grande

Dallas

New Orleans

Houston

Cape Canaveral

Miami

BAHAMAS

Tropic of Cancer

Lower California

MEXICO

Monterrey

Gulf of Mexico

Havana ⭐ CUBA

West Indies

HAITI DOMINICAN REPUBLIC PUERTO RICO (to U.S.)

20°

Guadalajara

Mexico City ⭐
Veracruz

Yucatán Peninsula

JAMAICA

CARIBBEAN SEA

BELIZE

GUATEMALA
EL SALVADOR
HONDURAS
NICARAGUA

CENTRAL
AMERICA

COSTA RICA PANAMA

CANAL ZONE (to U.S.)

Panama Canal

VENEZUELA

10°

COLOMBIA

ECUADOR

SOUTH

AMERICA

BRAZIL

Galápagos Islands (Ecuadoran)

Equator

PERU

BOLIVIA

10°

PACIFIC OCEAN

ATLANTIC OCEAN

120° 110° Longitude 100° West of 90° Greenwich 80° 70°